The Design of Single Story Rigid Frames

George C. Lee

Professor of Engineering and Applied Sciences
State University of New York at Buffalo

Robert L. Ketter

Professor of Engineering and Applied Sciences
State University of New York at Buffalo

T. L. Hsu

Research Assistant in Civil Engineering
State University of New York at Buffalo

1981

Metal Building Manufacturers Association
1230 Keith Building
Cleveland, Ohio 44115

i

LIBRARY OF CONGRESS CATALOG CARD NUMBER 81-80609

The Design of
Single Story Rigid Frames

Table of Contents

Preface   vi

Nomenclature   ix

Chapter I   Introduction   1

  1.1   Scope   1
  1.2   Fabrication   3
  1.3   Mechanical Properties of Steel   7
  1.4   References   8

Chapter II   Simple Indeterminate Frame Analysis   9

  2.1   Introduction   9
  2.2   Flexibility and Stiffness   13
  2.3   Flexibility Method: The Method of Consistent
      Deformations   24
  2.4   Stiffness Method: The Slope-Deflection Method   40
  2.5   The Finite Element Method: The Direct Stiffness
      Method   47

Chapter III   Behavior and Design Information for
Steel Structural Members   58

  3.1   Introduction   58
  3.2   Compression   62
  3.3   Bending   69
  3.4   Combined Bending and Compression   76
  3.5   Alternate Approach to Beam-Column Design   82
  3.6   Other Design Considerations   89

Chapter IV   Design Examples   92

Chapter V   References   162

Appendices   164

  A.   Introductions and Listings of a Finite Element Computer
     Program for the Analysis of Two-Dimensional
     Frame Structures   164

B. Selected AISC Specification Design Formulas for
    Prismatic Members   182
C. Determination of End Restraints for Members of
    Rigid Frames Consisting of Tapered and Prismatic
    Members   197
D. AISC Specifications for Web-Tapered Members
    (effective 11/1/78)   205
E. Effective Length Factors for Multi-Segment Tapered
    Members   219
F. Effective Length Factors for Laterally Continuous Beams   256
G. Design Aids for Tapered Beam-Columns with
    Unequal Flanges   258

Preface

For a number of years single span, single story, rigid, steel frames—both portal and gable types—have been used in industrial building construction. In the past, most designs presumed rolled shapes, and applications were limited by economic and other considerations to particular span lengths. In the more recent years, however, with advancement in welding and cutting technology, in methods of structural analysis and design, and in the production of higher strength steels, single story rigid frames have been much more popular. At the present time, this type of construction is used widely—for industrial plants, warehouses, laboratories, office buildings, schools, churches, shopping centers, and recreational facilities, to name but a few of the more obvious applications.

It is the primary purpose of this book to summarize all of the pertinent results of research and investigations achieved in recent years having to do with the design of steel, single story, rigid frames, and thereby facilitate their application by structural engineers. There are available a large number of texts and design literature concerning prismatic members. For this as well as other reasons, in this book every effort will be made to coordinate the material on tapered members with that on prismatic ones. Moreover, wherever possible, presentation will be consistent with the current AISC Specification.

The material contained in this book is in large part the result of research investigations that have been conducted by the authors at the State University of New York at Buffalo since 1966. This work has been carried out under the technical guidance and financial support of a number of organizations. Particular individuals in those groups were especially helpful, and we would like to here acknowledge them:

American Institue of Steel Construction
    Theodore R. Higgins
    William A. Milek (*Director of Engineering and Research*)
    Frederick Palmer
    The Specification Committee (Frank W. Stockwell, *Secretary*)

American Iron and Steel Institute
    Ivan M. Viest
    William Hansell

Metal Building Manufacturers Association
  Duane S. Ellifritt (*Director of Engineering and Research*)
  The Technical Committee (William Sontag, *Chairman*)
  The Subcommittee on Tapered Members (Donald Johnson, *Chairman*, Cooper Patrick, Durwood Graddy, and Paul Klim)

Naval Facilities Engineering Command
  Michael Yachnis (*Chief Engineer*)

Structural Stability Research Council
  Jerome S. F. Iffland (*Chairman*)
  Lynn S. Beedle (*Director*)

Welding Research Council
  Kenneth H. Koopman (*Director*)
  C. R. Felmley, Jr. (*Technical Secretary*)

Joint Structural Stability Research Council/Welding Research Council Group on Tapered Members
  A. Amirikian (*Chairman*)
  D. J. Butler
  C. R. Felmley, Jr.
  D. S. Ellifritt
  T. R. Higgins
  D. L. Johnson
  K. H. Koopman
  G. C. Lee
  C. J. Miller
  F. J. Palmer
  M. Yachnis

Finally, the authors wish to publicly express their appreciation to Louise Dumain and Edna Thill for their typing of the manuscript.

G. C. LEE
R. L. KETTER
T. L. HSU

December 1980

Nomenclature

a	The clear distance between stiffeners
A	Area of cross section
A_f, A_1, A_2	Area of one flange
A_w	Area of web
b, b_f	Width of flange
b, b_T, b_B	Length of the adjacent member
b_{ib}, b_{ic}	Coefficients defined in Section 2.3
B	(1) Bending coefficient for a tapered member defined in AISC Spec. App. D, Sect. D3 or
	(2) Coefficient defined in Eq. (3.3)
c	Spring constant defined in Section 2.2
c_{ij}	Carry-over factor which is the ratio of k_{ij}^c to k_{ij}
C	(1) Coefficient defined in Eq. (3.3) or
	(2) A numerical constant contained in Eq. (3.41) which depends on the properties of the material.
C_b	Bending coefficient for a prismatic member, which is a function of moment gradient (α).
C_c	Slenderness ratio of (KL/r) of elastic column corresponding to a stress of $(\sigma_y - \sigma_r^*)$
C_m	Equivalent moment coefficient defined in AISC 1.61.
C_v	Coefficient defined in AISC Eq. (1.10-1)
C_1	A modification factor contained in Eq. (3.17), which accounts for different loading conditions
d_0	The smallest depth of a tapered member or segment
d_1, d_2, d_l, d_L	The larger depth of a tapered member
$\bar{d}_0$	The smallest depth of the adjacent tapered member
$\bar{d}_1, \bar{d}_2$	The larger depth of the adjacent tapered member
d_p	Depth of the beam at the location of application of the concentrated load
d_z	Depth of the tapered member at the location of a distance z along the member
$[D]$	Displacement matrix
E	Modulus of elasticity
E_T	Tangent modulus
f	(1) Actual computed stress or
	(2) The vertical height of roof girder in a gable frame
f_a	Calculated axial stress

f_b	Calculated bending stress
f_v	Calculated shear stress
F	Allowable stress
$[F]$	Force matrix
$F_a, F_{a\gamma}$	Allowable compressive stress
$F_b, F_{b\gamma}$	Allowable bending stress
F_b'	Modified allowable bending stress defined by AISC Eq. (1.10-5)
$F_s, F_{s\gamma}, F_{b2}$	St. Venant torsion resistance bending stress
$F_w, F_{w\gamma}, F_{b1}$	Flange warping torsion resistance bending stress
F_v	Allowable shear stress
F_y	Yield point of structural steel
g	The equivalent column length factor shown in Appendix C
$g*$	Length modification factor defined by Eq. (3.10)
g_e	The modified equivalent length factor described in Appendix E
G	Elastic shear modulus
G_B, G_T	Joint stiffness ratio defined in Appendix E [subscripts apply to (or R_B, R_T) the top and bottom ends]
h	(1) The vertical height of column in a gable frame (2) Length modification factor for tapered beam (3) Height of web
h_s, h_w	Factors applied to the unbraced length of a tapered member (subscripts s and w refer to very thick and shallow shape of section, and very thin and deep shape of section, respectively)
H	Horizontal reaction at the base of a gable frame
I	Moment of inertia (subscripts 0 and l refer to the smallest and larger cross sections of the tapered members; B and T refer to the adjacent members at the bottom and top ends of a member; x and y refer to the strong and weak axes; C and G refer to the column and girder, respectively)
I_p	Moment of inertia at the location of application of the concentrated loading
I_w	Warping moment of inertia
J	Polar moment of inertia
k	(1) Stiffness of the member (2) Plate buckling coefficient in Eq. (3.39)

	(3) A coefficient defined in AISC Eq. (1.10-1)
	(4) Constant defined in Section 2.3
k_B, k_T	Rotational spring constants at the ends of a member
k_{ij}	Stiffness at the i'th position due to a unit deformation at the j'th position
k_{ij}^c	Carry-over stiffness coefficient
$[K]$	Stiffness matrix
$[K^c]$	Carry-over stiffness matrix
K_s, K_w	Effective length factor of the restraint beam (subscripts s and w refer to very thick and shallow shape of section, and very thin and deep shape of section, respectively)
K_x, K_y, K_z	Effective length factor (subscripts x, y, and z refer to buckling about strong and weak, and twisting about the longitudinal axes, respectively)
l	Length of a segment or a member
L	(1) Length of a member
	(2) Distance between the bases of a gable frame
m	(1) Moment function of the structure due to unit load applied at the location of the desired deflection (subscript i refers to a unit load at i'th position)
	(2) Coefficient defined in Eq. (3.1)
m_F	Flange moment function due to unit load applied at the location where deformation is desired.
M, M_{det}	Bending moment function of the (determinate) structure due to applied load
M_{cr}	Critical moment which causes lateral buckling of a beam
M_F	Flange moment function due to applied load
M_0	Applied equal end moment
M_u	Maximum bending moment due to applied transverse loading or end moments
n	Nondimensional coefficient defining the residual stress in web of tapered member
N	Coefficient defined in Eq. (3.1)
p	Axial force function due to unit load at the location where deformation is desired
P	Axial force function due to applied loads
P_{cr}	Critical axial load
P_e	Euler's flexural buckling load (subscripts x, y, and z refer to buckling about strong, weak and longitudinal axes, respectively)

P_u	The axial force carrying capacity of the member when axial force alone exists.
q,q_V,q_H	Distributed transverse load (subscripts V and H refer to vertical and horizontal components, respectively)
Q	Concentrated load
Q_{ib},Q_{ic}	Coefficients defined in Section 2.3
r_0	(1) Radius of gyration at the smallest depth of a tapered member
	(2) Cross-sectional coefficient defined by Eq. (3.24)
r_x,r_y	Strong and weak axis radius-of-gyration
r_T	Radius of gyration of a section comprising the compressive flange plus $\frac{1}{3}$ of the compression web area taken about an axis in the plane of the web
r_{Te}	Equivalent radius of gyration defined in the commentary of AISC Spec. (Sect. 1.5.1.4.5)
R	Reaction force
s	Length of a girder
S_x	Section modulus about the x-axis
t,t_f	Thickness of the flange
t_w	Thickness of the web
T_{sv}	St. Venant's torsional moment function due to unit load applied at the location where deformation is desired.
t_{sv}	St. Venant's torsional moment function due to applied load.
u	(1) Flexibility coefficient of a member
	(2) Displacement
u_{ij}	The flexibility at the i'th point resulting from the application of a unit load at the j'th point
$[U]$	Flexibility matrix
U	Nondimensional coefficient defined in Section 2.3
v	Shear force function due to unit load applied at the location where deformation is desired
V	(1) Vertical reaction at the base of a gable frame
	(2) Shear force
w	Uniformly distributed vertical load
z	Centroidal longitudinal axis
α	(1) Ratio of small end moment to large end moment
	(2) A nondimensional coefficient indicating the position of a concentrated load on a member
β	(1) Ratio of the length of one segment to the length of the

	whole tapered member
	(2) A constant which is dependent on the elastic value of residual stress (defined in Eq. 3.12)
$\bar{\beta}$	Ratio of the length of one segment to the length of the whole adjacent tapered member
γ	Tapering ratio (subscripts b and c refer to beam and column, respectively)
$\bar{\gamma}$	Tapering ratio of adjacent tapered member
Δ	(1) Relative deflection between the ends of the member
	(2) Lateral displacement at the roller base of a determinant gable frame (subscript i refers to the i'th position)
ΔL	Elongation of a member with length L
θ	End slope, rotation
λ	Cross-sectional constant for shearing stress
μ	(1) Nondimensional coefficient defined in Section 2.3
	(2) Poisson's ratio
ξ	Coefficient to determine the equivalent uniform moment in a beam-column
ρ	(1) Ratio of the tension flange area to the compression flange area
	(2) Coefficient defined in Section 2.3 (subscripts c and b refer to column and beam, respectively)
σ_a	Critical axial buckling stress
σ_b	Critical lateral torsional buckling stress
σ_{cr}	Critical buckling stress
σ_r^*	Maximum residual compressive stress
σ_y	Yield strength
τ	Ratio of the tangent modulus to the Young's modulus
ϕ	(1) Angle of twisting about shear center
	(2) Slope of roof girder of a gable frame
κ_T	St. Venant's torsional coefficient

Chapter One

Introduction

1.1 Scope

Tapered steel members have been used for a number of years in a large variety of structural applications. For the most part design of these members has been quite conservative. This has been primarily due to the fact that data were not available upon which more realistic designs could be based. Recognizing the need for such basic investigations, a joint task committee of the Structural Stability Research Council (formerly the Column Research Council) and the Welding Research Council was established in 1966 to facilitate the study and formulation of design information relating to tapered steel members.

Since 1966 research studies on the behavior of tapered steel members have been carried out at the State University of New York at Buffalo. These have been under the joint sponsorship of the American Institute of Steel Construction, the American Iron and Steel Institute, the Metal Building Manufacturers Association, and the Naval Facilities Engineering Command. In recent years, funding has been made available through the latter two organizations.

The Subcommittee on Tapered Members of the Technical Committee of the Metal Building Manufacturers Association (MBMA) has been actively involved in the research investigation at Buffalo. They provided invaluable technical assistance in the preparation of design recommendations for tapered members. These recommendations, which presume a linearly-tapered web member whose flanges are of constant width and thickness, were subsequently adopted by the American Institute of Steel Construction (AISC) and were incorporated in its 1974 "Specification for the Design, Fabrication, and Erection of Structural Steel for Buildings." While this AISC specification contains much basic information of help to the designer, there were a variety of situations encountered in tapered member design that were not covered. Therefore, further studies were undertaken. Since 1974 financial support of MBMA and the Naval Facilities Engineering Command (NFEC) have made possible the development of additional design data.

In 1977 the Technical Committee of MBMA, upon recommendation of its Subcommittee on Tapered Members, authorized financial support for the development of a book that would summarize all of the available relevant information regarding the design of steel frames composed of tapered members. This book is the product of that effort.

It is the purpose of Chapter I to provide a brief introduction to the type of steel frames that are most suitable for tapered member designs. These types of frames possess certain unique characteristics, and, where appropriate, these will be noted. This will be followed by a description of present day fabrication procedures. Finally, relevant material properties will be summarized and references listed.

Chapter II is a hurried review of several of the available methods of analysis for single-story rigid frames consisting of non-prismatic members. Only the fundamental concepts of the flexibility and stiffness approaches are discussed—and even then this is done mostly by illustration. The direct stiffness finite element method, however, is discussed in considerably more detail because of its suitability for use by a design engineer having access to a small digital computer.

Chapter III summarizes the behavior and design information available for the proportioning of individual tapered members. It is to be recognized that the entire spectrum of design cannot be covered—basic information is still lacking. Wherever possible, these deficiencies will be noted. For example, certain information regarding the design of lateral bracing is still undeveloped, and it will be necessary to continue to make conservative assumptions for those unknowns in the design process. Specifically, Chapter III will describe the influence of axial compression, bending, combined bending and compression and local buckling on tapered members.

Chapter IV will be devoted to design examples. The coverage will be comparatively complete and will include analysis. The design information contained in Chapter III will be extensively used in solving these problems.

As noted earlier in this chapter, tapered steel members have been used in a variety of building applications for a number of different reasons. To mention but two of these reasons: (1) tapered member framing provides a framing outline of pleasing appearance, and (2) comparatively large reductions in the weight of the main frame are realized when tapered members constitute the main components.

Tapered members are best suited to *elastic allowable stress* solutions based on elastic methods of analysis. While *plastic design* solutions could be carried out for structures composed of tapered members, the two ideas are philosophically in conflict. Tapered members are proportioned more or less so that they realize their allowable elastic stress at a number of different cross sections along the length simultaneously. Plastic design, on the other hand, presumes early realization of inelastic action at a limited number of cross sections, followed by inelastic rotation at those locations sufficient to allow redistribution of bending moments to other, less heavily stressed locations. In the limit, the moment diagram associated with the "best" elastic tapered member design will be the moment diagram associated with the plastic design—appropriate factors of safety being taken into account.

First, and foremost, the magnitude and distribution of the elastic stresses in frames depend upon the condition and position of the imposed loading. If the structure is indeterminate, the relative bending stiffnesses of the various members also must be taken into account. If the members themselves vary in stiffness along their lengths, as would tapered members, then these variations also must be included in the analysis. Fortunately, the use of tapered members in rigid frames results in a restrictive form of the moment diagram which tends to reinforce the chosen taper selection. Therefore, tapered members are ideally suited to the design of single and multi-span, single story, pinned-base rigid frames. Moreover, these types of structures can be pre-engineered, and the advantages of repetition of fabrication realized. Tapered members also can be used to an advantage in other situations.

1.2   Fabrication

It is to be understood that the individual members to be considered in this book are tapered only in the web with flanges presumed to be constant in both width and thickness. Although flange tapering could be approximated by changing the flange thickness and/or width in discrete steps, which is commonly done in the metal building systems industry, and some of the material contained in Chapter II could be directly applied to that situation, this book will not be concerned with those cases. Moreover, the fabrication techniques discussed herein will be restricted to structural I-shaped, welded members having constant flange dimensions and a linearly tapering web.

There are a number of methods available for fabricating members of the type under consideration. A rolled beam may be cut along a line not parallel to the flanges, one half turned end-for-end, and the two halves welded back together along the same cut, as shown in Figs. 1.1(a) and 1.1(b). Or, a rolled beam may be cut in the web parallel to one flange and then a tapered web

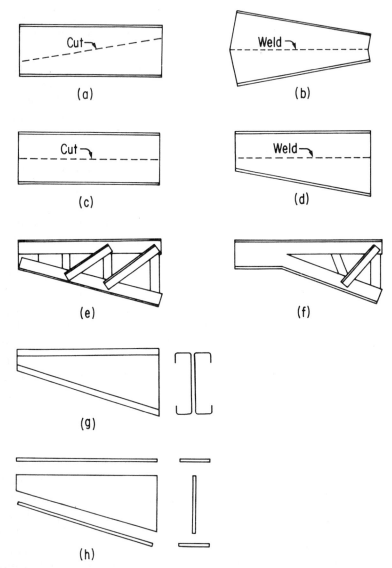

Figure 1.1 Several illustrative examples of various types of tapered members.

is welded to one half of the beam, as indicated in Figs. 1.1(c) and 1.1(d). A tapered truss-girder member can be made by splitting a wide flange shape, or using structural tees and welding web members to these tees which are now the top and bottom chords of the truss. This is shown in Fig. 1.1(e). The original rolled beam may not even be cut continuously, but simply spread apart as in Fig. 1.1(f). One earlier form of tapered member was made of brake-formed channels placed back to back, as in Fig. 1.1(g).

By far the most common method of fabricating tapered members is by welding three plates together to produce an I-shape as shown in Fig. 1.1(h). The remaining discussion of fabrication methods will be restricted to this one form.

The process of fabricating the flanges and web of a tapered member varies from one manufacturer to another, and with the dimensions of the member itself. Thin flanges may be split to width from plate material. Thicker flanges may be sheared from plates or ordered to correct width from bar stock (Universal Mill).

To eliminate scrap in plate or bar material, flanges are sometimes welded end-to-end in a continuous strip after being cut to the correct width. This sometimes results in a flange splice very close to the end of a finished member, and may be viewed by some as an attempt to patch up a fabrication error by welding on a short piece, but this is not the case. It simply is more efficient to weld bars and plates together and then cut them to exact length rather than to cut, say 9-foot flanges from 10-foot bars and have a foot of scrap on every flange. It is to be noted, however, that some companies have restrictions on where splices may occur. If holes are required in the flanges, these are punched before the beam is welded.

Tapered webs are sheared from plate stock to the correct dimensions. By alternating ends of webs, several may be cut from one plate to minimize scrap. There is usually some scrap from the web preparation, however, regardless of how it is done. Webs are prepunched for brace rods, girts, and any other necessary connectors prior to the welding on of flanges.

When two flanges and a web have been cut to their proper sizes and punched, they are placed in a *welding jig* with the flanges in a vertical position and the web horizontal. Hydraulic cylinders force the flanges tightly against the web and the connecting welds are made with a single pass of an automatic welder (see Fig. 1.2).

The minimum thickness of a beam or column web is sometimes dictated by its buckling strength in the welding jig rather than its performance under the service loads that will be experienced in the finished structure. When the hydraulic cylinders are activated to insure a snug fit between the flanges and the web prior to welding, the web must be capable of withstanding the axial force from the cylinders without buckling.

Frame members are welded in a horizontal position by an automatic welder, usually with a submerged arc. An uncoated weld rod is fed continuously from a spool to the welding head where it is submerged in a pool of

Figure 1.2   Typical example of the automatic welding process.

granular flux material, such that no flash is visible. The unused flux is re-claimed through a vacuum hose after the weld is completed.

There are two basic types of automatic submerged arc welders. In one type, the pieces to be welded remain stationary while the welding apparatus traverses the length of the member. This is known as *track welding*. The weld head is guided by a roller that rides in the junction of the flange and web. Another type is known as a *Conrac welder*, wherein two welding heads are held stationary while the pieces move past them. Tapered frame parts present little problem to either type of welder, although some Conrac welders have a maximum taper restriction.

The weld is normally made on only the top side of the member as it is positioned in the jig. This way the member does not have to be picked up and turned over. Some webs are thin enough that full penetration can be achieved with a fillet applied only on one side. However, full penetration is not a necessity of design in most cases. The fillet need only be large enough to transfer the horizontal shearing stresses between the flanges and the web and satisfy the minimum requirements of the AISC. Where structural members are subjected to dynamic loads, the notch which is sometimes produced by welding on one side only may lead to fatigue problems. In such a case, fatigue stresses should be checked according to the procedures defined in the AISC Manual.

When the three elements have been welded to form a tapered I-shape,

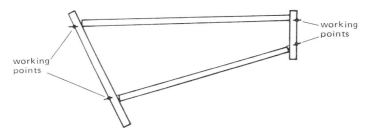

Figure 1.3 Illustration of welding arrangement in tapered member fabrication.

it is then removed from the welding jig and taken to a fitting area where end plates and any other attachments that are required are welded on by hand. For the attachment of end plates, a fillet weld is usually run down both sides of the web. It is usually desirable to get a full penetration weld between the flanges and the end plate, so they are handled differently, depending on their thickness and the angle the end plate makes with the flange. A flange larger than $\frac{1}{4}$ in. will usually be bevelled before it is attached to the web. Where the end plate makes an angle of other than $90°$ with the flange, the natural groove thus provided may eliminate the necessity for prior edge preparation (see Fig. 1.3).

To insure that the finished column or beam will match with other elements of the building to produce the desired overall height, length, and width, the fabricators work to specific *points* on the assembly that will match similar points on adjoining parts. These are called *working points,* examples of which are shown in Fig. 1.3. During fabrication, certain tolerances must be held to insure proper erection of the frame work and the predicted structural behavior under service loads.

The last step in the fabrication of tapered members is at the paint line where the finished piece is given a coat of primer. If surface preparation is required, this may be done by a *Wheelabrator,* shot blasting, wire brushing by hand, or by chemical washing.

1.3 Mechanical Properties of Steel

While a number of basic material properties would be required to fully describe the unit response of members subjected to all of the various types and kinds of loading that might be applied, the more important ones for the design of tapered steel members used in building construction are (1) the *Modulus of Elasticity,* (2) *Poisson's Ratio,* and (3) *Yield Point Stress.* In this book it will be assumed that these basic material properties are the same for both tensile and compressive loadings. Moreover, yield point stress values are presumed to be equal to those minimum values required by the American Institute of Steel Construction. For all steels, it will be assumed that the Modulus of Elasticity is equal to 29×10^6 psi, and Poisson's Ratio is 0.3.

Present day fabrication practice for the production of tapered steel members is by welding. This welding produces longitudional *residual stresses* which have an influence upon the behavior of the member. This is especially true for buckling. Based upon studies carried out at Buffalo*, it has been observed that although welding normally is done on one side only at the junction of the flange and web plates, the magnitude and distribution of the resulting residual stresses do not vary significantly from those established values for fabricated members welded on both sides. The maximum compressive residual stress for such cases occurs at the flange tips and has a value approximately equal to 0.5 σ_y. At the weld it would equal σ_y and be in tension.

1.4   References

A large number of books and research reports will be referred to in the material which follows. Full details concerning these references are given in Chapter 5. For convenience these references have been arranged in the following fashion: Group 1 are relevant specifications. Group 2 lists two text books that provide supplementary information concerning methods of analysis for simple indeterminate structures. The third group lists research publications where the basic background information concerning the design criteria for tapered members can be found. Many of the publications in this third group are research studies on tapered members carried out at the State University of New York at Buffalo. As noted earlier, these studies were financially supported by the American Institute of Steel Construction, the Metal Building Manufacturers Association, and the Naval Facilities Engineering Command. It is to be recognized that no attempt has been made to include all pertinent references having to do with the design of steel members composed of prismatic members.

---

* Pertinent research reports and other references are listed in Chapter Five.

Chapter Two

Simple Indeterminate Frame Analysis

2.1 Introduction

Without a doubt, analysis is the most important step in the entire structural design process. Analysis can be used to predict internal stresses, displacements, and failure loads. Equally true, it can be used to prescribe structural geometries, cross-sectional shapes and sizes, and required material properties.

Analysis is oftentimes repeated, over and over, by the designer in a given design situation in his attempt to find a relatively optimum design, considering among other factors economy and safety.

Although building structures (frames) by the very nature and requirements of the spaces they enclose are three-dimensional, it is common practice in civil engineering-type structures to arrange members and/or groups of members in such a manner that there exist a number of planar frames which transmit the loads to the ground. Such practice makes it possible to deal with relatively complex three-dimensional situations through the use of more elementary forms which are considerably less difficult to solve. Such idealizations yield reasonably satisfactory results for most frame structures. It should be noted, however, that the rapid development in electronic computing, both in hardware and in software, may some day provide justification for structural engineers to deal with three-dimensional analysis directly in their design process rather than to consciously analyze and construct structures in the above described fashion.

In this chapter no attempt will be made to introduce the entire spectrum of frame analysis principles or methods of solution. Attention will be given to a few selected approaches which are the more suitable ones for the type of rigid frames considered in this book—ones which are basically very simple, indeterminate frames. In fact, most of the attention will be given to single span, one-story, rigid frames with pinned bases.

From both historical and methodological points of view, analysis of indeterminate structures may be classified into the following three categories: the differential equation approach, the energy approach, and the finite element approach. Differential equation solutions follow the traditional elasticity approach, which is conceptually quite clear, but which in many practical cases is complicated in its solution procedure. Energy methods are of a variety of types and forms, and prior to the introduction of digital computers had been one of the major tools in structural analysis. Many of these methods are still popular in practice today, especially for the analysis of simple indeterminate structures. For the more complicated cases, the finite element approach developed within the past 20 years or so is undisputedly the most suitable solution method—especially when it is used in conjunction with an electronic computer.

Stiffness and *flexibility* approaches are generally recognized in modern structural analysis as the approaches most suitable for computer solutions. These classifications—and their development—will be the major discussions of this chapter.

Indeterminate frame analysis requires as part of the solution process the determination of deformations of suitably loaded determinate structures. It is explicitly required in the flexibility methods. And, since the basic concept of that method is so logical and clear, it is often included in a first introduction to indeterminate structural analysis.

Before proceeding, it is considered desirable to briefly review the so-called "unit load method"*—which also is frequently referred to as the "dummy unit load method"—for the determination of structural deformations. This method is based on the principle of minimum complementary energy. (For linear materials it is quantitatively equal to the principle of minimum potential energy.) This method will be used to develop certain of the terms required in the "other methods" that hereinafter will be discussed.

The unit load method may be written in the general form of Eq. (2.1).

$$\left.\begin{array}{c} \Delta_0 \\ \theta_0 \\ \phi_0 \end{array}\right\} = \Sigma \left[\int \frac{Mm}{EI} \, dz + \int \frac{Pp}{AE} \, dz + \int \frac{\lambda Vv}{AG} \, dz \right.$$

$$\left. + \int \frac{T_{sv} t_{sv}}{G_{KT}} \, dz + \int \frac{4M_F m_F}{EI_y} \, dz \right] \quad (2.1)$$

where

$$\left.\begin{array}{c} \Delta_0 \\ \theta_0 \\ \theta_0 \end{array}\right\} = \text{the displacement, slope and twisting angle at locations 0 in the determinate structure}$$

---

* For a complete development of this method see Ref. 4, p. 388.

M = bending moment function in the (determinate) structure due to the applied loads

m = bending moment function in the structure due to the application of a unit load at the location where deformation is desired

P = axial force function in the structure due to the applied loads

p = axial force function in the structure due to the application of a unit load at the location where deformation is desired

V = shearing force function in the structure due to the applied loads

v = shearing force function in the structure due to the application of a unit load at the location where deformation is desired

T_{sv} = St. Venant's torsional moment function in the structure due to the applied loads

t_{sv} = St. Venant's torsional moment function in the structure due to the application of a unit load at the location where deformation is desired

M_F = flange bending moment function (warping torsion) in the structure due to the applied loads

m_F = flange bending moment function in the structure due to the application of a unit load at the location where deformation is desired

EI = bending rigidity

AE = axial rigidity

AG = shear rigidity

$G\kappa_T$ = St. Venant's torsional rigidity

EI_y = lateral bending rigidity

λ = cross-sectional constant for shearing stress

In Eq. (2.1) it is assumed that each of the terms $M, m, P, p, V, v, T_{sv}, t_{sv}, M_F$, and m_F, as well as E, G, A, I, I_y, and κ_T can vary along the length(s) of the various members of the structure. It is to be recognized, however, that in "real" structures it is not unusual for members to have constant cross sections. For those cases the material and cross-sectional properties can be taken outside of the integral. Moreover, for truss-type, axial force members, where both the axial thrust and the cross-sectional areas are constants over the lengths of the members, integration is readily accomplished, that is,

$$\Sigma \int \frac{Pp}{AE}\, dz = \Sigma \left(\frac{PL}{AE}\right)p$$

Considering the bending term, and assuming a member of constant cross-section, the integration can be expressed as

$$\int \frac{Mm}{EI}\, dz = \frac{1}{EI} \int Mm\, dz$$

Given distributions of M and m as functions of z it is possible to obtain algebraic expressions for the integral in question.

For example, if both M and m vary linearly as indicated in Fig. 2.1, the algebraic expression corresponding to the integral would be

$$\frac{1}{EI} \int_0^L Mm\, dz = \frac{L}{3EI}\, [M_L m_L + M_R m_R + \tfrac{1}{2}(M_L m_R + M_R m_L)]$$

(2.2)

For other assumed variations, similar expressions would be obtained.

It should be recognized that since m is due to the application of a single unit load (force or moment), m will always vary linearly if the members are straight. M, however, may vary in a variety of ways depending on the actual applied loading and the structural form. Table 2.1 summarizes a number of the cases more frequently encountered. In the left-hand column are shown various forms for M. Across the top are shown m diagrams. Each table entry is the algebraic result of the integration of the corresponding product. The use of Table 2.1 now will be illustrated.

For the rigid frame shown in Fig. 2.2(a), which is fixed ended at A and free at D, the rotation at point D is to be determined by the unit load method. The M moment diagrams are shown in sketch (b). The m diagrams are in sketch c. (It is to be noted that both of these sets of bending moment diagrams have been shown on the tension side of the members. Between the two, then,

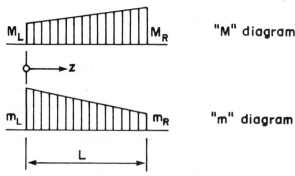

Figure 2.1.   Moment diagram due to applied loading and unit loading, respectively, in the unit load method for determining deformations.

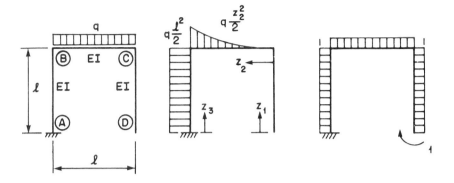

(a) Structure and loading   (b) "M" diagram   (c) "m" diagram

Figure 2.2.   Illustrative example of using the unit load method.

the signs are consistent.) The unit bending moment at D has been chosen in the clockwise direction. A computed plus value for θ_D, therefore, will correspond to a clockwise rotation at that point.

Assuming that only bending deformations are significant [that is, considering only the first term of Eq. (2.1)], the rotation at point D can be determined from the following equation

$$\theta_D = \underbrace{\int_0^l \frac{(0)(1)}{EI}\, dz_1}_{\text{Member C-D}} + \underbrace{\int_0^l \frac{q(z_2)^2(1)}{EI}\, dz_2}_{\text{Member B-C}} + \underbrace{\int_0^l \frac{q(l^2)(1)}{2EI}\, dz_3}_{\text{Member A-B}}$$

Using the algebraic values tabulated in Table 2.1,

$$\theta_D = 0 + \frac{l}{6EI}\left[(1)\left(\frac{ql^2}{2} + \frac{4ql^2}{8}\right)\right] + \left[\frac{l}{EI}\left(\frac{ql^2}{2}\right)(1)\right] = \frac{2}{3}\frac{ql^3}{EI}$$

Deflections in the horizontal and vertical directions at D would be obtained in a similar fashion.

2.2   Flexibility and Stiffness

As noted earlier, there are two basic methods that are used to solve most statically indeterminate structural problems: the *force* (or *flexibility*) *method* and the *displacement* (or *stiffness*) *method*. In the force method the redundant forces (or redundant stress resultants) are taken as the unknown quantities to be determined. In the stiffness method, on the other hand, the

Table 2.1.   Expressions for the typical moment diagrams used by the unit load method.

Evaluation of the integral $\displaystyle\int_0^L Mm\,dz$.

M diagram \\ m diagram	$m_R = m_L$	$m_L \;/\; m_R$	$m_L \;/\; 0$	$m_R = -m_L$	$0 \;/\; m_R$
Linear variation in M					
$M_R = M_L$	$L(M_L m_L)$	$\dfrac{L}{2}[M_L(m_L + m_R)]$	$\dfrac{L}{2}(M_L m_L)$	0	$\dfrac{L}{2}(M_L m_R)$
$M_L \;/\; M_R$	$\dfrac{L}{2}[(M_L + M_R)m_L]$	$\dfrac{L}{3}\big[M_L(m_L + \tfrac{1}{2}m_R) + M_R(m_R + \tfrac{1}{2}m_L)\big]$	$\dfrac{L}{3}[(M_L + \tfrac{1}{2}M_R)m_L]$	$\dfrac{L}{6}(M_L m_L - M_R m_L)$	$\dfrac{L}{3}[(M_R + \tfrac{1}{2}M_L)m_R]$
$M_L \;/\; 0$	$\dfrac{L}{2}(M_L m_L)$	$\dfrac{L}{3}[M_L(m_L + \tfrac{1}{2}m_R)]$	$\dfrac{L}{3}(M_L m_L)$	$\dfrac{L}{6}(M_L m_L)$	$\dfrac{L}{6}(M_L m_R)$
$M_R = -M_L$	0	$\dfrac{L}{6}[M_L(m_L - m_R)]$	$\dfrac{L}{6}(M_L m_L)$	$\dfrac{L}{3}(M_L m_L)$	$-\dfrac{L}{6}(M_L m_R)$
$0 \;/\; M_R$	$\dfrac{L}{2}(M_R m_L)$	$\dfrac{L}{3}[M_R(m_R + \tfrac{1}{2}m_L)]$	$\dfrac{L}{6}(M_R m_L)$	$-\dfrac{L}{6}(M_R m_L)$	$\dfrac{L}{3}(M_R m_R)$

Parabolic variation in M

Diagram					
M_L ⎮⎮⎮⎮ M_C ⎮⎮⎮⎮⎮ M_R (M_C = central ordinate)	$\dfrac{L}{6}[(M_L + 4M_C + M_R)m_L]$	$\dfrac{L}{6}[(M_L + 2M_C)m_L + (2M_C + M_R)m_R]$	$\dfrac{L}{6}[(M_L + 2M_C)m_L]$	$\dfrac{L}{6}[(M_L + M_R)m_L]$	$\dfrac{L}{6}[(2M_C + M_R)m_R]$
0 ⎮ M_C ⎮ 0	$\dfrac{2L}{3}[M_Cm_L]$	$\dfrac{L}{3}[M_C(m_L + m_R)]$	$\dfrac{L}{3}(M_Cm_L)$	0	$\dfrac{L}{3}(M_Cm_L)$
M_L ⎮ M_C ⎮ 0	$\dfrac{L}{6}[(M_L + 4M_C)m_L]$	$\dfrac{L}{6}[(M_L + 2M_C)m_L + 2M_Cm_R]$	$\dfrac{L}{6}[(M_L + 2M_C)m_L]$	$\dfrac{L}{6}(M_Lm_L)$	$\dfrac{L}{3}(M_Cm_R)$
0 ⎮ M_C ⎮ M_R	$\dfrac{L}{6}[(4M_C + M_R)m_L]$	$\dfrac{L}{6}[(2M_C)m_L + (2M_C + M_R)m_R]$	$\dfrac{L}{3}(M_Cm_L)$	$\dfrac{L}{6}(M_Rm_L)$	$\dfrac{L}{6}[(2M_C + M_R)m_R]$

This table is Table 5.1 of Ref. 4.

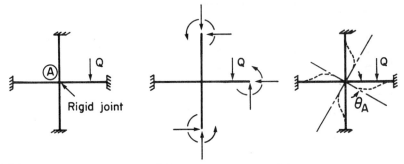

(a) Structure and loading   (b) Force method   (c) Displacement method

Figure 2.3.   Definitions of force method and displacement method in structural analysis.

unknowns are presumed to be translations and/or rotations at one or more joints of the structure. (The unknown forces and/or moments selected in the first method are frequently referred to as *static redundants.* The unknown displacements chosen in the second method are, correspondingly, *kinematic redundants.*)

   Problem formulation using either of these methods relies heavily on the principle of superposition. In both cases there results sets of simultaneous algebraic equations which must be solved. The size (order) of the set that results from the application of the force method corresponds to the number of static redundants in the problem. Similarly, the set resulting from use of the displacement method has a size equal to the number of kinematic redundants. (It is to be understood that since superposition holds only when the behavior is elastic and deformations are small, and since superposition is presumed in both of these procedures, these methods are valid only for linear systems.) In general, the question of which method should be used to solve a particular problem is relatively easy to answer; the method used should be the one which involves the least number of unknowns.

   Consider the four member indeterminate structure shown in Fig. 2.3(a). Each of the members has its outer end fixed—both translationally and rotationally. At A they are all rigidly joined one to the other. A concentrated load Q is applied as indicated. To solve the problem by the force method, it is first necessary to determine the total number of static redundants for the entire system. As shown in sketch (b), there are 9 of these. Thus for this rigid frame to be solved, the force method would involve the solution of a 9×9 set of equations. On the other hand, as indicated in sketch (c), the entire deformed shape of the structure can be described in terms of the single angle

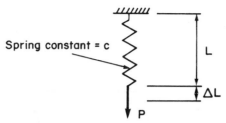

Spring constant = c

Figure 2.4.   Illustration of the concepts of stiffness and flexibility.

θ_A. For the displacement method, then, only one equation need be solved. The choice of method for this problem should be obvious.

The basic concepts of *stiffness* and *flexibility* can be illustrated by considering the behavior of the axially loaded spring shown in Fig. 2.4. The spring in question—by definition—is linearly elastic. For an applied load of P, there results a total change in length of the spring of ΔL. Denoting the spring constant as c, where the units are, for example, lbs/in./in.

$$k = \frac{P}{\Delta L} = cL \text{ (lbs/in.)}$$

where "k" is defined as the *stiffness* of the member. (Note that k is the amount of force that is required to produce one unit of displacement of the total spring.) *Flexibility* (usually denoted by the symbol "u") is defined as the deformation that corresponds to a unit value of the applied load P. That is,

$$u = \frac{\Delta L}{P} \text{ (in./lb)}$$

It should be evident, at least for this case, that stiffness and flexibility are the inverse of each other.

$$k = \frac{1}{u} = u^{-1}, \text{ and } u = \frac{1}{k} = k^{-1}$$

These concepts can be readily extended to real structures and structural members. For example, if a uniform cross-section, axially loaded, tension member of length L and cross-sectional area A is deformed by a length ΔL, the flexibility and stiffness coefficients may be respectively defined as

$$u = \frac{\Delta L}{P} = \frac{L}{AE}$$

$$k = \frac{P}{\Delta L} = \frac{AE}{L} = u^{-1}$$

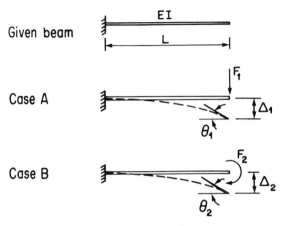

Figure 2.5.   A cantilever beam illustrating the definitions of stiffness and flexibility.

where E is the modulus of elasticity of the material.

Consider as a second example the cantilever beam shown in Fig. 2.5. In this case, presume that two separate and distinct loading conditions exist. The first (Case A) is a vertical force of F_1, applied at the free-end of the member. The second (Case B) is an applied end-bending moment of magnitude F_2. Both of these loadings produce at the free-end of the beam (and for that matter, everywhere along the beam) vertical displacements and bending-type rotations. Defining the vertical deflection at the free-end as "direction 1" and the rotation at the same point as "direction 2," and noting that flexibility has been defined as "displacement per unit of applied load," four separate flexibility quantities must be defined for the beams and loadings in question. For ease of solution and to facilitate discussion, a double subscript notation will be used to identify these various quantities. u_{ij} will stand for the flexibility at the i'th point (or in the i'th direction/or both) resulting from the application of a unit load/or moment at the j'th point (or in the j'th direction/or both). The four flexibilities in question are indicated in Fig. 2.6, where

$$\text{Flexibility} = u_{ij} \underset{\displaystyle\searpoint}{\overset{\displaystyle\text{(position/or direction of displacement)}}{\underset{\text{(position/or direction of unit load or moment)}}{}}}$$

The values of these flexibilities are computed readily using the unit load method discussed in the preceding section of this book.

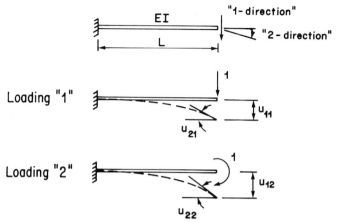

Figure 2.6.   Explanation of the definition of flexibility coefficients.

$$u_{ij} = \int_0^L \frac{m_j m_i}{EI} \, dz \tag{2.3}$$

m_j is the moment resulting from a unit load (or moment) in the j'th direction, and m_i is the moment caused by a unit load (or moment) in the i'th direction/or at the i'th position. For this example, m_1 and m_2 are shown in Fig. 2.7. (In both of these cases, the moment values are shown on the compression side of the member.) Therefore,

$$u_{11} = \int_0^L \frac{m_1{}^2}{EI} \, dz = \frac{L^3}{3EI}$$

$$u_{21} = \int_0^L \frac{m_2 m_1}{EI} \, dz = \frac{L^2}{2EI}$$

$$u_{22} = \int_0^L \frac{m_2{}^2}{EI} \, dz = \frac{L}{EI}$$

$$u_{12} = \int_0^L \frac{m_1 m_2}{EI} \, dz = \frac{L^2}{2EI} = u_{21}$$

If the concentrated load F_1 is applied as shown in Fig. 2.5, Δ and θ can be computed directly from these flexibility values.

$$\Delta_1 = F_1 u_{11}$$

$$\theta_1 = F_1 u_{21}$$

If the moment F_2 is applied,

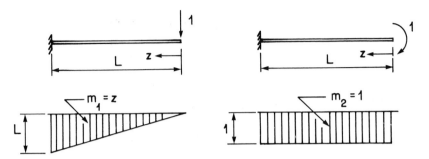

Figure 2.7.   Use of unit load methods to determine the flexibility coefficient of a cantilever beam.

$$\Delta_2 = F_2 u_{12}$$

$$\theta_2 = F_2 u_{22}$$

If both F_1 and F_2 are applied simultaneously, and Δ is the total vertical displacement of the free end, and θ is the total bending rotation at that same point, then

$$\Delta = F_1 u_{11} + F_2 u_{12}$$

$$\theta = F_1 u_{21} + F_2 u_{22}$$

In matrix form, this would be written as

$$\underbrace{\begin{bmatrix} u_{11} & u_{12} \\ u_{21} & u_{22} \end{bmatrix}}_{\substack{\text{Flexibility} \\ \text{Matrix}}} \underbrace{\begin{bmatrix} F_1 \\ F_2 \end{bmatrix}}_{\substack{\text{Force} \\ \text{Matrix} \\ \text{(or Vector)}}} = \underbrace{\begin{bmatrix} \Delta \\ \theta \end{bmatrix}}_{\substack{\text{Displacement} \\ \text{Matrix} \\ \text{(or Vector)}}}$$

It also could be written as

$$[U][F] = [D]$$

in which

$$[U] = \begin{bmatrix} \left(\dfrac{L^3}{3EI}\right) & \left(\dfrac{L^2}{2EI}\right) \\ \left(\dfrac{L^2}{2EI}\right) & \left(\dfrac{L}{EI}\right) \end{bmatrix} = \text{Flexibility Matrix}$$

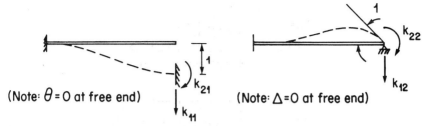

Figure 2.8. Definitions of stiffness coefficient.

The flexibility matrix $[U]$ will always be square and symmetrical, and will have as many rows as the number of degrees of freedom of the system being described.

It should be recognized that this formulation is nothing more than a direct application of the method of superposition.

The *stiffness* of the beam at its free-end can be derived in a similar fashion, noting that stiffness—by definition—is the stress resultant necessary to produce a unit deformation in the direction in question. It also can be obtained by *inverting* the flexibility matrix*.

$$\text{Stiffness Matrix} = [K] = [U]^{-1} = \begin{bmatrix} k_{11} & k_{12} \\ k_{21} & k_{22} \end{bmatrix}$$

$$= \begin{bmatrix} \left(\dfrac{12EI}{L^3}\right) & \left(\dfrac{-6EI}{L^2}\right) \\ \left(\dfrac{-6EI}{L^2}\right) & \left(\dfrac{4EI}{L}\right) \end{bmatrix} \quad (2.4)$$

By definition, each element k_{ij} of the stiffness matrix represents the stress resultant induced in the i'th direction (or in the i'th position) by a unit of deformation in the j'th direction (or the j'th position) *with all other deformations prevented*. This is shown diagrammatically in Fig. 2.8. (It should be recognized that a direct solution for the various k_{ij}'s requires the solution of two indeterminate structural problems.)

It is to be noted in Fig. 2.8 that the force and moment vectors indicated, which in effect are the various terms of the stiffness matrix, are shown in assumed directions consistent with those of Fig. 2.7. This is in spite of the fact that one could reasonably conclude in advance, from elementary equilibrium considerations, that certain of the vectors would actually act in the

---

* For a review of various methods of matrix inversion see R. L. Ketter and S. P. Prawel, *Modern Methods of Engineering Computation*, Chapter 6, McGraw-Hill Book Company, 1969.

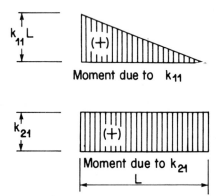

Figure 2.9. Use of moment-area method to determine the stiffness coefficient of a cantilever beam.

opposite sense. For the cases shown, it has been assumed that forces and moments acting on the ends of the member are plus when they tend to produce clockwise rotations. Similarly, clockwise rotations at the ends and/or relative end deflections that cause overall clockwise rotations of the entire member are presumed positive.

For the first of the loading conditions shown in Fig. 2.8 the moment diagrams would be those shown in Fig. 2.9. Using the moment-area method, for example, to define the deformations of the right-hand end of the member

$$\theta = 0 = \frac{1}{2}\left(\frac{k_{11}L}{EI}\right)(L) + \left(\frac{k_{21}}{EI}\right)(L)$$

and

$$\Delta = 1 = \frac{1}{2}\left(\frac{k_{11}L}{EI}\right)(L)\left(\frac{2L}{3}\right) + \left(\frac{k_{21}}{EI}\right)(L)\left(\frac{L}{2}\right)$$

Solving these equations simultaneously yields

$$k_{11} = \left(\frac{12EL}{L^3}\right)$$

and

$$k_{21} = \left(\frac{-6EI}{L^2}\right)$$

If the same procedure were used for the second of the two indicated loading conditions, the following would be obtained:

$$\theta = 1 = \frac{1}{2}\left(\frac{k_{12}L}{EI}\right)(L) + \left(\frac{k_{22}}{EI}\right)(L)$$

$$\Delta = 0 = \frac{1}{2}\left(\frac{k_{12}L}{EI}\right)(L)\left(\frac{2L}{3}\right) + \left(\frac{k_{22}}{EI}\right)(L)\left(\frac{L}{2}\right)$$

from which it can be determined that

$$k_{12} = \left(\frac{-6EI}{L^2}\right)$$

$$k_{22} = \left(\frac{4EI}{L}\right)$$

[These are the same values that are given in Eq. (2.4), which were determined by inverting the earlier derived flexibility matrix.]

   The above discussion was concerned with stiffness at the free-end of the
cantilever. Using the same definition, stiffness at the fixed-end due to deformations and/or loads at the free-end could be developed. For example,
a unit deformation in the "1-direction" at the free-end produces in addition
to the force and moment k_{11} and k_{21} at the free-end, k^c_{11} and k^c_{21} at the
fixed-end as shown in Fig. 2.10. Similarly a unit rotation at the free-end
produces a vertical reaction k^c_{12} and a bending moment k^c_{22} at the left-end.
These are in addition to k_{12} and k_{22} at the right-hand, unit-displacement
end. In both of these cases, the superscript c has been used to indicate the
carry-over effect.

   The *carry-over stiffness matrix* is defined as

$$[K^c] = \begin{bmatrix} k^c_{11} & k^c_{12} \\ k^c_{21} & k^c_{22} \end{bmatrix} \tag{2.5}$$

The values of the individual elements in this matrix can be determined from
a consideration of static equilibrium, knowing the values of k_{11}, k_{12}, k_{21},
and k_{22}.

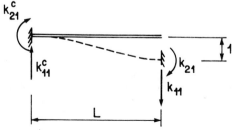

Figure 2.10.   Definitions of the stiffness coefficient of a beam.

$$[K^c] = \begin{bmatrix} (k_{11}) & (k_{12}) \\ (-k_{21} - k_{11}L) & (-k_{22} - k_{12}L) \end{bmatrix} = \begin{bmatrix} \left(\dfrac{12EI}{L^3}\right) & \left(\dfrac{-6EI}{L^2}\right) \\ \left(\dfrac{-6EI}{L^2}\right) & \left(\dfrac{2EI}{L}\right) \end{bmatrix}$$

The ratio k_{ij}^c/k_{ij} is referred to as the *carry-over factor* c_{ij}. For example,

$$c_{22} = \frac{k_{22}^c}{k_{22}} = \frac{\left(\dfrac{2EL}{L}\right)}{\left(\dfrac{4EI}{L}\right)} = +\frac{1}{2}$$

$$c_{21} = \frac{k_{21}^c}{k_{21}} = \frac{\left(\dfrac{-6EI}{L^2}\right)}{\left(\dfrac{-6EI}{L^2}\right)} = +1$$

The plus signs denote that the carry-over moment and shear at the far-end of the member will act in a direction and in a sense consistent with the chosen "clockwise positive" sign system. This is not to say that they necessarily will act upward or clockwise—since ratios have been taken—but that the two ends will act consistently, as per the assumed directions.

2.3   Flexibility Method: The Method of Consistent Deformations

An indeterminate structure, made determinate by the introduction of unknown forces and/or moments for the chosen redundants, will have an infinite number of possible values or combinations of values of those redundants that will satisfy the equations of static equilibrium. There will be one and only one set, however, that will yield deformations that are geometrically compatible with the originally defined problem.

The procedure that normally is used when solving problems by this method requires that the given indeterminate structure first be made determinate by the removal of a "sufficient number" of unknowns. (The choice of one particular set of unknowns as opposed to another set will depend on a variety of factors, not the least of which is the personal preference of the analyst. It is to be noted, however, that in a number of cases a judicious selection can materially reduce the amount of work required to obtain an answer.)

The determinate structure that results from the removal of the redundants is often referred to as the *Base Structure*. For that structure, deformations in the directions of each of the chosen redundants can be determined using the unit load method. Assigning reference numbers to these locations and directions, a flexibility matrix can be established. Since each of the coefficients u_{ij} represents a displacement in the "i'th" direction due to the application of a unit force in the "j'th" direction, superposition can be used to define the composite effect of the various applied and redundant forces and/or moments, and these expressions can be written in such a fashion that they "force" the originally specified geometry at the redundant locations. There results a set of simultaneous algebraic equations equal in number to the number of redundants for the structure which must be satisfied. The unknowns are the magnitudes of the redundants.

As an example of the process just described, consider the structure and loading shown in Fig. 2.11. The structure is a "propped cantilever beam" which is one-time redundant. It is subjected to a uniformly distributed vertical load of q lbs/ft. applied over the entire length of the member. Since no horizontal loads are specified, and since only the reaction at A can resist horizontal forces, it can be concluded that the horizontal reaction at end A is zero. The remaining components of reactions are $M_A, R_A,$ and R_B. Any one of these reactions—or for the matter, any internal stress resultant—could be selected as the redundant. The three separate cases indicated in the figure will be considered for this example.

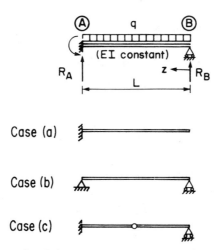

Figure 2.11.   Solutions of an indeterminate beam by the method of consistent deformations.

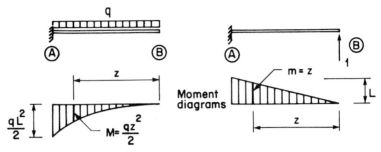

Figure 2.11a.

Case (a):

In this case the base structure is a cantilever beam. The governing loadings, moment diagrams and deflections are those shown in Fig. 2.11(a).

Using the unit load method, the deflection of the base structure at location B, the end of the cantilever beam, is

$$\Delta_B = \int_0^L \frac{Mm}{EI}\, dz = \int_0^L \frac{qz^2}{2EI}(-z)\, dz = -\left(\frac{qL^4}{8EI}\right)$$

(The negative sign indicates that end B deflects in a direction opposite to that assumed by the unit upward vertical force applied at B.)

The vertical deflection of point B due to the application of the redundant force R_B can be determined by multiplying by R_B the response of the structure to a unit load at that point. That is,

$$\Delta_B' = R_B(u_{11}) = R_B \int_0^L \frac{m^2}{EI}\, dz = R_B \int_0^L \frac{z^2}{EI}\, dz = R_B\left(\frac{L^3}{3EI}\right)$$

For zero deflection at point B in the indeterminate (real) structure,

$$\Delta_B + \Delta_B' = 0$$

or

$$\left(\frac{-qL^4}{8EI}\right) + R_B\left(\frac{L^3}{3EI}\right) = 0$$

This gives for the redundant reaction

$$R_B = +\frac{3}{8}qL$$

Case (b):

In this case the base structure is presumed to be a simple beam. (The se-

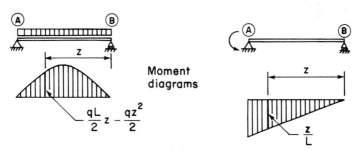

Applied Loading on Base Structure   Redundant Loading on Base Structure

Moment
diagrams

$$-\frac{qL}{2}z - \frac{qz^2}{2}$$

$$\frac{z}{L}$$

Figure 2.11b.

lected redundant is the end-moment M_A.) The deformation in question—
that is, the one to be "forced" by the formulation—is the bending rotation
at end A. The necessary condition for a solution is, therefore,

$$\theta_A + \theta'_A = 0$$

In terms of the applied and unit-load moments,

$$\int_0^L \frac{Mm}{EI}\, dz + M_A \int_0^L \frac{m^2}{EI}\, dz = 0$$

or

$$\int_0^L \frac{\left(\frac{qLz}{2} - \frac{qz^2}{2}\right)\left(\frac{-z}{L}\right) dz}{EI} + M_A \int_0^L \frac{\left(\frac{-z}{L}\right)\left(\frac{-z}{L}\right) dz}{EI} = 0$$

This yields the control equation

$$\left(\frac{-qL^3}{24EI}\right) + M_A\left(\frac{L}{3EI}\right) = 0$$

The redundant end-moment is therefore

$$M_A = +\frac{1}{8}qL^2$$

Case (c):

Next consider the same problem, but this time presume that the structure
is made determinate by the introduction of a "pin" (hinge) at the midspan

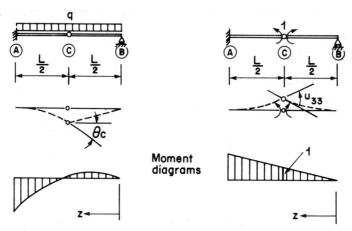

Figure 2.11c.

of the beam as shown in Fig. 2.11(c). Deformation consistent with the original geometry (at the location of the chosen redundant) requires that

$$\theta_C + M_C(u_{33}) = 0$$

or

$$\int_A^C \frac{M_{AC} m_{AC}}{EI} \, dz + \int_C^B \frac{M_{BC} m_{BC}}{EI} \, dz + M_C \left[\int_A^C \frac{m^2_{AC}}{EI} \, dz \right.$$

$$\left. + \int_C^B \frac{m^2_{BC}}{EI} \, dz \right] = 0$$

Carrying out these integrations and solving for M_C yields

$$M_C = + \frac{1}{16} qL^2$$

The analysis of pinned-base, gable frames consisting of tapered members now will be considered using the flexibility approach. A typical frame is shown in Fig. 2.12. (It must be noted at the outset that for frames such as this, the most convenient method of analysis is the finite element method, especially when it is used in conjunction with a digital computer. Such an approach will be developed later in this book. The purpose of considering the problem at this stage is to illustrate in a more general fashion the method of consistent deformations.)

For the structure shown in Fig. 2.12, the base determinate structure is

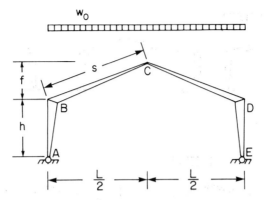

Figure 2.12. A typical pinned-base gable frame consisting of tapered members.

selected by removing the horizontal reaction at the hinge base, say, at point
E. Due to the applied loading, point E will move horizontally relative to
point A by an amount Δ. The magnitude of Δ can be determined by the unit
load method. This same base structure then can be subjected to a unit load
in the direction of the assumed redundant H_E and the displacement in that
same direction determined. (It is to be recognized that the resulting deformation will equal u, the flexibility coefficient for this single redundant
system.) With this information the unknown redundant H_E can be determined from the compatibility condition

$$\Delta + (H_E)(u) = 0 \tag{2.6}$$

where

$$\Delta = \sum \int \frac{(M_{\text{det}})(m_E)}{EI_z} \, dz$$

and

$$u = \sum \int \frac{(m_E)^2}{EI_z} \, dz$$

The variation in cross-sectional properties along the lengths of the various
members is taken into account by the general functional expression I_z.

   In these equations M_{det} is the moment in the base structure due to the
actual applied loading. m_E is the moment due to a unit load applied in the
horizontal direction at E. u is the resulting flexibility coefficient and is not
a function of the applied loading. It may be used, therefore, for all types and
kinds of loading conditions for the particular structure in question. Δ in Eq.

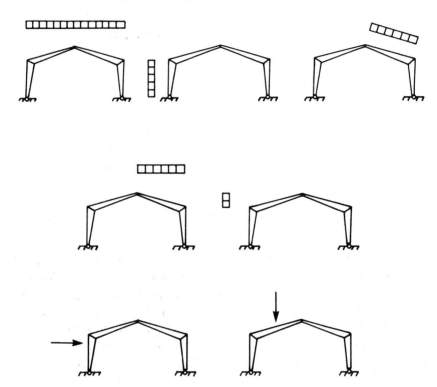

Figure 2.13.　Possible loading cases to be considered in typical gable frame design.

(2.6), on the other hand, is dependent upon the particular externally imposed loading condition under consideration. For a variety of different loadings applied to the same structure, then, Eq. (2.6) may be written in the following more general form:

$$H_E = \frac{\Delta_i}{(u)}, \text{ where } i = \text{I, II, III, } \ldots$$

(The various applied loading conditions are noted as I, II, III, ...)

In typical gable frame design, several different loading conditions must be considered. Figure 2.13 shows seven such cases. Proper combination of these will provide the important possibilities for most design situations.

In the example shown in Fig. 2.12, the first of these loading conditions was specified: a uniformly distributed vertical load of w_0 lbs/in. acting over the entire length of the structure. The bending moment diagrams $M_{\det}$ and m_E acting on the base structure (that is, after removing the redundant H_E) are shown in Fig. 2.14.

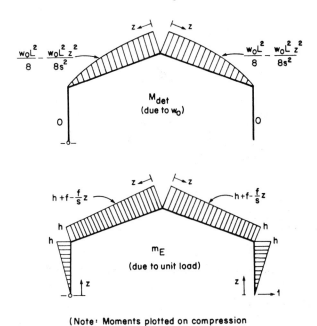

Figure 2.14. Moment diagrams of the frame of Fig. 2.12 due to applied load and unit load, respectively.

The resulting expressions are obtained:

$$\Delta_I = \sum \int \frac{(M_{\text{det}})(m_E)}{EI_{b_z}} \, dz$$

or

$$\Delta_I = 2 \int_0^s \frac{\left(\dfrac{w_0 L^2}{8} - \dfrac{w_0 L^2 z^2}{8s^2} \right)\left(h + f - \dfrac{f}{s} z \right)}{EI_{b_z}} \, dz \tag{2.7}$$

and

$$u = \sum \int \frac{(m_E)^2}{EI_z} \, dz$$

or

$$u = 2 \int_0^h \frac{(z)^2}{EI_{c_z}} \, dz + 2 \int \frac{\left(h + f - \dfrac{f}{s} z \right)^2}{EI_{b_z}} \, dz \tag{2.8}$$

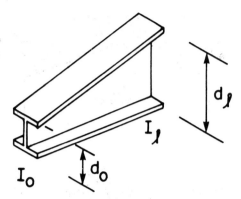

Figure 2.15.   Typical nomenclature defining the depth and moment of inertia variations in tapered members.

I_{b_z} and I_{c_z} are functions of the independent variable z. The evaluation of the integrals, therefore, obviously is not straightforward. If the variations in I along the lengths of the members are extremely simple algebraic functions or constants, direct integration may be considered, but such is seldom the case for "real" tapered member designs. Numerical integration procedures more often than not are required. A method of "Substitution Integration" used by Tuma and Munshi (Ref. 31) is one such procedure that appears to have rather wide applicability. (The equations contained in the remainder of this section are based upon that referenced work.)

The following definition of constants is necessary for all seven of the loading cases of Fig. 2.13 (see Fig. 2.15).

$$\gamma = \left(\frac{d_l}{d_0} - 1\right) = \text{taper ratio}$$

d_0 and I_0 = smaller end depth and moment of inertia, respectively

d_l and I_l = larger end depth and moment of inertia, respectively

$$\rho = \frac{\log I_l - \log I_0}{\log d_l - \log d_0}$$

$$I_l = I_0(1 + \gamma)^2(1 + \mu\gamma)$$

$$\mu = \left(\frac{d_0{}^3}{12}\right)\left(\frac{t_w}{I_0}\right)$$

t_w = web thickness

(γ and ρ will be subscripted with either b or c, depending on whether they refer to a beam or a column in the rigid frame.)

(i) *For the beams* (*girders*)—without concentrated loads

$$\gamma_b = \text{taper ratio}$$

$$\rho_b = \frac{\log I_l - \log I_0}{\log d_l - \log d_0}$$

$$Q_{0b} = \frac{b_{0b}}{\gamma_b} \qquad\qquad b_{0b} = \frac{(1 + \gamma_b)^{1-\rho_b} - 1}{(1 - \rho_b)}$$

$$Q_{1b} = \frac{b_{1b} - b_{0b}}{\gamma_b{}^2} \qquad\qquad b_{1b} = \frac{(1 + \gamma_b)^{2-\rho_b} - 1}{(2 - \rho_b)}$$

$$Q_{2b} = \frac{b_{2b} - 2b_{1b} + b_{0b}}{\gamma_b{}^3} \qquad\qquad b_{2b} = \frac{(1 + \gamma_b)^{3-\rho_b} - 1}{(3 - \rho_b)}$$

$$Q_{3b} = \frac{b_{3b} - 3b_{2b} + 3b_{1b} - b_{0b}}{\gamma_b{}^4} \qquad\qquad b_{3b} = \frac{(1 + \gamma_b)^{4-\rho_b} - 1}{(4 - \rho_b)}$$

(ii) *For the columns*—without concentrated loads.

$$\gamma_c = \text{taper ratio}$$

$$\rho_c = \frac{\log I_l - \log I_0}{\log d_l - \log d_0}$$

$$Q_{0c} = \frac{b_{0c}}{\gamma_c} \qquad\qquad b_{0c} = \frac{(1 + \gamma_c)^{1-\rho_c} - 1}{(1 - \rho_c)}$$

$$Q_{1c} = \frac{b_{1c} - b_{0c}}{\gamma_c{}^a} \qquad\qquad b_{1c} = \frac{(1 + \gamma_c)^{2-\rho_c} - 1}{(2 - \rho_c)}$$

$$Q_{2c} = \frac{b_{2c} - 2b_{1c} + b_{0c}}{\gamma_c{}^3} \qquad\qquad b_{2c} = \frac{(1 + \gamma_c)^{3-\rho_c} - 1}{(3 - \rho_c)}$$

$$Q_{3c} = \frac{b_{3c} - 3b_{2c} + 3b_{1c} - b_{0c}}{\gamma_c{}^4} \qquad\qquad b_{3c} = \frac{(1 + \gamma_c)^{4-\rho_c} - 1}{(4 - \rho_c)}$$

(iii) *For the beams*—with a concentrated load acting on the left-hand span, αL away from the top of the left-hand column (see Fig. 2.16).

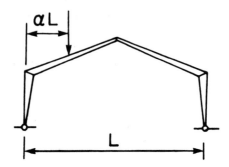

Figure 2.16.   A typical gable frame subjected to vertical concentrated load.

$$k = 1 - 2\alpha$$

$$Q'_{0b} = \frac{b'_{0b}}{\gamma_b} \qquad\qquad b'_{0b} = \frac{(1 + k\gamma_b)^{1-\rho_b} - 1}{(1 - \rho_b)}$$

$$Q'_{1b} = \frac{b'_{1b} - b'_{0b}}{\gamma_b{}^2} \qquad\qquad b'_{1b} = \frac{(1 + k\gamma_b)^{2-\rho_b} - 1}{(2 - \rho_b)}$$

$$Q'_{2b} = \frac{b'_{2b} - 2b'_{1b} + b'_{0b}}{\gamma_b{}^3} \qquad\qquad b'_{2b} = \frac{(1 + k\gamma_b)^{3-\rho_b} - 1}{(3 - \rho_b)}$$

$$Q'_{3b} = \frac{b'_{3b} - 3b'_{2b} + 3b'_{1b} - b'_{0b}}{\gamma_b{}^4} \qquad\qquad b'_{3b} = \frac{(1 + k\gamma_b)^{4-\rho_b} - 1}{(4 - \rho_b)}$$

Furthermore, for this particular loading it is necessary to break up the beam into two segments at the loading point by defining

$$\gamma''_b = \left(\frac{d_l}{d_p} - 1\right)$$

d_l = larger end depth

d_p = depth of the beam at the location of application of the concentrated load in the beam

$$\rho''_b = \frac{\log I_l - \log I_p}{\log d_l - \log d_p}$$

I_p = moment of inertia of the cross section at the load point

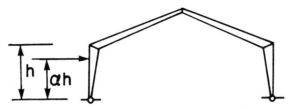

Figure 2.17.   A typical gable frame subjected to horizontal concentrated load.

$$Q''_{0b} = \frac{b''_{0b}}{\gamma''_b}$$

$$b''_{0b} = \frac{(1 + \gamma''_b)^{1-\rho''_b} - 1}{(1 - \rho''_b)}$$

$$Q''_{1b} = \frac{b''_{1b} - b''_{0b}}{(\gamma''_b)^2}$$

$$b''_{1b} = \frac{(1 + \gamma''_b)^{2-\rho''_b} - 1}{(2 - \rho''_b)}$$

$$Q''_{2b} = \frac{b''_{2b} - 2b''_{1b} + b''_{0b}}{(\gamma''_b)^3}$$

$$b''_{2b} = \frac{(1 + \gamma''_b)^{3-\rho''_b} - 1}{(3 - \rho''_b)}$$

$$Q''_{3b} = \frac{b''_{3b} - 3b''_{2b} + 3b''_{1b} - b''_{0b}}{(\gamma''_b)^4}$$

$$b''_{3b} = \frac{(1 + \gamma''_b)^{4-\rho''_b} - 1}{(4 - \rho''_b)}$$

(iv)   For the columns—with a concentrated load applied at αh from the base of the column (see Fig. 2.17).

$$k = \alpha$$

$$Q^*_{0c} = \frac{b^*_{0c}}{\gamma_c}$$

$$b^*_{0c} = \frac{(1 + k\gamma_c)^{1-\rho_c} - 1}{(1 - \rho_c)}$$

$$Q^*_{1c} = \frac{b^*_{1c} - b^*_{0c}}{\gamma_c^2}$$

$$b^*_{1c} = \frac{(1 + k\gamma_c)^{2-\rho_c} - 1}{(2 - \rho_c)}$$

$$Q^*_{2c} = \frac{b^*_{2c} - 2b^*_{1c} + b^*_{0c}}{\gamma_c^3}$$

$$b^*_{2c} = \frac{(1 + k\gamma_c)^{3-\rho_c} - 1}{(3 - \rho_c)}$$

$$Q^*_{3c} = \frac{b^*_{3c} - 3b^*_{2c} + 3b^*_{1c} - b^*_{0c}}{\gamma_c^4}$$

$$b^*_{3c} = \frac{(1 + k\gamma_c)^{4-\rho_c} - 1}{(4 - \rho_c)}$$

Moreover, defining

$$\gamma^{**} = \left(\frac{d_l}{d_p} - 1\right)$$

d_p and I_l = depth and moment of inertia at the location of application of the concentrated load in the column

$$\rho^{**} = \frac{\log I_l - \log I_p}{\log d_l - \log d_p}$$

$$Q_{0c}^{**} = \frac{b_{0c}^{**}}{\gamma_c^{**}}$$

$$b_{0c}^{**} = \frac{(1 + \gamma_c^{**})^{1-\rho_c^{**}} - 1}{(1 - \rho_c^{**})}$$

$$Q_{1c}^{**} = \frac{b_{1c}^{**} - b_{0c}^{**}}{(\gamma_c^{**})^2}$$

$$b_{1c}^{**} = \frac{(1 + \gamma_c^{**})^{2-\rho_c^{**}} - 1}{(2 - \rho_c^{**})}$$

$$Q_{2c}^{**} = \frac{b_{2c}^{**} - 2b_{1c}^{**} + b_{0c}^{**}}{(\gamma_c^{**})^3}$$

$$b_{2c}^{**} = \frac{(1 + \gamma_c^{**})^{3-\rho_c^{**}} - 1}{(3 - \rho_c^{**})}$$

$$Q_{3c}^{**} = \frac{b_{3c}^{**} - 3b_{2c}^{**} + 3b_{1c}^{**} - b_{0c}^{**}}{(\gamma_c^{**})^4}$$

$$b_{3c}^{**} = \frac{(1 + \gamma_c^{**})^{4-\rho_c^{**}} - 1}{(4 - \rho_c^{**})}$$

Using the above definitions and noting the following

$$I_z \div I_0 \left(1 + \gamma \frac{z}{L}\right)^{\rho} = I_0(U)^{\rho}$$

Equations (2.7) and (2.8) can be evaluated. Upon substitution of variables, Eq. (2.7) becomes

$$\Delta_I = \left(\frac{w_0 L^2 s}{4E(I_0)_b}\right) \int_0^1 \frac{[h + f - f\rho_b - h\rho_b^2 - f\rho_b^2 + f\rho_b^3]}{[U^{\rho_b}]} d\rho_b$$

or

$$\Delta_I = \left(\frac{w_0 L^2 s}{4E(I_0)_b}\right) [Q_{0b}(h + f) - Q_{1b}(f) - Q_{2b}(h + f) + Q_{3b}(f)]$$

For Eq. (2.8)

$$u = \left(\frac{2h}{E(I_0)_c}\right) \int_0^1 \frac{h^2 \rho_c^2}{(U)^{\rho_c}} d\rho_c +$$

$$\left(\frac{2s}{E(I_0)_b}\right) \times \int_0^1 \frac{h^2 + 2hf + f^2 - 2hf\rho_b - 2f^2\rho_b + f^2\rho_b^2}{(U)^{\rho_b}} d\rho_b$$

$$= \left(\frac{2h^3}{E(I_0)_c}\right) Q_{2c} + \left(\frac{2s}{E(I_0)_b}\right) [Q_{0b}(h + f)^2 - 2Q_{1b}(hf + f^2) + Q_{2b}f^2]$$

or

$$u = \left(\frac{2h^3}{E(I_0)_c}\right) Q_{2c} + \left(\frac{2s^3}{E(I_0)_b}\right) \left[\left(\frac{h}{s} + \frac{f}{s}\right)^2 Q_{0b} - 2\left(\frac{fh}{s^2} + \frac{f^2}{s^2}\right) Q_{1b} + \left(\frac{f^2}{s^2}\right) Q_{2b}\right]$$

The horizontal reaction H_E would be evaluated using Eq. (2.6).

For illustration, consider the frame defined in Fig. 2.12, with the following specified dimensions:

$$f = 5'$$

$$h = 18'$$

$$L = 60'$$

For the beams:

$$d_0 = 6''$$

$$b = 4''$$

$$t_f = 0.25''$$

$$t_w = 0.10''$$

For the columns:

$$d_0 = 12''$$

$$b = 6''$$

$$t_f = 0.25''$$

$$t_w = 0.10''$$

The following parameters can be calculated:

$$s = \sqrt{925} = 30.4'$$

$$I_{ob} = 17.93 \text{ in.}^4, \quad I_{lb} = 17.9 (1 + \gamma_b)^2 (1 + 0.088\gamma_b)$$

$$I_{oc} = 116.24 \text{ in.}^4, \quad I_{lc} = 116.24 (1 + \gamma_c)^2 (1 + 0.116\gamma_c)$$

Using these particular numerical values and relationships, the horizontal reaction can be obtained in non-dimensional form, as functions of γ_b and γ_c. This is shown in Fig. 2.18.

Assuming that the smaller end dimensions of the beams and columns as well as the overall frame geometry are prescribed, the curve given in Fig. 2.18 may be used for design purposes. They would allow selection of appropriate taper ratios for the beams and columns—since the resulting H_E can be used directly in the determination of the bending moment diagram (that is, the structure is statically determinate).

It should be evident that charts and/or curves similar to those given in Fig. 2.18 could be generated for a variety of loadings and variable param-

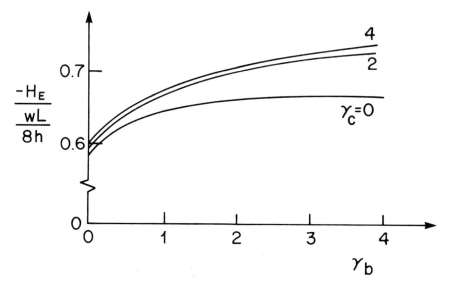

Figure 2.18.   Relationship of the horizontal reaction and the taper ratio.

eters. However, a large number of such curves would have to be developed to cover the entire range of dimensions and frame geometries used in present day engineering practice. For the special case of frame geometry where the span is relatively short and the beams and columns have approximately the same Q values, the horizontal reaction H_E for all seven of the basic loading conditions referred to earlier (Fig. 2.13) are summarized in Fig. 2.19.

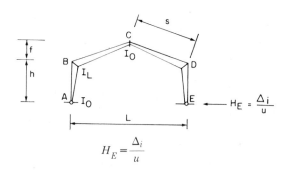

$$H_E = \frac{\Delta_i}{u}$$

where

$$u = \frac{2s^3}{4EI_0}\left[Q_0\left(\frac{h}{s}+\frac{f}{s}\right)^2 - Q_1\left(\frac{2fh}{s^2}+\frac{2f^2}{s^2}\right) + Q_2\left(\frac{f^2}{s^2}+\frac{h^3}{s^3}\right)\right]$$

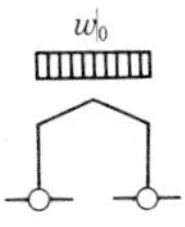

$$\Delta_I = \frac{w_0 L^2 s}{4EI_0}[Q_0(h + f) - Q_1(f) - Q_2(h + f) + Q_3(f)]$$

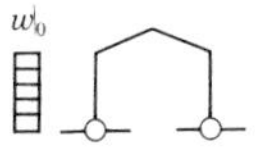

$$\Delta_{II} = \frac{w_0 h^2 s}{2EI_0}\left[Q_0(h + f) - Q_1(f) + Q_2\left(\frac{h^2}{s}\right) - Q_3\left(\frac{h^2}{s}\right)\right]$$

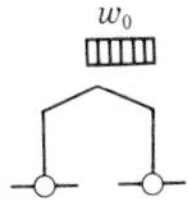

$$\Delta_{III} = \frac{w_0 L^2 s}{8EI_0}[(Q_0 - Q_2)(h + f) - (Q_1 - Q_3)(f)]$$

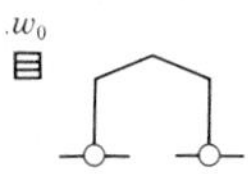

$$\Delta_{IV} = \frac{w_0 f^2 s}{2EI_0}\left[Q_0\left(3h + \frac{2h}{f} + f\right) - Q_1(f + 2h)\right.$$
$$\left. - Q_2\left(h - \frac{2h^3}{sf} + f\right) + Q_3(f)\right]$$

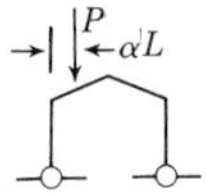

$$\Delta_V = \frac{PL\alpha s}{2EI_0}[Q_0(h + f) - Q_1(h + 2f) + Q_2(f)]$$
$$+ \frac{PL\alpha s}{2EI_0}[Q_0'(h + f)(1 - 2s) + Q_1'(h)(1 - 2\alpha)^2$$
$$- Q_2'(f)(1 - 2\alpha)^3] + \frac{PL\alpha^2 s}{2EI_p}[Q_0''(4h - 4\alpha h + 8\alpha f$$
$$- 4\alpha^2 f) + Q_1''(2\alpha h - 2h + 8\alpha^2 f - 8\alpha f)$$
$$+ Q_2''(2\alpha f + 2\alpha^2 f)]$$

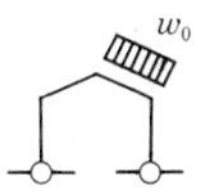

$$\Delta_{VI} = \frac{w_0 s^3}{2EI_0}\left[Q_0\left(5h\frac{f^2}{s^2} - \frac{hL^2}{4s^2} + \frac{2fh^2}{s^2} + \frac{3f^3}{s^2} - \frac{fL^2}{4s^2}\right)\right.$$
$$- Q_1\left(\frac{6hf^2}{s^2} + \frac{7f^3}{s^2} - \frac{fL^2}{4s^2}\right) + Q_2\left(h + f + \frac{4f^3}{s^2} + \frac{2fh^3}{s^3}\right)$$
$$\left. - Q_3(f)\right]$$

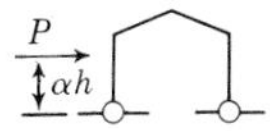

$$\Delta_{VII} = -\frac{\alpha Ph^3}{EI_0}\left\{\left[Q_0\left(\frac{s}{h} + \frac{fs}{h^2}\right) - Q_1\left(\frac{fs}{h^2}\right) + Q_2'(\alpha^2)\right]\right.$$
$$\left. + \frac{I_0}{I_p}[Q_0''(\alpha - \alpha^2) + Q_1''(1 - 2\alpha + \alpha^2)]\right\}$$

Note: These equations are exact for the case where d_0 and I_0 are the same at the three locations A, C, and E.

Figure 2.19. Horizontal reactions of a gable frame consisting of tapered members due to seven possible loadings.

2.4   Stiffness Method: The Slope-Deflection Method

When analyzing indeterminate structures by the stiffness method, the un-knowns to be assumed are deformations (deflections and/or rotations) at the various joints. The number of independent deformational quantities required to fully describe the deformed shape of the total structure is fre-quently referred to as the *degrees of freedom* of the structure.

To facilitate solution, it is necessary that there be available for the various types and kinds of members used in the structure expressions describing the interrelationships that must necessarily exist between the forces (and/or moments) acting at the "ends" of the member and the resulting end dis-placements and/or rotations. These relationships are—by definition—the stiffness coefficients defined in Section 2.2 of this book. For rigidly connected structures where the individual members are primarily subjected to bending, these relationships are usually written in what has become known as the *slope-deflection* form:

$$M_{AB} = k_{AA}\theta_A + c_{AB}k_{BB}\theta_B - k_\Delta \left(\frac{\Delta}{L}\right) + M_{AB}^F \qquad (2.9)$$

$$M_{BA} = c_{BA}k_{AA}\theta_A + k_{BB}\theta_B - k_\Delta \left(\frac{\Delta}{L}\right) + M_{BA}^F \qquad (2.10)$$

where A and B are the ends of a given member A–B in a continuous struc-ture (for example, the one shown in Fig. 2.20); k_{AA} and k_{BB} are the rota-tional stiffnesses at A and B, respectively; c_{AB} and c_{BA} are the bending moment carry-over factors from A to B and B to A, respectively; k_Δ is the translational stiffness of the members; and M_{AB}^F and M_{BA}^F are the fixed-end moments at A and B for the imposed lateral loading. For prismatic members the various terms can be shown to be

$$k_{AA} = k_{BB} = \frac{4EI}{L}$$

$$c_{AB} = c_{BA} = +\frac{1}{2}$$

$$k_\Delta = -\frac{6EI}{L^2}$$

The slope-deflection equations for prismatic members are, therefore,

$$M_{AB} = \frac{2EI}{L}\left(2\theta_A + \theta_B - 3\frac{\Delta}{L}\right) + M_{AB}^F$$

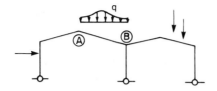

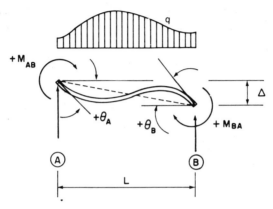

Figure 2.20.   Definition of the slope-deflection approach.

$$M_{BA} = \frac{2EI}{L}\left(\theta_A + 2\theta_B - 3\frac{\Delta}{L}\right) + M_{BA}^F$$

In these equations the fixed-end moment has been kept in its more general form. For a particular loading, the corresponding values would have to be ascertained before the frame problem could be approached.   (M_{AB}^F and M_{BA}^F are the moments induced at the ends of a single member due to the imposed lateral loading—if it is presumed that the ends of the members are "fixed" against rotation.)   For a member of length L and of uniform cross-section, subjected to a uniformly distributed lateral load,

$$M_{AB}^F = -\frac{qL^2}{12}$$

$$M_{BA}^F = +\frac{qL^2}{12}$$

where q is the unit intensity of lateral loading.

In all of the above a "clockwise positive" sign system has been presumed: the end-moments are positive when acting clockwise, the end-slopes are positive when clockwise and the relative lateral deformation of the ends of the member (i.e., Δ) is positive if there is an overall clockwise rotation of the member.

To illustrate the slope-deflection approach, consider the one-time inde-terminate beam shown in Fig. 2.11. (It is given that the member is of uniform cross-section along its entire length, fully fixed at A, and constrained against lateral deflection at B. Bending rotations can occur at B.) For this member the rotation at B is the only independent deformational degree of freedom. The slope-deflection equations are therefore

$$M_{AB} = \frac{2EI}{L}(0 + \theta_B + 0) + M_{AB}^F = \frac{2EI}{L}(0 + \theta_B + 0) - \frac{qL^2}{12}$$

$$M_{BA} = \frac{2EI}{L}(0 + 2\theta_B + 0) + M_{BA}^F = \frac{2EI}{L}(0 + 2\theta_B + 0) + \frac{qL^2}{12}$$

It is known that the moment at hinge support B must be zero, that is,

$$M_{BA} = 0$$

Therefore, from the second of the equations,

$$\frac{4EI}{L}\theta_B = -\frac{qL^2}{12}$$

or

$$\theta_B = -\frac{qL^3}{48EI}$$

(The minus sign signifies that the member will rotate in the counterclockwise direction at end B.) Substituting this value of θ_B into the first of the slope-deflection equations yields the value of the end-moment at A;

$$M_{AB} = -\frac{qL^2}{8} \quad \text{(counterclockwise)}$$

To illustrate the application of the slope-deflection method to the solution of frames composed of tapered members, consider the single-span, rigid frame structure shown in Fig. 2.21. For this case, let it be assumed that the structure is subjected to a combined uniformly distributed gravity loading of q_V lbs/in. and a uniformly distributed horizontal loading of q_H lbs/in. These loadings and an exaggerated representation of the deformed config-uration of the frame under loading also are given in Fig. 2.21.

For this structure, there are seven independent degrees of deformational freedom: θ_A, θ_B, θ_C, θ_D, θ_E, Δ_1, and Δ_2. The displacements Δ_3 and Δ_4 can

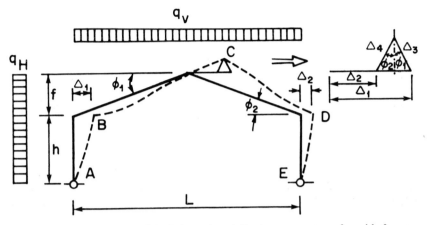

Figure 2.21. Relationship of the independent deflection parameters of a gable frame.

be expressed in terms of Δ_1 and Δ_2 as shown in Fig. 2.21. Considering the deformed structure

$$\frac{\Delta_1 - \Delta_2}{Sin\ (\phi_1 + \phi_2)} = \frac{\Delta_3}{Sin\ (90° - \phi_2)} = \frac{\Delta_3}{Cos\ \phi_2} = \frac{\Delta_4}{Sin\ (90° - \phi_1)} = \frac{\Delta_4}{Cos\ \phi_1}$$

or

$$\Delta_3 = Cos\ \phi_2\ \frac{\Delta_1 - \Delta_2}{Sin\ (\phi_1 + \phi_2)}$$

and

$$\Delta_4 = Cos\ \phi_1\ \frac{\Delta_1 - \Delta_2}{Sin\ (\phi_1 + \phi_2)}$$

Corresponding to the seven degrees of freedom, there will be seven equations of equilibrium. For the five rotational parameters—five moment equilibrium equations can be written at the joints:

$$M_{AB} = 0$$

$$M_{BA} + M_{BC} = 0$$

$$M_{CB} + M_{CD} = 0$$

$$M_{DC} + M_{DE} = 0$$

$$M_{ED} = 0$$

The two remaining equations can be determined from considerations of shear

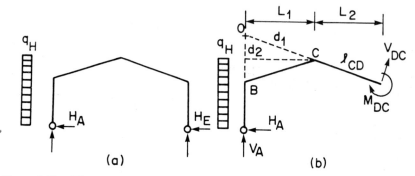

Figure 2.22. Illustrative example of using the slope-deflection approach for the solution of a gable frame consisting of tapered members.

equilibrium. The first of these would be a consideration of the horizontal forces acting on the total frame. The second would be a moment balance of the shear force and end-moments acting on a part of the frame. These two distinct and separate cases are shown in Fig. 2.22.

From the first sketch of Fig. 2.22,

$$H_A + H_E = q_H(h + f)$$

But H_A and H_E can be related to the unknown moments M_{BA} and M_{DE} by considering free-body diagrams of each of the columns AB and DE. Substituting these into the overall horizontal equilibrium equation gives

$$M_{BA} + M_{DE} = -h \left(q_H f + q_H \frac{h}{2} \right)$$

Considering the second sketch in Fig. 2.22 and summing moments about location "0", the following would be obtained:

$$H_A \left(f + h + \frac{d}{2} \right) + M_{DC} - V_{DC}(l_{CD} + d_1) + q_V \frac{(L_1 + L_2)^2}{2}$$

$$- q_W(f + h) \left(\frac{f + h + 2d_2}{2} \right) = 0$$

Again H_A and V_{DC} can be expressed in terms of the end-moments M_{BA}, M_{CD}, and M_{DC}. The resulting equation would be

$$M_{BA} \left(\frac{f + h + d_2}{h} \right) + M_{CD} \left(1 + \frac{d_1}{l_{CD}} \right) + M_{DC} \left(\frac{d_1}{l_{CD}} \right) = -R$$

where

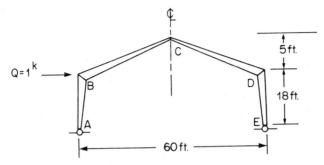

Figure 2.23. Numerical example of slope-deflection method.

$$R = \left(\frac{q_V L_2{}^2}{2}\right) + \left(\frac{d_1}{l_{CD}}\right)\left(\frac{q_V L_2{}^2}{2}\right) - \left(q_H \frac{h}{2}\right)(f + h + d_2)$$

$$- \left(q_V \frac{L^2}{2}\right) + q_H(f + h)\left(\frac{2 + h + 2d_2}{2}\right)$$

These seven equilibrium equations may be solved simultaneously for the seven deformational unknowns θ_A, θ_B, θ_C, θ_D, θ_E, Δ_1, and Δ_2—once the appropriate expressions based on Eqs. (2.9) and (2.10) for each of the members of the frame are substituted. [It is to be noted that Eqs. (2.9) and (2.10) contain not only stiffness terms—which vary depending on the taper of the member—but also "fixed-end moment" terms—which also depend upon the shape of the particular member selected.]

Since it is the primary purpose of this section to illustrate the general method of solution under consideration—the slope-deflection method—and since the inclusion of lateral loads does not present any real additional complication, the loading case shown in Fig. 2.23 will be solved.

In addition, assume the following particular values for the various members:

For the columns	For the beams
$d_0 = 12''$	$d_0 = 6''$
$b = 6''$	$b = 4''$
$t_f = 0.25''$	$t_f = 0.25''$
$t_w = 0.10''$	$t_w = 0.10''$
$\gamma = 2.0$	$\gamma = 2.0$

b is the flange width, t_f is the flange thickness and t_w is the web thickness.

The moment-slope equations corresponding to Eqs. (2.9) and (2.10) are as follows:

$$M_{AB} = \frac{(4E)(216.13)}{(18)(12)}\left[\theta_A + 0.84\theta_B - \frac{\Delta_1}{(18)(12)}(1 + 0.84)\right]$$

$$M_{BA} = \frac{(4E)(644.91)}{(18)(12)}\left[\theta_B + 0.28\theta_A - \frac{\Delta_1}{(18)(12)}(1 + 0.28)\right]$$

$$M_{BC} = \frac{(4E)(99.9)}{(30.4)(12)}\left[\theta_B + 0.28\theta_C + \frac{3(\Delta_1 - \Delta_2)}{(30.4)(12)}(1 + 0.28)\right]$$

$$M_{CB} = \frac{(4E)(33.48)}{(30.4)(12)}\left[\theta_C + 0.84\theta_B + \frac{3(\Delta_1 - \Delta_2)}{(30.4)(12)}(1 + 0.84)\right]$$

$$M_{CD} = \frac{(4E)(33.48)}{(30.4)(12)}\left[\theta_C + 0.84\theta_D - \frac{3(\Delta_1 - \Delta_2)}{(30.4)(12)}(1 + 0.84)\right]$$

$$M_{DC} = \frac{(4E)(99.9)}{(30.4)(12)}\left[\theta_D + 0.28\theta_C - \frac{3(\Delta_1 - \Delta_2)}{(30.4)(12)}(1 + 0.28)\right]$$

$$M_{DE} = \frac{(4E)(644.91)}{(18)(12)}\left[\theta_D + 0.28\theta_E - \frac{\Delta_2}{(18)(12)}(1 + 0.28)\right]$$

$$M_{ED} = \frac{(4E)(216.13)}{(18)(12)}\left[\theta_E + 0.84\theta_D - \frac{\Delta_2}{(18)(12)}(1 + 0.84)\right]$$

These equations were obtained using the methods described in Ref. 22. Substituting these expressions into the seven equilibrium equations defined above, the following set is obtained:

$$\left[\quad K \quad\right]\begin{bmatrix}\theta_A \\ \theta_B \\ \theta_C \\ \theta_D \\ \theta_E \\ \Delta_1 \\ \Delta_2\end{bmatrix} = \begin{bmatrix}0 \\ 0 \\ 0 \\ 0 \\ 0 \\ -216 \\ -120\end{bmatrix}$$

where the stiffness matrix is given by

$$[K] = \begin{bmatrix}
4E & 3.36E & 0 & 0 & 0 & -0.034E & 0 \\
0 & 0 & 0 & 3.36E & 4E & 0 & -0.034E \\
3.34E & 13.04E & 0.31E & 0 & 0 & -0.0591E & -0.0116E \\
0 & 0.31E & 0.74E & 0.31E & 0 & 0 & 0 \\
0 & 0 & 0.31E & 13.04E & 3.34E & -0.0116E & -0.0591E \\
3.34E & 11.94E & 0 & 11.94E & 3.34E & -0.0707E & -0.0707E \\
52E & 18.6E & 1.04E & 1.72E & 0 & -0.133E & 0.0227E
\end{bmatrix}$$

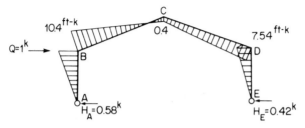

Figure 2.24.   The moment diagram of the frame defined in Fig. 2.23.

Solution of these equations yields the following results:

$$\theta_A = \frac{143.35}{E} \qquad\qquad \theta_E = \frac{136.13}{E}$$

$$\theta_B = \frac{118.60}{E} \qquad\qquad \Delta_1 = \frac{28585.13}{E}$$

$$\theta_C = -\frac{99.39}{E} \qquad\qquad \Delta_2 = \frac{27740.83}{E}$$

$$\theta_D = \frac{118.65}{E}$$

By substituting these values into the moment-slope relationships, the moments at the joints can be obtained:

$M_{AB} = 0$	$M_{CD} = -0.4$ kip-ft.
$M_{BA} = -10.4$ kip-ft.	$M_{DC} = +7.54$ kip-ft.
$M_{BC} = +10.4$ kip-ft.	$M_{DE} = -7.54$ kip-ft.
$M_{CB} = +0.4$ kip-ft.	$M_{ED} = 0$

The moment diagram is plotted in Fig. 2.24.

2.5   The Finite Element Method: The Direct Stiffness Approach

As described in the preceding section, the stiffness coefficient k_{ij} of a structural element may be described as follows:

k_{ij} = force (or moment) corresponding to coordinate i due to a unit displacement (or rotation) of coordinate j with all other displacements maintained at zero.

Applied forces and resulting deformations (at the points of load application, and in the directions of the applied forces) therefore can be written in the following matrix form:

$$[K]\{D\} = \{F\}$$

where $[K]$ is the stiffness matrix, $\{D\}$ is a column matrix (vector) of displacements, and $\{F\}$ is a column matrix of forces.

If the element in question is a planar bending element, there are two degrees of freedom at each of the ends of the member—one rotational and the other translational. The bending element stiffness matrix for a prismatic member of length l constrained to deform in the plane of the applied forces, would be as follows:

$$[K] = \begin{bmatrix} \left(\dfrac{-4EI}{l}\right) & \left(\dfrac{-6EI}{l^2}\right) & \left(\dfrac{2EI}{l}\right) & \left(\dfrac{6EI}{l^2}\right) \\[2mm] \left(\dfrac{-6EI}{l^2}\right) & \left(\dfrac{12EI}{l^3}\right) & \left(\dfrac{-6EI}{l^2}\right) & \left(\dfrac{-12EI}{l^3}\right) \\[2mm] \left(\dfrac{2EI}{l}\right) & \left(\dfrac{-6EI}{l^2}\right) & \left(\dfrac{4EI}{l}\right) & \left(\dfrac{6EI}{l^2}\right) \\[2mm] \left(\dfrac{6EI}{l^2}\right) & \left(\dfrac{-12EI}{l^3}\right) & \left(\dfrac{6EI}{l^2}\right) & \left(\dfrac{12EI}{l^3}\right) \end{bmatrix} \quad (2.11)$$

As would be expected from Maxwell's Principle, the elements of the matrix are diagonally symmetrical; that is,

$$k_{ij} = k_{ji}$$

The forces and moments corresponding to each of the entries in the above defined stiffness matrix are shown in Fig. 2.25.

In a somewhat more general form, consider the structure element shown in Fig. 2.26(a)—an element subjected to four separate and distinct forces F_1, F_2, F_3, and F_4. At each of the points of load application (*node points*), there results deformations in the directions of the applied forces: D_1, D_2, D_3, and D_4. The relationship between these forces and deflections can be written in the general form

$$[K]\{D\} = \{F\} \quad (2.12)$$

where, again $[K]$ is the stiffness matrix of the element in question. The in-

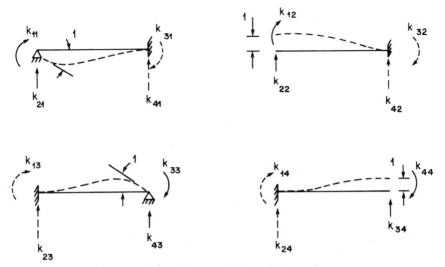

Figure 2.25.   Definitions of the stiffness coefficient of a beam element.

dividual entries in the stiffness matrix would be determined by displacing the element a unit amount in the j'th direction (at the appropriate node point) while holding it "in place" in all of the other numbered directions, and then calculating the forces necessary to maintain that resulting deformed shape. The particular force in the i'th direction would be k_{ij}. Knowing the stiffness matrix, equilibrium of the element in the 3-direction, for example, would be written as

$$k_{31}D_1 + k_{32}D_2 + k_{33}D_3 + k_{34}D_4 = F_3$$

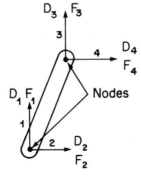

(a) **Element 1**

Figure 2.26.   Equilibrium of individual structural elements. See (a) and (b).

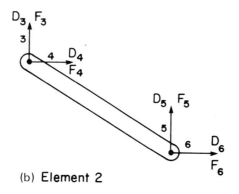

(b) **Element 2**

Figure 2.26.

If a second element is now defined, for example, the one shown in Fig. 2.26(b), and if there is contained in that second element a node point C which—by definition—is the same as C in the first element, the two members can be joined at that point of connection. The ability of the two to react to forces at that point of connection is then the sum of the contributions of each of the elements.

For element (2) in Fig. 2.26(b), equilibrium is given by the algebraic set

$$\begin{bmatrix} k_{33} & k_{34} & k_{35} & k_{36} \\ k_{43} & k_{44} & k_{45} & k_{46} \\ k_{53} & k_{54} & k_{55} & k_{56} \\ k_{63} & k_{64} & k_{65} & k_{66} \end{bmatrix} \begin{bmatrix} D_3 \\ D_4 \\ D_5 \\ D_6 \end{bmatrix} \begin{bmatrix} F_3 \\ F_4 \\ F_5 \\ F_6 \end{bmatrix}, \qquad (2.13)$$

Equilibrium in the 3 direction is

$$k_{33}D_3 + k_{34}D_4 + k_{35}D_5 + k_{36}D_6 = {}_2F_3$$

where ${}_2F_3$ represents the force in direction 3 resulting from the deformation of element 2.

If elements 1 and 2 are joined at node point C, the force in the 3 direction resulting from the combination is

$$_TF_3 = {}_1F_3 + {}_2F_3$$

where the pre-subscript T indicates the "total" and 1 and 2 refer to elements 1 and 2, respectively. Thus

$$k_{31}D_1 + k_{32}D_2 + {}_1k_{33}D_3 + {}_1k_{34}D_4$$

$$+ {}_2k_{33}D_3 + {}_2k_{34}D_4 + k_{35}D_5 + k_{36}D_6 = {}_TF_3$$

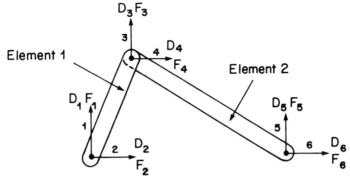

Figure 2.27. Formulation of stiffness equations.

The elements joined together are shown in Fig. 2.27. The complete equilibrium statement of this composite in each of the six prescribed directions is then given in matrix form by Eqs. (2.14).

$$
\begin{bmatrix}
k_{11} & k_{12} & k_{13} & k_{14} & 0 & 0 \\
k_{21} & k_{22} & k_{23} & k_{24} & 0 & 0 \\
k_{31} & k_{32} & {}_1k_{33}+{}_2k_{33} & {}_1k_{34}+{}_2k_{34} & k_{35} & k_{36} \\
k_{41} & k_{42} & {}_1k_{43}+{}_2k_{43} & {}_1k_{44}+{}_2k_{44} & k_{45} & k_{46} \\
0 & 0 & k_{53} & k_{54} & k_{55} & k_{56} \\
0 & 0 & k_{63} & k_{64} & k_{65} & k_{66}
\end{bmatrix}
\begin{bmatrix}
D_1 \\ D_2 \\ D_3 \\ D_4 \\ D_5 \\ D_6
\end{bmatrix}
=
\begin{bmatrix}
F_1 \\ F_2 \\ {}_1F_3+{}_2F_3 \\ {}_1F_4+{}_2F_4 \\ F_5 \\ F_6
\end{bmatrix}
$$

$$(2.14)$$

As indicated by the dashed rectangular boxes on the matrix itself, the resulting set is simply the superimposed effects of elements 1 and 2 written in "expanded form". The expanded form contains zeros as indicated in the following:

Element 1

$$
\begin{bmatrix}
k_{11} & k_{12} & k_{13} & k_{14} & 0 & 0 \\
k_{21} & k_{22} & k_{23} & k_{24} & 0 & 0 \\
k_{31} & k_{32} & {}_1k_{33} & {}_1k_{34} & 0 & 0 \\
k_{41} & k_{42} & {}_1k_{43} & {}_1k_{44} & 0 & 0 \\
0 & 0 & 0 & 0 & 0 & 0 \\
0 & 0 & 0 & 0 & 0 & 0
\end{bmatrix}
\begin{bmatrix}
D_1 \\ D_2 \\ D_3 \\ D_4 \\ D_5 \\ D_6
\end{bmatrix}
=
\begin{bmatrix}
F_1 \\ F_2 \\ {}_1F_3 \\ {}_1F_4 \\ F_5 \\ F_6
\end{bmatrix}
$$

$$\text{Element 2} \quad \begin{bmatrix} 0 & 0 & 0 & 0 & 0 & 0 \\ 0 & 0 & 0 & 0 & 0 & 0 \\ 0 & 0 & {}_2k_{33} & {}_2k_{34} & k_{35} & k_{36} \\ 0 & 0 & {}_2k_{43} & {}_2k_{44} & k_{45} & k_{46} \\ 0 & 0 & k_{53} & k_{54} & k_{55} & k_{56} \\ 0 & 0 & k_{63} & k_{64} & k_{65} & k_{66} \end{bmatrix} \begin{bmatrix} D_1 \\ D_2 \\ D_3 \\ D_4 \\ D_5 \\ D_6 \end{bmatrix} = \begin{bmatrix} F_1 \\ F_2 \\ {}_2F_3 \\ {}_2F_4 \\ F_5 \\ F_6 \end{bmatrix}$$

In general, the procedure for the finite element approach may be described in the following fashion:

1. The stiffness matrix for each of the elements used in the structure is written in terms of its end deformational parameters (in its own, "local" coordinate system).
2. The *element stiffness matrix* is then "translated" from its local coordinate system to a *global coordinate system* for the whole structure.
3. The *master stiffness matrix* is then assembled by adding the stiffness terms of each of the elements that contribute at a common node to the appropriate position in the matrix.
4. Substitute into the system the boundary conditions prescribed. (This is done by striking the appropriate rows and columns of the displacement, stiffness, and load matrices.)
5. Solve for the displacement matrix in the global coordinate system.
6. Based upon the resulting displacements, determine the reactions.
7. Translate the displacements from the global coordinate system to the local coordinate systems of each element.
8. Substitute the known local displacements back into the element equilibrium equations, and determine the internal stress resultants in the various members.

While the above described procedure may seem unduly long and cumbersome, advantage can be taken of the repetitive nature of the entire process and the availability of computer programs for frame analysis. The entire process can be made "almost automatic." As noted, there are a large number of computer programs available, but many of these are written in very general terms and are unnecessarily large for the analysis of frames of the type considered in this book. A small and relatively simple computer program that is sufficient for the purposes of this coverage is given in Appendix A. Instructions for its use also are provided.

For frames composed of tapered members, it is common practice to assume that each member can be subdivided into a number of distinct and separate segments—each of which is considered to act as a prismatic element. Ex-

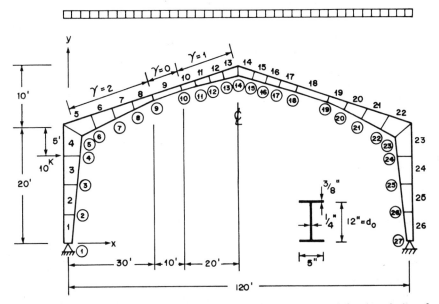

Figure 2.28. Illustrative example of using the true stiffness approach for the solution of a gable frame.

perience has shown that relatively few elements are required to provide adequate accuracy. However, the computer can be programmed to "carry" as many as desired.

To illustrate the use of the computer program given in Appendix A, the tapered member, rigid frame shown in Fig. 2.28 will be analyzed. The roof girders of this frame are made up of two tapered and one prismatic segment on each side. (Node point numbers are shown in circles.) As indicated, there are assumed 26 elements to represent the frame. The following cross-sectional dimensions are presumed at the smallest depths (for both the columns and the girders):

$$b = 5 \text{ in.}$$

$$t_f = \frac{3}{8} \text{ in.}$$

$$t_w = \frac{1}{4} \text{ in.}$$

$$d_0 = 12 \text{ in.}$$

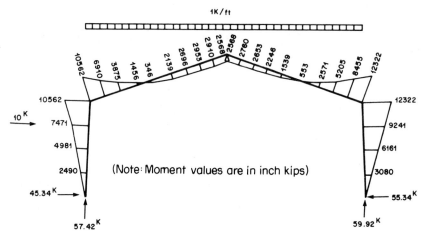

Figure 2.29.   Moment diagram of the frame defined in Fig. 2.28.

The depths of the members at other locations can be calculated from d_0, γ, and the distances to the section in question.

The bending moment diagram obtained by using the program of Appendix A is plotted in Fig. 2.29. For the convenience of the reader, in the event Appendix A is to be used, the necessary input data together with the computer output are given in the following several pages.

Input Data

```
ONE STORY GABLE FRAME
26   27    1    9    0    6
 1 29000.
 1    8.563       0.           377.537
 2   10.563       0.           650.485
 3   12.563       0.          1141.433
 4   14.563       0.          1914.381
 5    7.563       0.           302.813
 6    8.063       0.           335.862
 7    9.063       0.           428.836
 8   10.063       0.           564.31
 9   11.063       0.           750.284
 1    1.4428      3.51          51.362      0.         3.51       -51.362
 2    1.57185     4.9378       100.0        0.         4.9378    -100.
 3    0.62421     2.4804        25.0        0.         2.4804     -25.0
 4    0.          3.51          51.362     -1.4428     3.51       -51.362
 5    0.          4.9378       100.0       -1.57185    4.9378    -100.
 6    0.          2.4804        25.0       -0.62421    2.4804     -25.0
 1  110    0.            0.
 2         4.           60.
 4        12.          180.          10.
 5        16.          240.
 9       360.          310.7
10       480.          329.8
14       720.          360.
18       960.          329.8
19      1080.          310.7
23      1424.          240.
27  110 1440.            0.
 1    1    2    1    1
 2    2    3    1    2
 3    3    4    1    3
 4    4    5    1    4
 5    5    6    1    4    1
 6    6    7    1    3    1
 7    7    8    1    2    1
 8    8    9    1    1    1
 9    9   10    1    5    2
10   10   11    1    9    3
11   11   12    1    8    3
12   12   13    1    7    3
13   13   14    1    6    3
14   14   15    1    6    6
15   15   16    1    7    6
16   16   17    1    8    6
17   17   18    1    9    6
18   18   19    1    5    5
19   19   20    1    1    4
20   20   21    1    2    4
21   21   22    1    3    4
22   22   23    1    4    4
23   23   24    1    4
24   24   25    1    3
25   25   26    1    2
26   26   27    1    1
```

Output

```
 1  ONE STORY GABLE FRAME

NUMBER OF ELEMENTS                   =    26
NUMBER OF NODAL POINTS               =    27
NUMBER OF MATERIALS                  =     1
NUMBER OF ELEMENT TYPES              =     9
NUMBER OF ELASTIC SUPPORT TYPES =          0
NUMBER OF FIXED END FORCE TYPES =          6
```

1MATERIAL	YOUNG S MODULUS	POISSON S RATIO
1	29000.	0.00000

ELEMENT TYPE	AXIAL AREA	SHEAR AREA	MOMENT OF INERTIA
1	8.563	0.000	377.537
2	10.563	0.000	650.485
3	12.563	0.000	1141.433
4	14.563	0.000	1914.381
5	7.563	0.000	302.813
6	8.063	0.000	335.862

```
        7          9.063      0.000      428.836
        8         10.063      0.000      564.310
        9         11.063      0.000      750.284
1
                        FIXED END FORCES IN LOCAL COORDINATES
```

TYPE	AXIAL I	SHEAR I	MOMENT I	AXIAL J	SHEAR J	MOMENT J
1	1.443	3.510	51.362	0.000	3.510	-51.362
2	1.572	4.938	100.000	0.000	4.938	-100.000
3	.624	2.480	25.000	0.000	2.480	-25.000
4	0.000	3.510	51.362	-1.443	3.510	-51.362
5	0.000	4.938	100.000	-1.572	4.938	-100.000
6	0.000	2.480	25.000	-.624	2.480	-25.000

```
1              NODAL COORDINATES            BOUNDARY CONDITIONS       ELASTIC SUPPORT
```

NODE	CODE	X	Y	X	Y	Z	TYPE
1	110	0.000	0.000	0.000	0.000	0.000	0
2	0	4.000	60.000	0.000	0.000	0.000	0
3	0	8.000	120.000	0.000	0.000	0.000	0
4	0	12.000	180.000	10.000	0.000	0.000	0
5	0	16.000	240.000	0.000	0.000	0.000	0
6	0	102.000	257.675	0.000	0.000	0.000	0
7	0	188.000	275.350	0.000	0.000	0.000	0
8	0	274.000	293.025	0.000	0.000	0.000	0
9	0	360.000	310.700	0.000	0.000	0.000	0
10	0	480.000	329.800	0.000	0.000	0.000	0
11	0	540.000	337.350	0.000	0.000	0.000	0
12	0	600.000	344.900	0.000	0.000	0.000	0
13	0	660.000	352.450	0.000	0.000	0.000	0
14	0	720.000	360.000	0.000	0.000	0.000	0
15	0	780.000	352.450	0.000	0.000	0.000	0
16	0	840.000	344.900	0.000	0.000	0.000	0
17	0	900.000	337.350	0.000	0.000	0.000	0
18	0	960.000	329.800	0.000	0.000	0.000	0
19	0	1080.000	310.700	0.000	0.000	0.000	0
20	0	1166.000	293.025	0.000	0.000	0.000	0
21	0	1252.000	275.350	0.000	0.000	0.000	0
22	0	1338.000	257.675	0.000	0.000	0.000	0
23	0	1424.000	240.000	0.000	0.000	0.000	0
24	0	1428.000	180.000	0.000	0.000	0.000	0
25	0	1432.000	120.000	0.000	0.000	0.000	0
26	0	1436.000	60.000	0.000	0.000	0.000	0
27	110	1440.000	0.000	0.000	0.000	0.000	0

```
1
```

ELEMENT	NODE I	NODE J	MATERIAL TYPE	ELEMENT TYPE	ELEMENT CODE	FIXED END FORCE TYPE	RELATIVE STIFFNESS KIJ	KJI	CARRY OVER FACTOR
1	1	2	1	1	0	0	4.00000	4.00000	.50000
2	2	3	1	2	0	0	4.00000	4.00000	.50000
3	3	4	1	3	0	0	4.00000	4.00000	.50000
4	4	5	1	4	0	0	4.00000	4.00000	.50000
5	5	6	1	4	0	1	4.00000	4.00000	.50000
6	6	7	1	3	0	1	4.00000	4.00000	.50000
7	7	8	1	2	0	1	4.00000	4.00000	.50000
8	8	9	1	1	0	1	4.00000	4.00000	.50000
9	9	10	1	5	0	2	4.00000	4.00000	.50000
10	10	11	1	9	0	3	4.00000	4.00000	.50000
11	11	12	1	8	0	3	4.00000	4.00000	.50000
12	12	13	1	7	0	3	4.00000	4.00000	.50000
13	13	14	1	6	0	3	4.00000	4.00000	.50000
14	14	15	1	6	0	6	4.00000	4.00000	.50000
15	15	16	1	7	0	6	4.00000	4.00000	.50000
16	16	17	1	8	0	6	4.00000	4.00000	.50000
17	17	18	1	9	0	6	4.00000	4.00000	.50000
18	18	19	1	5	0	5	4.00000	4.00000	.50000
19	19	20	1	1	0	4	4.00000	4.00000	.50000
20	20	21	1	2	0	4	4.00000	4.00000	.50000
21	21	22	1	3	0	4	4.00000	4.00000	.50000
22	22	23	1	4	0	4	4.00000	4.00000	.50000
23	23	24	1	4	0	0	4.00000	4.00000	.50000
24	24	25	1	3	0	0	4.00000	4.00000	.50000
25	25	26	1	2	0	0	4.00000	4.00000	.50000
26	26	27	1	1	0	0	4.00000	4.00000	.50000

```
1
```

JOINT	X-DISPLACEMENT	Y-DISPLACEMENT	Z-ROTATION
1	0.00000	0.00000	.02447
2	-1.33244	.07419	.01763
3	-2.07355	.11174	.00572
4	-2.10087	.10358	-.00559
5	-1.48989	.05415	-.01535
6	-1.10170	-1.90106	-.02909
7	-.46531	-5.07276	-.04326
8	.40616	-9.40044	-.05543
9	1.42205	-14.44875	-.05947
10	2.38844	-20.72334	-.04089
11	2.66192	-22.98218	-.03410
12	2.86872	-24.71854	-.02357
13	2.97963	-25.70195	-.00919
14	2.96884	-25.72969	.00797
15	3.07718	-24.75472	.02467

```
    16        3.30119         -22.87189          .03795
    17        3.61162         -20.31137          .04710
    18        3.97793         -17.31441          .05243
    19        5.07197         -10.23643          .06063
    20        6.03933          -5.42338          .04851
    21        6.73954          -1.92824          .03065
    22        7.12009           -.00076          .01267
    23        7.19532            .43225         -.00368
    24        6.60687            .40207         -.01536
    25        5.23694            .32124         -.02935
    26        2.98416            .18354         -.04408
    27        0.00000          0,00000         -.05254
  1
```

```
                            MEMBER END FORCES
ELEMENT     AXIAL I    SHEAR I     MOMENT I      AXIAL J    SHEAR J     MOMENT J
   1        60.305    -41.417        -.000      -60.305     41.417    -2490.551
   2        60.305    -41.417      2490.551     -60.305     41.417    -4981.102
   3        60.305    -41.417      4981.102     -60.305     41.417    -7471.652
   4        60.970    -51.395      7471.652     -60.970     51.395   -10562.203
   5        65.763     45.101     10562.203     -64.320    -38.081    -6910.633
   6        64.320     38.081      6910.633     -62.877    -31.061    -3875.401
   7        62.877     31.061      3875.401     -61.434    -24.041    -1456.508
   8        61.434     24.041      1456.508     -59.992    -17.021      346.046
   9        59.168     19.694      -346.046     -57.596     -9.818     2139.068
  10        57.245     11.694     -2139.068     -56.621     -6.733     2696.257
  11        56.621      6.733     -2696.257     -55.996     -1.773     2953.451
  12        55.996      1.773     -2953.451     -55.372      3.188     2910.650
  13        55.372     -3.188     -2910.650     -54.748      8.149     2567.853
  14        55.060      5.669     -2567.853     -55.684      -.708     2760.650
  15        55.684       .708     -2760.650     -56.308      4.253     2653.451
  16        56.308     -4.253     -2653.451     -56.933      9.214     2246.257
  17        56.933     -9.214     -2246.257     -57.557     14.175     1539.068
  18        57.989    -12.287     -1539.068     -59.561     22.163     -553.954
  19        60.495    -19.470       553.954     -61.938     26.490    -2571.508
  20        61.938    -26.490      2571.508     -63.381     33.510    -5205.401
  21        63.381    -33.510      5205.401     -64.823     40.530    -8455.633
  22        64.823    -40.530      8455.633     -66.266     47.550   -12322.203
  23        63.465     51.229     12322.203     -63.465    -51.229    -9241.652
  24        63.465     51.229      9241.652     -63.465    -51.229    -6161.102
  25        63.465     51.229      6161.102     -63.465    -51.229    -3080.551
  26        63.465     51.229      3080.551     -63.465    -51.229       -.000
  1
```

```
              APPLIED JOINT LOADS AND REACTIONS
NODE         FORCE X        FORCE Y        MOMENT Z
   1         45.337         57.417          -.000
   2           .000          -.000          -.000
   3           .000           .000          -.000
   4         10.000          -.000          -.000
   5          -.000          -.000          -.000
   6          -.000           .000           .000
   7          -.000          -.000          -.000
   8          -.000          -.000           .000
   9           .000          -.000           .000
  10          -.000          -.000          -.000
  11          -.000           .000           .000
  12           .000          -.000           .000
  13          -.000          -.000           .000
  14           .000          -.000           .000
  15           .000           .000           .000
  16           .000          -.000           .000
  17           .000          -.000           .000
  18          -.000          -.000           .000
  19           .000          -.000           .000
  20           .000           .000           .000
  21           .000          -.000           .000
  22           .000          -.000           .000
  23           .000          -.000           .000
  24           .000           .000          -.000
  25           .000          -.000          -.000
  26           .000           .000          -.000
  27        -55.337         59.917          -.000
  1
```

```
NUMBER OF ELEMENTS               =      0
NUMBER OF NODAL POINTS           =      0
NUMBER OF MATERIALS              =      0
NUMBER OF ELEMENT TYPES          =      0
NUMBER OF ELASTIC SUPPORT TYPES =      0
NUMBER OF FIXED END FORCE TYPES =      0


0PROBLEMS COMPLETED OR CONTROL CARD ERROR
```

Chapter Three

Behavior and Design Information for Steel Structural Members

Background information necessary for the establishment of design guides for tapered members will be summarized and discussed in this chapter. More detailed information concerning the various topics is contained in the references listed in Chapter V.

3.1 Introduction

Indeterminate frame design traditionally is carried out in the following fashion: Selecting an initial set of assumed relative stiffness values, the indeterminate structures problem would be solved, and there would be obtained shears, thrusts and bending moments acting on each of the members of the frame in question. Based upon these, particular cross-sectional dimensions of the various elements would be chosen. The resulting members should have *relative stiffness* values that are reasonably close to those assumed. If not, additional analyses and member selections must be carried out until a satisfactory solution is obtained. The proportioning of the individual members would be based upon given specifications, the provisions of which ensure adequate safety against the various possible failure modes. For steel members, stability is more often than not the condition to be guarded against.

Steel structural members must be proportioned such that there is adequate safety against failure in compression, bending, combined bending and compression, and local buckling. *Local buckling,* the last of these criteria, provides the basis for prescribing *minimum width-to-thickness ratios* for the plate elements which make up the cross-section. The other criteria are concerned with the more general problem of the overall stability of the various members as they exist in the structure. It is most important for the designer to remember that the critical buckling load of a given structural member relates not only to the length and cross-sectional dimensions of the member itself, but also to the laterally unsupported length of that member, and the support conditions that exist at its ends.

Two end conditions are of major importance in the determination of the buckling strength of members in frames. The first of these has to do with the rotational and torsional restraints at the ends of the member in question. (This will result in an *effective unsupported length* for that member.) The second deals with the relative translational deformation that can occur between the two ends of the member at the time of buckling. (The buckling load of a given member can be considerably reduced if one end of the member is allowed to translate with respect to the other end in the direction of buckling. Cross bracing in the plane of the frame frequently is used in high-rise structures in order to minimize the lateral deflections, increase the buckling load, and thereby increase the allowable stresses in the columns.)

For single-story gable frames, springs representing the influence of "the rest of the structure" may be presumed at the ends of the members. These spring restraints can be determined theoretically by considering the "stiffness coefficients for the remainder of the structure.* For frames composed of prismatic members, a simplified and reasonably accurate approach has been adopted by the AISC. Reference 25 provides adequate information for the determination of an equivalent length factor "g", which can be used to "convert" a tapered, adjacent member of length "l" into a prismatic member of length "gl", so that the AISC prismatic provisions can be directly applied. These conversion curves and examples of their usage are given in Appendix C.

Also discussed in Ref. 25 for two typical loading cases is the estimation of the relative translation of the ends of a member in a typical gable frame. This should help the designer determine the appropriate effective length factors. (The importance of this consideration is illustrated in Fig. 3.1. For the first of the idealized columns—where *sidesway* is prevented—the critical buckling load is eight times greater than that for the second column—where sidesway is allowed.) To ascertain the possibility of the relative translation of the ends of a member that is a part of a rigid frame requires that there be carried out an analysis of the entire structure for all of its prescribed loading conditions. Since for indetermediate analysis only the relative stiffnesses of the various members are initially assumed, the deformed configuration must be calculated for each iteration of design. (This is comparatively easy to do

---

* This method is described in Chapter 2 of Ref. 4.

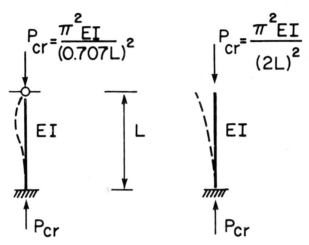

Figure 3.1. Illustration of the influence of support conditions on the critical buckling load of a column.

using the finite element approach described in Chapter Two and the computer programs of Appendix A.)

For illustrative purposes, consider the gable frame shown in Fig. 3.2. (In this example, the members, both girders and columns, will be assumed to be prismatic.) Under a specified loading condition—say, gravity loading plus wind from one side—there will be relative deflections occuring between the ends of the roof girders; that is, $\Delta_3 \neq 0$. Therefore, the girders should be designed presuming that sidesway can occur. For the wind loading case alone, however, assuming that suction as well as pressure exists, no relative deflection of the roof girders will take place; that is, $\Delta_3 = 0$.

To have more precise information on which to ascertain which of the two conditions—sidesway allowed or sidesway prevented—should be presumed in a given design situation, indeterminate structural solutions are required. For the two cases shown, these are as follows:

a). Uniform vertical loading:

$$H_E = \frac{w_1 l^2 (3 + 5m)}{16Nh} \tag{3.1}$$

$$\Delta_1 = \Delta_2 = \frac{h^3 H_E}{3EI_c} + \frac{1}{12EI_g}[(12h^2 s + 6\,hsf)H_E - hsl^2 w_1] \tag{3.2}$$

$$\Delta_3 = \frac{s}{f}\Delta_1 \tag{3.3}$$

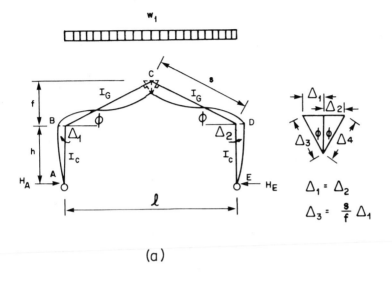

(a)

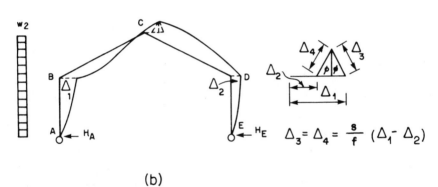

(b)

Figure 3.2. Relationships among deformational parameters of a gable frame.

where

$$A = \frac{I_g}{I_c} \frac{h}{s}, \quad m = 1 + \frac{f}{s}, \quad B = 2(A + 1) + m$$

$$C = 1 + 2m$$

$$N = B + mC$$

b). Uniform horizontal loading:

$$H_E = w_2 \left[\frac{-f^2(C + m)}{8Nh} + \frac{f}{2} + \frac{h[2(B + C) + A]}{8N} \right] \quad (3.4)$$

$$\Delta_1 = \frac{1}{24EI_c}\left[(5h^4 + 8h^3 f)w_2 - 8h^3 H_E\right]$$

$$+ \frac{1}{48EI_g}\left[(16h^3 s + 32h^2 sf + 9hsf^2)w_2 - (48h^2 s + 24hsf)H_E\right] \quad (3.5)$$

$$\Delta_2 = \Delta_1 - \frac{1}{24EI_g}\left[(24hsf + 16sf^2)H_E - 6(6h^2 sf + 12hsf^2 + 5sf^3)w_2\right]$$

$$(3.6)$$

and

$$\Delta_3 = \frac{s}{f}\left[\frac{\Delta_1 - \Delta_2}{2}\right] \quad (3.7)$$

Displacements may be evaluated from the above equations by inserting the appropriate values for the loadings and the various bending stiffness and dimensional parameters. Some comparisons of the displacements are given in Ref. 21.

3.2 Compression

Generally, centrally loaded columns do not exist in "real", rigid frame structures. Most of the members are subjected to a combination of axial forces, lateral forces, shearing forces and bending moments. In three-dimensional structures, members also may be subjected to torsional moments. For two-dimensional planar cases, members are usually assumed to be subjected to the combined action of axial force and bending moments, and are proportioned according to the convenient specification *interaction formula*. In this approach the designer must first determine the allowable stresses that the member can sustain under the two—theoretically possible—extreme loading conditions of pure axial thrust and pure bending.

A perfectly straight member subjected to compressive forces at its ends may fail in two distinct and separate ways: 1) it could reach a predictable maximum uniform stress over the entire cross-section, at which load the member would continue to deform axially, or 2) the member could, at a given load, suddenly bend out of the straight line form, and support the applied axial loading in a laterally bent configuration. This second phenomena is known as buckling, and is one of the ways in which a structural member can become unstable. In general, for axially loaded steel members, unless the column is exceedingly stocky, buckling failure governs design.

For doubly symmetrical cross-sections a column may fail by flexural buckling (i.e., bending) about either of its principal axes. It also may buckle about the longitudinal axis of the member in what is known as pure torsional

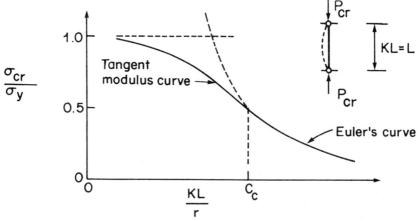

Figure 3.3. A typical curve of column buckling strength. The elastic buckling (Euler's curve) and the tangent modulus inelastic buckling regions join at the point C_c.

buckling (i.e., twisting). The smallest critical load associated with one of these three distinct and separate possibilities controls the design. (It should be recognized that all three critical loads are influenced by the restraints that exist at the ends of the member, as well as by any lateral supports that might be present along the member.) For most H-shaped cross-section columns restrained only at their ends, weak-axis buckling usually controls the design.

Details concerning the determination of the elastic and the inelastic buckling curves for axially loaded columns will not be given here. (The reader is referred to Refs. 4 and 16 for this type of information.) A typical column buckling curve is shown in Fig. 3.3. It is to be recognized from this figure that column strength is governed by two separate curves. For larger *effective slenderness ratios* strength is predicted by the Euler equation. In the inelastic range, that is, for shorter effective length members, depending upon the magnitude and pattern of residual stresses in the member, a Tangent Modulus type of behavior occurs.

It should be noted that the abscissa of the column strength curve shown in Fig. 3.3 contains the effective length factor "K". (This is the same parameter which appears in the column buckling equations in Fig. 3.1—though for those cases actual numerical values were given. Other idealized cases are shown in Fig. 3.4, which is taken from Ref. 1.) In actual structures "K" is dependent upon the support conditions that exist at the ends of the columns. These, in turn, can be related to the behavior of the entire frame of which the column under consideration is one of the parts.

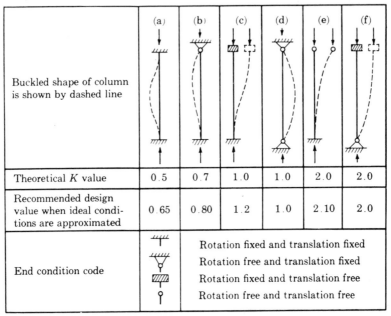

	(a)	(b)	(c)	(d)	(e)	(f)
Buckled shape of column is shown by dashed line						
Theoretical K value	0.5	0.7	1.0	1.0	2.0	2.0
Recommended design value when ideal conditions are approximated	0.65	0.80	1.2	1.0	2.10	2.0

End condition code	Rotation fixed and translation fixed
	Rotation free and translation fixed
	Rotation fixed and translation free
	Rotation free and translation free

Figure 3.4. Effective-length factors K for centrally loaded columns with various end conditions.

   In the determination of the allowable axial stress which can be applied to a given roof girder, the question often arises as to what should be the effective length factor for weak-axis buckling. Present day engineering practice uses the following approach: If the ends of a segment of a roof girder have purlins attached at the top flange only, then the effective length factor about the weak-axis for that segment should be taken as unity. On the other hand, if the bottom flange at these purlin locations also is braced, then the effective length factor for the segment may be computed to be a value less than unity by considering appropriately the restraining effects from adjacent segments. For this latter case, the far-ends of the adjoining members normally would be considered to be simply supported.

   For axial buckling of tapered columns, two sets of effective length factors have been developed. The first are for columns having a constant linear variation in depth along the length of the member. These curves are given in Ref. 22. (The research results reported in Ref. 22 provided the basis for the present AISC Design Specification, Ref. 1, and are included in the commentary to that document. The AISC design provisions for tapered members, including the effective length factors, are reproduced as Appendix D of this book.) A second set of curves for columns with multi-segmented

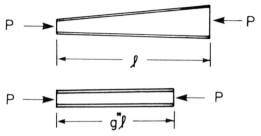

Figure 3.5. A tapered column is converted into a prismatic column for the purpose of using prismatic member design format in tapered member design.

tapered members has been developed in Ref. 21, and are reproduced here as Appendix E.

The basic concept for developing both of these effective length factors was to "convert" the tapered member into a prismatic one of different length which has a constant cross-sectional form equal to the smaller end of the tapered member, as shown in Fig. 3.5. This approach is illustrated by the following equations:

$$\sigma_{\text{tapered}} = [\sigma_{\text{prismatic}}][f(\gamma, d_0, b, t_f, t_w, l)]$$

where

$$\sigma_{\text{prismatic}} = \frac{\pi^2 E}{\left(\dfrac{l}{r_0}\right)^2}$$

$$\left.\vphantom{\begin{array}{c} a \\ b \\ c \end{array}}\right\} \quad (3.8)$$

For strong-axis buckling, the critical buckling stress may be written as Eq. (3.9).

$$\sigma_{\text{tapered}} = \frac{\pi^2 E}{\left(\dfrac{g^* l}{r_{x0}}\right)^2} \qquad (3.9)$$

For weak-axis buckling, because of the negligible variation in the radius of gyration along the length of the member, the prismatic column buckling formula may be used. This is given by Eq. (13.10).

$$\sigma_{\text{tapered}} = \frac{\pi^2 E}{\left(\dfrac{l}{r_{y0}}\right)^2} \qquad (3.10)$$

In Eq. (3.9) the length modification factor "$g*$" has been determined considering typical tapered columns used in present day engineering practice (Ref. 22). It has been shown that this length modification factor can be approximated by

$$g^* = 1.000 - 0.375\gamma + 0.080\gamma^2 (1.000 - 0.0775\gamma) \qquad (3.11)$$

where

$$\gamma = \left(\frac{d_L}{d_0} - 1\right) \qquad (3.12)$$

and d_L and d_0 are, respectively, the larger and smaller end depths. Between the ends, the depth of the member varies with the distance along the member "z", measured from the smaller end, according to the relationship

$$d_z = d_0 \left(1 + \frac{z}{L}\gamma\right)$$

When buckling occurs in the inelastic range, the allowable stress for a tapered column would be determined using the *transition curve* approach specified for prismatic members. The curve is of the general form

$$\sigma_{\text{inelastic}} = \sigma_y - \frac{\beta}{\sigma_{\text{elastic}}} \qquad (3.13)$$

where β depends upon the maximum compressive value for the residual stress.

Based on the above, allowable axial stress for linearly tapered columns can be determined from equations D2-1 and D2-2 of Appendix D of the AISC Specifications. These are reproduced here as Eqs. (3.14) and (3.15).

$$F_{a\gamma} = \frac{12\pi^2 E}{23\left(\frac{K_\gamma L}{r_0}\right)^2}, \quad \text{for } \frac{K_\gamma L}{r_0} \geq C_c \qquad (3.14)$$

and

$$F_{a\gamma} = \frac{\left[1.0 - \frac{(K_\gamma L/r_0)^2}{2C_c{}^2}\right] F_y}{\frac{5}{3} + \frac{3(K_\gamma L/r_0)}{8C_c} - \frac{(K_\gamma L/r_0)^3}{8C_c{}^3}}, \quad \text{for } \frac{K_\gamma L}{r_0} \leq C_c \qquad (3.15)$$

where

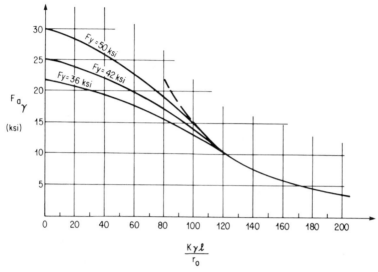

Figure 3.6. Buckling curves for centrally loaded tapered columns.

$$C_c = \sqrt{\frac{2\pi^2 E}{F_y}} \qquad (3.16)$$

and

$F_{a\gamma}$ is the axial compressive stress permitted in the tapered member in the absence of bending stress, and

F_y is the specified minimum yield point of the type of steel being used.

It should be noted that these design formulas are in the same format as those for prismatic columns. The only exception is the effective length factor for the tapered column (see Fig. 3.6). The effective length factor can be determined from the curves contained in Appendix D.

There are several additional cases of tapered members that are commonly used in metal building construction which the current AISC Specification does not cover. The first of these is for tapered roof girders that consist of two or more tapered elements. For these, more than one taper ratio is required to fully describe the geometry of the girder. The second case has to do with tapered columns where the flanges of the member in question have unequal areas.

For the multi-segmented tapered roof girder case (Fig. 3.7), the allowable axial stress may be obtained in a fashion similar to that contained in Ap-

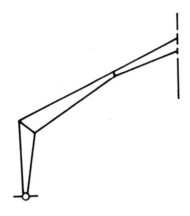

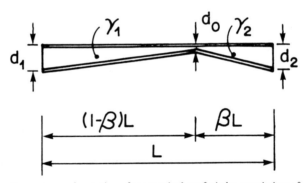

Figure 3.7. Geometry and notations for a typical roof girder consisting of tapered segments.

pendix D; that is, an equivalent effective length factor can first be determined and the girder "converted" into a prismatic member of different length. This is discussed in detail in Ref. 21. (Effective length factors for such members are given in Appendix E. This design information will be used in the illustrated examples contained in Chapter Four.)

For tapered columns with unequal flange areas, a similar approach can be used, as is documented in Ref. 25. Typical cross-sections and parameters are defined in Fig. 3.8. In this case the parameters required to formulate design equations are too many and too varied to allow simple algebraic expressions to be written. Therefore, only curves are presented here for use by the designer. (It is to be noted that the inelastic buckling strength problem

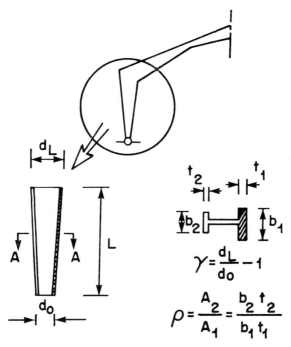

Figure 3.8. Geometry and notations for tapered columns having unequal flanges.

has been considered.) Allowable axial stresses for members of this type are contained in Appendix G. Again, this material will be used in the illustrative examples contained in Chapter Four.

3.3 Bending

When a structural member is subjected to bending or combined bending and thrust, one of two types of failure is observed. If bending is about the weak-axis of the cross-section, or if it is about the strong-axis and the member is "adequately supported" to resist any tendency toward movement in the weak direction, failure will eventually occur by excessive bending. The ultimate load carrying capacity of such a member can be predicted by the methods of *Simple Plastic Theory.* For pure bending it would be the fully plastic moment value "M_p" of the section in question. Allowable stress design of steel beams against in-plane excessive bending failure is governed by the yield stress of the material, modified by an appropriate factor of safety.

Beams and beam-columns subjected to bending about the strong-axis of the cross-section also fail by lateral-torsional bending; that is, at a particular

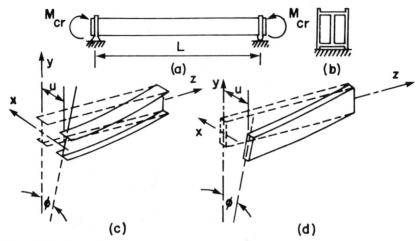

Figure 3.9.   Lateral-torsional buckling of a beam subjected to end moments.

value of the applied moments and thrust the member suddenly moves out of the plane of the moments and twists. As was the case for axially loaded compression members, lateral-torsional buckling can occur in either the elastic or the inelastic ranges of material behavior, and is profoundly influenced by the end-conditions of the beam and the restraints offered from adjacent spans.

For a beam subjected to a uniform bending moment about the strong-axis of the cross-section as shown in Fig. 3.9, the critical lateral-torsional buckling moment is given by Eq. (3.17).

$$(M_{ox})_{cr} = \frac{\pi}{L} \sqrt{EI_y G \kappa_T + EI_y \frac{\pi^2}{L^2} EI_\omega} \tag{3.17}$$

where

L is the unsupported length of a simply supported member,
EI_y is the lateral bending rigidity,
EI_ω is the warping torsional rigidity, and
$G\kappa_T$ is the St. Venant's torsional rigidity.

In Eq. (3.17) the first term under the radical represents the combined resistance of the beam to lateral bending and *uniform torsion*. The second term is the contribution of the combined lateral bending and *warping torsion*. The relative importance of these two terms depends upon the unsupported length of the beam as well as the cross-sectional geometry. For relatively short beams the first term is generally of lesser importance, and in many cases can be ignored for design purposes. For long members the first term is usually dominant. (These two conditions form the basis for the two AISC equations which define the allowable bending stress for laterally unsupported beams–AISC 1.5–6 and 1.5–7.)

As indicated above, Eq. (3.17) is the solution for the elastic lateral-torsional buckling strength of beams subjected to a uniform bending moment. In actual design situations, however, other moment conditions exist and should be taken into account. For example, lateral loads produce non-uniform bending moment diagrams, and have associated with them other lateral-torsional buckling solutions. It has been shown, however (see Ref. 4), that these "other situations" can be related to the uniform moment case by the introduction into the solution of a *modification factor* which depends primarily upon the shape of the moment diagram. Several typical cases are given here in Fig. 3.10. (The "C_1" values listed in the table are those referred to above as the "modification factor".)

A further important consideration in beam design is in the influence of end-conditions on the buckling moment. The in-plane restraint from adjacent spans on a critical span is automatically taken into account through the modification of the moment diagram. The lateral and torsional restraints provided to the critical span from adjacent spans, however, normally have not been considered. (The current AISC Specifications do not contain provisions for designers to estimate the lateral torsional restraints of a continuous beam.) In Ref. 15 this problem is discussed, and a set of design curves is developed for the estimation of these values. Curves are included as Appendix F of this book. (With the curves of Appendix F, one may determine an equivalent length parameter associated with either the uniform torsion term or the warping term. These were derived separately because they are not related to the unsupported length of the beam in the same fashion. For the warping term, the influence of "effective length" on buckling strength is more profound.)

In general terms, the elastic lateral-torsional buckling strength of beams is given by Eq. (3.18).

$$(M_{x,\max})_{cr} = C_1 \frac{\pi}{K_y L} \sqrt{EI_y G K_T + \left(\frac{\pi}{K_z L}\right)^2 EI_y EI_\omega} \qquad (3.18)$$

where

$(M_{x,\max})_{cr}$ is the maximum primary bending moment that can be supported,

Lateral buckling coefficients

Beam and loading	Boundary conditions	$K = K_y = K_z$	C_1
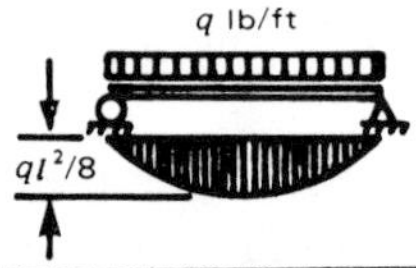 q lb/ft, $ql^2/8$	$u = u'' = \phi = \phi'' = 0$ $u = u' = \phi = \phi' = 0$	1.00 0.50	1.13 0.97
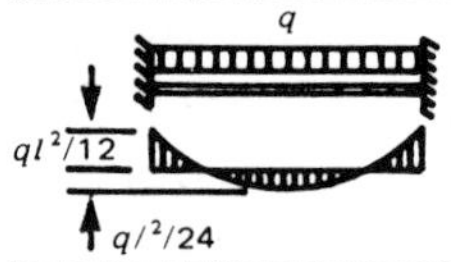 q, $ql^2/12$, $ql^2/24$	$u = u'' = \phi = \phi'' = 0$ $u = u' = \phi = \phi' = 0$	1.00 0.50	1.30 0.86
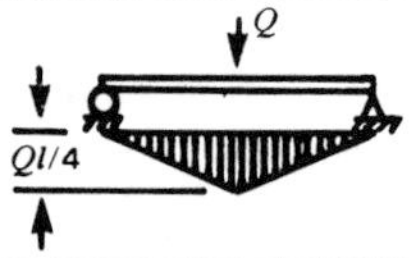 Q, $Ql/4$	$u = u'' = \phi = \phi'' = 0$ $u = u' = \phi = \phi' = 0$	1.00 0.50	1.35 1.07
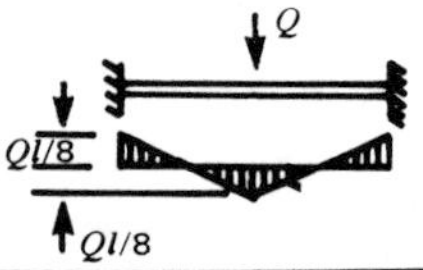 Q, $Ql/8$, $Ql/8$	$u = u'' = \phi = \phi'' = 0$ $u = u' = \phi = \phi' = 0$	1.00 0.50	1.70 1.04
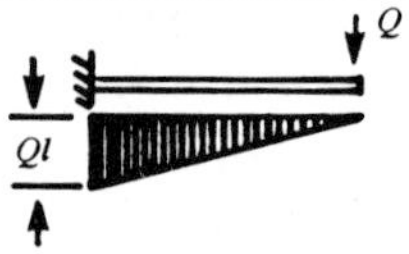 Q, Ql	$u = u' = \phi = \phi' = 0$	1.00	1.30
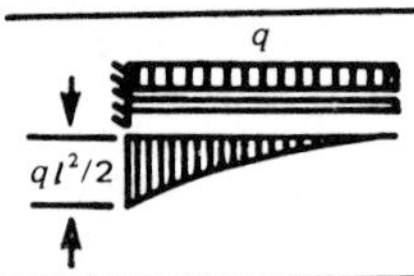 q, $ql^2/2$	$u = u' = \phi = \phi' = 0$	1.00	2.05
 M, αM, $-1.0 \leqslant \alpha \leqslant +1.0$	$u = u'' = \phi = \phi'' = 0$	1.00	(1) $C_1 \leqslant 2.3$ (2) $C_1 = 1.75 - 1.05\alpha$ $+ 0.3\alpha^2$

Figure 3.10. Lateral buckling coefficients for various loading and support conditions (from Ref. 4).

C_1 is the modification factor (or function) which accounts for different conditions of loading,

K_y is the effective length factor for lateral buckling, and

K_z is the effective length factor for twisting about the longitudinal axis of the member.

Values for "C_1", as indicated above, are given in Fig. 3.10 for a variety of different loading conditions.

The critical stress corresponding to the lateral buckling moment can be obtained by dividing Eq. (3.18) by the section modulus of the cross-section about the strong-axis.

$$\sigma_{cr} = C_1 \frac{\pi}{S_x(K_y L)} \sqrt{EI_y G_{KT} + \left(\frac{\pi}{K_z L}\right)^2 EI_y EI_\omega} \qquad (3.19)$$

For buckling in the inelastic range, the AISC transition curve (Eq. 3.20) approximates reasonably well the exact solutions, and may be used for design purposes.

$$(\sigma_{cr})_{\text{Inelastic}} = \sigma_y - \frac{\sigma_r^*(\sigma_y - \sigma_r^*)}{(\sigma_{cr})_{\text{Elastic}}} \qquad (3.20)$$

where

$(\sigma_{cr})_{\text{Elastic}}$ is the elastic buckling stress given by Eq. (3.19),
(σ_y) is the yield stress of the type of steel being used, and
(σ_r^*) is the maximum compressive residual stress in the cross-section.

For welded shapes of the type and kind referred to in this book, $\sigma_r^* = 0.5\sigma_y$, as indicated in Chapter 1. [It should be noted that Eqs. (3.13) and (3.20) are the same relationships, expressed in slightly different forms. Eq. (3.20) is the more usable equation for design.]

Beam buckling strength curves similar to those for column buckling shown earlier as Fig. 3.3 can be constructed using Eqs. (3.19) and (3.20). It is to be recognized, however, that such curves would correspond to buckling, per se, and would contain no reserve in strength against that mode of failure.

In the AISC Specifications, design allowable stresses may be calculated based upon either one or both terms of Eq. (3.19), depending upon the length and proportions of the member in question. For those cases where warping torsion governs (AISC 1.5-6) there are two formulas for the elastic and inelastic ranges, respectively. When St. Venant's torsion controls (AISC 1.5-7) only one formula (elastic buckling) is used. Both terms should be included to obtain the more economical design.

[It should be noted here that AISC (1.5-7) is based on elastic buckling for the entire range of Ld/A_f. In using the total strength—that is, both terms of the equation—by combining AISC (1.5-6) and (1.5-7), the formulas overestimate the lateral buckling stress over a small range of Ld/A_f values.]

The above discussion is primarily concerned with the behavior and design of prismatic beams. For tapered members, the case of uniform moment is not a reasonable or realistic basis for design. The most severe loading condition for using a tapered member occurs when the maximum bending stress at both the larger and smaller ends are equal. This corresponds to a moment gradient equal to the value given by Eq. (3.21).

$$\alpha = \pm \frac{1}{(1 + \gamma)(1 + \mu\gamma)} \tag{3.21}$$

where

$$\mu = \frac{d_0^3 t_\omega}{12 I_{x0}}$$

and γ is the taper ratio previously defined. For most design cases, information derived from a consideration of a moment gradient equal to zero will be satisfactory for tapered member design.

Solutions for the allowable bending stresses in tapered beams are given in Ref. 22. There, length modification factors similar to those developed for columns are prescribed. Moreover, it was possible to develop a simple modification of the present AISC prismatic beam formulas to take into account the "tapered member problem". The only change in the AISC prismatic beam formulas (1.5-6 and 1.5-7) is the length. Modifications would be governed by Eqs. (3.22) and (3.23).

$$h_s = 1.0 + 0.0230\gamma \sqrt{\frac{L d_0}{A_f}} \tag{3.22}$$

$$h_w = 1.0 + 0.00385\gamma \sqrt{\frac{L}{r_{T_0}}} \tag{3.23}$$

For AISC Eq. (1.5-7), Eq. (3.22) would be used; for (1.5-6), Eq. (3.23). The variation of these parameters is shown in Fig. 3.11.

In comparison with procedures for axially loaded columns, present day design of bending members is less sophisticated. There are improvements that can be made. As will be demonstrated in the examples given in Chapter Four, savings can be realized by taking into consideration the lateral-torsional restraints from adjacent spans. The design aids presented in Appendix F (which are based on the information contained in Ref. 15) can be used to estimate the effective length factors for laterally continuous beams. This is similar in concept to the effective length factors for axially loaded columns. (The effective length factors obtained from Appendix F, K_s and K_w, would

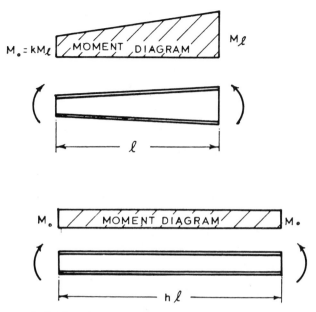

$M_o = kM\ell$ /MOMENT DIAGRAM/ $M\ell$

ℓ

M_o /// MOMENT DIAGRAM /// M_o

$h\ell$

Definition of the length modification factor h for beams

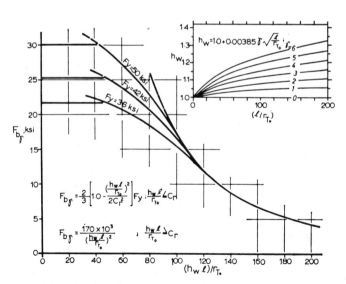

$h_W = 1.0 + 0.00385 \delta \cdot \sqrt{\dfrac{\ell}{r_{T_o}}}$; $\dfrac{f}{6}$

(ℓ/r_{T_o})

F_{b_f} , ksi

Fy=50 ksi

Fy=42ksi

Fy=36 ksi

$$F_{b_f} = \frac{2}{3}\left[1.0 - \frac{(\frac{h_w \ell}{r_{T_o}})^2}{2C_f^2}\right]F_y \; ; \; \frac{h_w \ell}{r_{T_o}} \leq C_r$$

$$F_{b_f} = \frac{170 \times 10^3}{(\frac{h_w \ell}{r_{T_o}})^2} \; ; \; \frac{h_w \ell}{r_{T_o}} \geq C_r$$

$(h_w \ell)/r_{T_o}$

Allowable bending stress for thin, deep smaller end
cross sections $C_{b_\gamma} = 1.0$

Figure 3.11. Lateral buckling curves for tapered beams subjected to end moments. The concept of converting the tapered beam into a prismatic beam, similar to the case of centrally loaded columns is used.

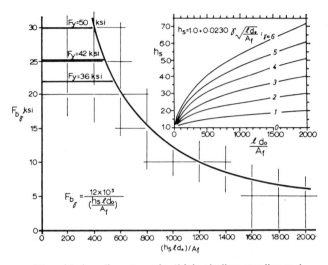

Allowable bending stress for thick, shallow smaller end
cross sections $C_{b_\gamma} = 1.0$

Figure 3.11. (continued)

be multiplied by the modified lengths of the beams "$h_s L$" and "$h_w L$" to achieve a better design.)

Information concerning the lateral buckling strength of unbraced, multi-segmented, roof girders currently is not available. In the design of these types of members (see Fig. 3.7), the in-plane strength usually governs because the girders usually are closely braced by purlins. To check the adequacy of the member between braced points, the element in question is a singly tapered member and the provisions of Appendix D apply.

In Appendix G, allowable bending stresses for tapered members with unequal flange areas are given. These solutions (Ref. 25) consider both possibilities of torsional buckling and lateral-torsional buckling for an applied bending moment acting only at the top of the column (see Fig. 3.8).

3.4   Combined Bending and Compression

Beam-columns respond to imposed loadings in a variety of fashions, depending upon the type of cross-section, the lateral and torsional restraints provided, the stress-strain properties of the material, etc. For example, consider the wide-flange cross-section beam-column loaded as shown in Fig. 3.12. The member in question is of length L and is subjected to an axial thrust P plus two equal but opposite end-moments that cause a single curvature type of deformation. The applied moments are about the strong axis of bending of the cross-section.

Assume that a constant axial thrust less than the buckling value is first applied to the member, and that the end-bending moments are then increased from zero to their maximum values. At first, an elastic, straight-line, end-moment versus end-rotation response is observed. As end-moments are increased, however, there eventually will be reached a particular value for which initial yielding occurs in the member. (This has been indicated as point A on the graph.) For increases in M_{0x} beyond this value, the member responds in a more flexible fashion as indicated by the dashed curve "a".

If the member continues to deflect in the plane of the applied moments, it is possible to define the entire load-deformational response curve in the inelastic range. However, for most real structural members, at some point along the dashed curve, say at point B, the member will deflect both laterally and torsionally. The load-deformational response curve beyond that point then will be of the type shown in curve "b". (It is to be recognized that for very slender members, buckling may occur in the elastic range, such as curve "c" in Fig. 3.12.)

In discussing the behavior of beam-columns, two distinct and separate modes of failure must be considered. The first is the in-plane deformational response in which the member realizes its maximum load carrying capacity in the inelastic range by excessive bending. The second case is lateral-torsional buckling. The member may buckle either in the elastic or the inelastic range.

For the in-plane response of beam-columns, the most important design considerations are (i) the magnification of the bending moment due to axial force times the primary bending deformation, and (ii) the reduction in the maximum bending moment capacity at a given section along the member due to the presence of axial force. For example, the maximum bending moment for the loading defined in Fig. 3.12—which occurs at the mid-point of the member—may be written as

$$\frac{M_{\max}}{M_0} = \sec\left[\frac{\pi}{2}\sqrt{\frac{P}{P_e}}\right] \tag{3.24}$$

where

M_0 is the applied, equal end-moments,

P is the applied axial compression, and

P_e is the Euler flexural buckling load and equals $\pi^2 EI/L^2$.

The relationship between $M_{\max}$ and P is shown in Fig. 3.13.

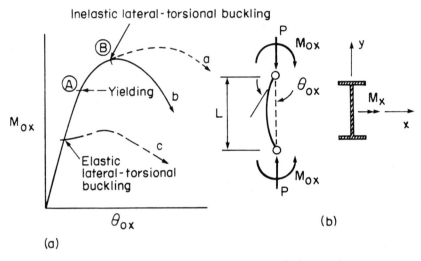

Figure 3.12.   The typical load vs. deformation response of a beam-column.

In the inelastic range, it is exceedingly difficult to derive a closed form solution for I-shaped cross-section, beam-columns. Interaction curves, however, have been numerically determined, such as the ones illustrated in Fig. 3.14.

For the out-of-plane failure modes, buckling loads must be determined for both elastic and inelastic cases. For elastic lateral-torsional buckling, direct solution of the differential equations of equilibrium yields

$$\frac{M_{0x}^2}{r_0^2 P_{ey} P_{ex}} = \left(1 - \frac{P}{P_{ey}}\right)\left(1 - \frac{P}{P_{ey}} \cdot \frac{P_{ey}}{P_{ez}}\right) \qquad (3.25)$$

where

$$P_{ex} = \frac{\pi^2 E I_x}{L^2}$$

$$P_{ey} = \frac{\pi^2 E I_y}{L^2}$$

$$P_{ez} = \frac{1}{r_0^2}\left(\frac{\pi^2 E I_\omega}{L^2} + G_{K_T}\right)$$

$$r_0^2 = \frac{1}{A}(I_x + I_y)$$

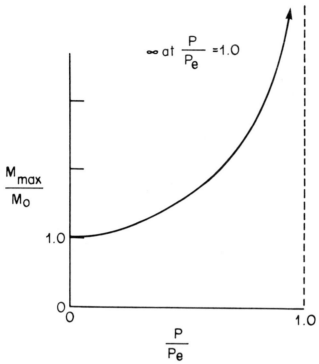

$$\infty \text{ at } \frac{P}{P_e} = 1.0$$

Figure 3.13.   Illustration of the influence of axial force on moment carrying capacity of beam-columns.

Equation (3.25) is shown graphically in Fig. 3.15.

For inelastic lateral-torsional buckling, numerical solutions for particular cross-sections and loadings are presented in many references. A summary of the state-of-the art is given in Ref. 16. The inelastic buckling stress can be approximated using the AISC transition curve approach. That is,

$$(\sigma_{cr})_{\text{Inelastic}} = \sigma_y - \frac{\sigma_r^*(\sigma_y - \sigma_r^*)}{(\sigma_{cr})_{\text{Elastic}}} \tag{3.26}$$

where, as before, σ_r^* represents the value of the maximum compressive residual stress in the member, and $(\sigma_{cr})_{\text{Elastic}}$ is the lateral-torsional buckling stress based on Eq. (3.25).

In actual design situations, rather than compute the various solutions associated with the different modes of failure referred to above for all of the combinations of loading possible, the *interaction equation* approach is more often used. The interaction equation is of the general form given in Eq. (3.27).

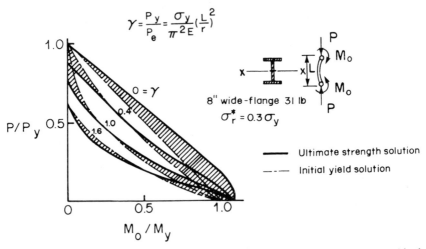

Figure 3.14. Beam-column interaction curves for a W 8 × 31 member containing residual stresses.

$$\frac{P}{P_u} + \xi \frac{M}{M_u} = 1.0 \tag{3.27}$$

where

   P is the axial compressive thrust applied to the member in question,
   M is the primary bending moment due to applied transverse loading or end-moments,
   P_u is the compressive force carrying capacity of the member when axial force alone is applied, and
   M_u is the bending-moment carrying capacity of the member when moment alone exists.

   It is to be understood that M does not include the induced secondary moment in the member due to axial thrust times deflection. Moreover, it is assumed that M acts only in the plane of symmetry of the cross-section.

   P_u may be the elastic or the inelastic buckling load, depending upon the effective slenderness of the member. Furthermore, it may correspond to either buckling about the x-x axis or about the y-y axis, depending upon the end conditions and/or intermediate lateral supports available along the member. (For very short length members, P_u approaches the yield load $A\sigma_y$.)

   M_u may be either the elastic or the inelastic lateral buckling moment, when the member is laterally unsupported. When it is supported, it is the

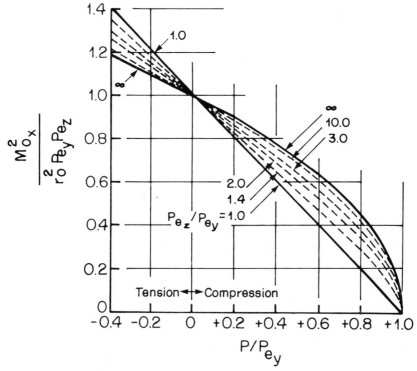

Figure 3.15. Elastic interaction curves for lateral-torsional buckling of beam columns subjected to equal end moments.

maximum moment that the cross-section can sustain, that is, the fully plastic moment, M_P.

ξ is a modification factor to M_u which takes into account the influence of moment gradient, different loading conditions, support conditions, as well as an amplification factor $(1 - P/P_e)$. The amplification factor is a conservative approximation of the effect of axial force on maximum bending moment. For prismatic beam-columns, the value of ξ is either unity (for most cases where $f_a/F_a < 0.15$) or equal to the expression defined by Eq. (3.28).

$$\xi = \frac{C_m}{1 - \dfrac{f_a}{F'_e}} \tag{3.28}$$

"C_m" is a factor which takes into account end-moment ratios as well as several other factors. (It must be noted here that there remain today several questions concerning the best definition of C_m which remain to be answered by further research.)

For tapered beam-columns, the basic interaction equation listed above as (3.27) is presumed to hold. (The tapered beam-column design provisions developed in Ref. 22 were of this type. They were adopted by the AISC with minimum modifications.) P_u and M_u are the force and bending moment carrying capacities, respectively, of the tapered member. ξ, however, takes on a somewhat different form from that given as Eq. (3.28). (The appropriate AISC provisions are included in Appendix D. Their applications are illustrated in Chapter Four.)

In a recent study by Hsu and Lee (Ref. 15), the adequacy of the modification factor ξ was examined. It is their conclusion that beam-column design can be achieved best by considering two separate definitions for the factor ξ: one for the in-plane, and the other for the out-of-plane failure modes. This approach will be discussed in the following section.

3.5   Alternate Approach for Beam-Column Design

It is generally agreed that interaction Eq. (3.27) is a relatively simple and convenient formula for the design of beam-columns. Moreover, the moment modification function ξ, as defined by Eq. (3.28), is well suited to the solution of in-plane strength problems. Unfortunately, when members have relatively long unsupported lengths and fail by lateral-torsional buckling, this is not the case. Furthermore, if a beam-column is continuous (lateral-torsionally), current design formulas do not provide a procedure for the designer to estimate the effective length factor for the critical span, in order to take advantage of the restraining effects of the adjacent spans.

For these as well as other reasons, an alternate approach for beam-column design is included in this section. This procedure which is somewhat different from the present AISC interaction equation retains the same AISC formulas for design against in-plane instability failure modes, but contains a different ξ function for use in design against lateral-torsional buckling failure. Alternate formulas for the allowable stresses F_a and F_b also are suggested. A procedure for estimating the effective length factors in determining the allowable bending stress is included (Ref. 15).

This alternate approach for prismatic member design may be summarized as follows:

i).   For the allowable axial compressive stress when axial force alone exists, the AISC allowable stress formulas based upon the SSRC basic column strength curve is a compromise among various types of cross-sections, methods of fabrication, and between strong and weak axis buckling curves. Provisions are available, however, for the designer to estimate the effective length of columns in rigid frames (see Fig. 3.16).

If the end-conditions are such that weak-axis buckling governs the design when axial force alone exists, the weak-axis column buckling curve may be used instead of the AISC formula. This can be approximated by a straight line in the inelastic range. Euler type buckling would exist for the longer members. The appropriate equations are therefore

$$F_a = \left[\frac{1 - 0.3 \dfrac{KL}{r_y C_c}}{\text{F.S.}} \right] F_y, \quad \text{for } \frac{KL}{r_y} \leq C_c \tag{3.29}$$

$$F_a = \frac{12\pi^2 E}{23\left(\dfrac{KL}{r_y}\right)^2}, \quad \text{for } \frac{KL}{r_y} \geq C_c \tag{3.30}$$

where

$$C_c = \sqrt{\frac{\pi^2 E}{0.7 F_y}} \cong \sqrt{\frac{14 E}{F_y}}$$

[It is to be observed that the difference between Eqs. (3.29) and (3.30) and the current AISC column design formulas is relatively small.]

ii). For the allowable stress in bending when no axial forces are present, the current AISC formulas yield conservative design solutions. There are two major reasons for this: First, there is currently lacking a procedure for the designer to estimate the effective length factor for lateral buckling. Secondly, only one portion of the total resistance of the beam to lateral buckling is presumed in the design equations. [This latter problem may be avoided if recognition is given to the provisions contained in the Commentary to the AISC Specifications (1.5.1.4.5.).]

These conservative characteristics of the AISC Specifications have been addressed in Ref. 15. In the alternate approach there proposed, and upon which this section is based, effective length is defined separately for St. Venant's parameter $K_s L d / A_f$ and the warping torsion parameter $K_\omega L / r_T$. Furthermore, inelastic buckling is distinguished from elastic buckling for both of the component terms of the lateral buckling solution. The inelastic buckling strength is further approximated by the standard

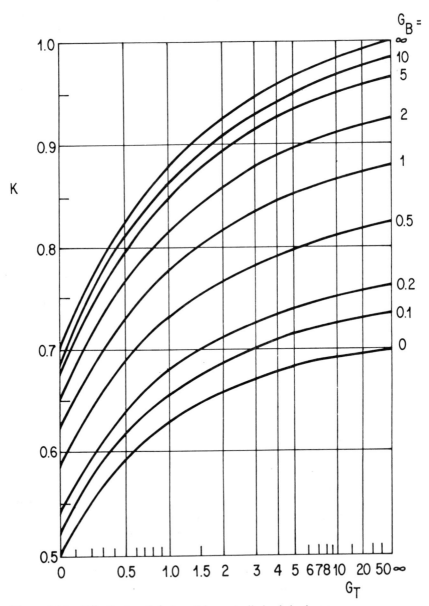

Figure 3.16. Effective length factors K for centrally loaded columns.

transition curve between $0.7\sigma_y$ and $1.11\sigma_y$. (This assumes that the maximum compressive residual stress is $0.3\sigma_y$.)

The alternate design equation for F_b would be as follows:

$$F_b = \sqrt{F_{b1}^2 + F_{b2}^2}, \quad \text{for } 0 \le F_b \le 0.42F_y \tag{3.31}$$

and

$$F_b = \frac{2}{3}\left[1.0 - \frac{F_y}{6.435\sqrt{F_{b1}^2 + F_{b2}^2}}\right]F_y, \quad \text{for } 0.42F_y \le F_b \le 0.6F_y \tag{3.32}$$

where

$$F_{b1} = \frac{170,000\, C_b}{\left(\dfrac{K_w L}{r_T}\right)^2} \tag{3.33a}$$

$$F_{b2} = \frac{12,000\, C_b,}{\left(\dfrac{K_s L d}{A_f}\right)} \tag{3.33b}$$

and

$$C_b = 1.75 - 1.05\alpha + 0.3\alpha^2 \tag{3.34a}$$

For a concentrated load applied at the midspan,

$$C_b = 1.75 \tag{3.34b}$$

iii). For combined axial compression and bending, the interaction equation based on Eq. (3.27) is to be used. This design equation may be written as

$$\frac{f_a}{F_a} + \xi\frac{f_b}{F_b} \le 1.0 \tag{3.35}$$

For in-plane failure (laterally supported)

F_a is determined from strong-axis buckling curves (or AISC 1.5–1 and 1.5–2),

F_b is $0.6\,F_y$, and

ξ is defined by Eq. (3.28) with F_e' equal to the strong-axis buckling stress.

For out-of-plane failure (laterally unsupported)

F_a is determined from weak-axis buckling curves–Eqs. (3.29) and (3.30) (or AISC 1.5–1 and 1.5–2),

F_b is defined by Eqs. (3.31) and (3.32), and
ξ is to be determined from one of the following:

$$\left.\begin{array}{ll} \xi = 1.0 - 0.5\left(\dfrac{P}{P_{cr}}\right), & \text{for } \dfrac{KL}{r_y} \geq 100 \\[3ex] \xi = 1.0, & \text{for } \dfrac{KL}{r_y} \leq 100 \end{array}\right\} \qquad (3.36)$$

where K is the effective length factor of the beam-column associated with lateral-torsional buckling failure. (The weak axis effective length factor K_y may be used with sufficient accuracy.) P/P_{cr} is equal to the ratio f_a/F_a if a factor of safety of 1.0 is applied to F_a. [For a laterally unsupported beam-column whose dimensions are such that in-plane failure may govern design, ξ must be checked both by Eq. (3.36) and the AISC formula—Eq. (3.28). It also should be noted that both strong and weak axis situations must be considered and F_a and F_b values determined. The smaller values would govern.]

For the design of tapered members of equal flange area, there first must be determined an equivalent prismatic member for the element in question. For example, for the case of laterally unsupported beams, the equations to be used for determining allowable bending stress in the elastic range would be

$$F_{b1} = \frac{170,000}{\left(\dfrac{K_w h_w L}{r_T}\right)^2} \qquad (3.37)$$

$$F_{b2} = \frac{12,000}{\left(\dfrac{K_s h_s L d}{A_f}\right)} \qquad (3.38)$$

and

$$F_b = \sqrt{F_{b1}^2 + F_{b2}^2}$$

In these equations h_w and h_s are, respectively, the modified length factors for warping and St. Venant's torsion that were defined by Eqs. (3.22) and (3.23). K_w and K_s are the effective length factors for a prismatic beam with lateral-torsional end restraints. Their values can be estimated from Figs. 3.17 and 3.18. For tapered beam-columns, the ξ values would be those given by Eqs. (3.36).

For tapered columns with unequal flanges of the type defined in Fig. 3.8, the alternate approach just defined is the only procedure now available.

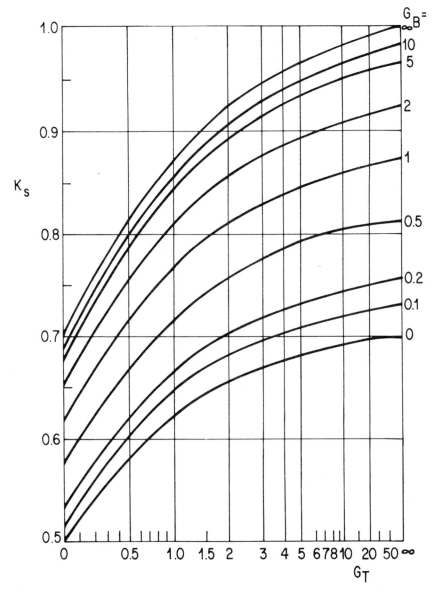

Figure 3.17. Effective length factors, K_s, for the "St. Venant's" term of laterally unsupported beams.

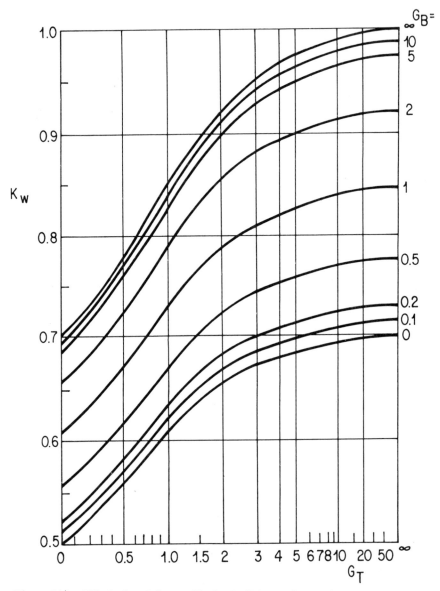

Figure 3.18. Effective length factors, K_w, for the "Warping" term of laterally unsupported beams.

[Equation (3.35), therefore, should be used unless other, more rational, methods can be clearly demonstrated.] For the design of beam-columns with unequal flanges—both tapered and prismatic—the allowable stresses F_a and F_b and the moment modification factor ξ are given in graphical form in Appendix G. Design examples using this material are contained in Chapter Four.

3.6   Other Design Considerations

Within the general framework of design based upon strength and stability, there still are other limiting situations that must be handled—in addition to those discussed above for main member design. Examples of a few of these would be the allowable tensile stress for cables and rods, allowable shearing stresses in the web plate of a *knee*, and the maximum allowable normal stress in a laterally supported beam. An acceptable design criteria for most of these would be

$$f \le F = \frac{F_y}{\text{F.S.}} \tag{3.39}$$

where F is the allowable stress, and would be equal to the yield stress of the material divided by the desired factor of safety. f would be the actual stress computed from static equilibrium considerations. (In the case of limiting shearing stress, F_y is to be converted to the yield stress in shear via the use of von Mise's yield condition.)

An important aspect of the proportioning of members that thus far has not been discussed in this book is the limitations that must necessarily be placed on the width-to-thickness ratios of the various plate elements of the cross-section so that there will not occur premature *local buckling* failure. The requirements normally are based upon plate buckling solutions, as-suming various edge conditions for the element in question.

There are basically two types of models used in arriving at local buckling design criteria. The first of these presumes a "long" plate strip subjected to applied longitudinal stresses due to compressive forces and/or bending moments. For such elements, it can be shown that the buckling strength (that is, the strength associated with "wrinkling" of the element) is governed primarily by the plates width-to-thickness ratio "b/t", and the restraint conditions that exist along the longitudinal boundaries of the element. The buckling equation is

$$\sigma_{cr} = k \, \frac{\pi^2 E \sqrt{\tau}}{12 \, (1 - \mu^2)\left(\dfrac{b}{t}\right)^2} \tag{3.40}$$

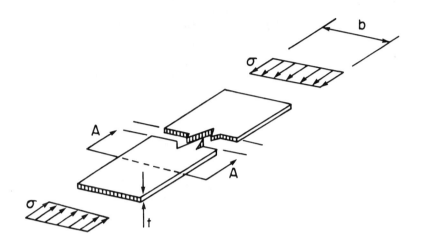

Case	Description of edge support	k value	Sketch of section A-A
1	One edge simply supported the other edge free	0.42	
2	One edge fixed, the other edge free	1.28	
3	Both edges simply supported	4.00	
4	One edge simply supported the other edge fixed	5.42	
5	Both edges fixed	6.97	

Figure 3.19. Local buckling coefficients of plate elements with various support conditions.

where $\tau = E_T/E$, μ = Poisson's ratio, b and t are the width and thickness of the plate element, respectively, and k is a factor depending upon the longitudinal boundary conditions. (k values for several different cases are given in Fig. 3.19.)

A second type of local buckling failure occurs in the web plate of a thin-web bending member (for example, a plate-girder). For these cases, it is generally more economical—and, therefore, more desirable—to attach to the web at intermediate locations transverse stiffeners so that the plate element under consideration can be presumed to be supported along four sides, rather than two. The loading condition also is different. In these situations the applied stresses must include the possibility of normal stresses in both directions, as well as shearing stresses—all in the plane of the plate. Again, an equation corresponding to buckling can be obtained and can be written in the general form of Eq. (3.40). The parameter "k", however, now would be a function of the aspect ratio of the element under consideration (that is, the ratio of its length and width), as well as to the pattern of applied stress (for example, shearing stresses, biaxial compressive stresses, etc.). Limiting values of b/t have been established and are the design basis for the current AISC Specifications.

It is to be emphasized that in the application of local buckling criteria, the designer has a choice when the width-to-thickness requirements are not met. He may either revise the overall design, or choose to take the prescribed reduction in allowable stress. Provisions for this latter option are contained in the AISC Specifications, Sections 1.9, 1.10, and Appendix C.

(It should be noted that rigorous inelastic solutions for local buckling requirements are lacking. Current AISC plastic design provisions are based upon a simple model that assumes that the material is either fully elastic or fully strain-hardened.)

For the design of thin-web plate girders, AISC Section 1.10 provides design formulas for the web which take into consideration the tension field action (post-buckling strength) of rectangular web panels. For web-tapered girders, it is current engineering practice to use the average width (or depth) in computing the width-to-thickness ratio in conjunction with the AISC tension field formulas for prismatic members (Refs. 11 and 15).

There are, of course, many additional topics that are important to the design of single story rigid frames. These include, but are not limited to, connections, splices, welds and bolts, and dynamic effects. More recent design information on some of these topics may be found in Refs. 18, 19, and 31.

Chapter Four

Design Examples

Six examples will be presented in this chapter. None, however, will be complete designs. Each has been selected to illustrate a particular point or demonstrate the use of curves given in the Appendices. It also should be noted that in all cases the structural analyses are not documented, and not all possible loading conditions have been explored.

Examples 1, 2, and 5 are three different gable frame designs for the same overall frame geometry and loading conditions. In Example 1, the roof girders are presumed to be composed of two tapered segments on each side. The columns are singly tapered. (Tapering is only in the depth of the web.) In Example 2 (for the same overall geometry and loadings presumed in Example 1) a prismatic member design is carried out. Again in Example 5 the same geometry and loadings are given, but for this case, it has been presumed that the columns have unequal flanges.

Example 3 is concerned with the design of a gable frame with a large slope to the roof girders. In Example 4, the problems associated with including a column at mid-span are illustrated. Finally, Example 6 is concerned with the design of a rectangular portal frame using the procedures defined in Section 3.5 of Chapter Three. These solutions are compared to ones which would have been obtained from direct application of the current AISC Specification.

In the design examples, the effective length factors K_y have been determined and used for the purpose of illustration. It should be noted that the weak axis effective length factor for the columns in many cases may appropriately be taken as unity for determining the allowable axial stress, when the segments of the column have similar length and axial load. For the case where segments of a column are unequal in length, a longer segment should not be considered to provide end restraint to a shorter one and K_y may be taken as unity.

Example No. 1 (See Fig. 4.1)

In this example the adequacy of column 1-3 and girders 5-12 of the frame of Fig. 4.1 will be determined. The dimensions and section properties of the

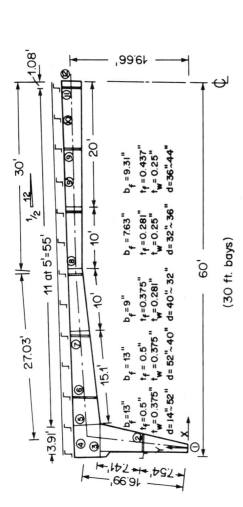

COORDINATES AND SECTION PROPERTIES

Point	1	2	3	4	5	6	7	8*	9	10	11	12
X(ft.)	0.00	0.79	1.58	1.80	3.65	7.75	17.73	28.75	47.73	52.73	57.73	58.75
Y(ft.)	0.00	7.50	14.87	16.89	17.03	17.34	18.08	18.91	19.38	19.51	19.63	19.66
d(in.)	14.00	33.16	52.00	—	52.00	48.73	40.78	32.00	39.59	41.59	43.59	44.00
A(in.^{2})	17.87	25.06	32.12	—	32.12	30.90	27.92	12.15	17.82	18.31	18.82	18.92
I_x(in.^{4})	661.2	4508	12765	—	12765	10960	7241	1726	4328	4851	5412	5531
S_x(in.^{3})	94.46	271.9	491.0	—	491.0	449.8	355.1	107.9	218.6	233.3	248.3	251.4
I_y(in.^{4})	183.1	183.2	183.3	—	183.3	183.3	183.3	20.8	58.8	58.8	58.8	58.8
r_y(in.)	3.54	3.28	3.07	—	3.07	3.11	3.19	1.74	2.28	2.25	2.24	2.24

*Smaller values of section properties of both sides.

Figure 4.1.   Dimensions and geometry of a gable frame consisting of tapered members (Example 1).

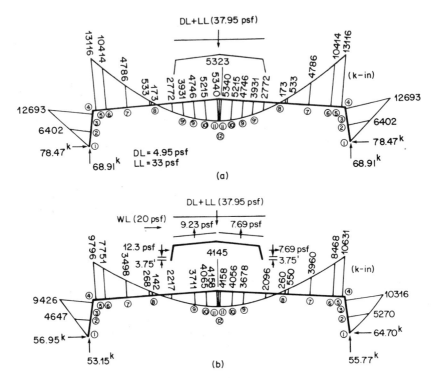

Figure 4.2. Moment diagrams of the frame of Fig. 4.1 due to two sets of loading conditions.

frame are those listed. The outside flanges of the columns and girders are supported laterally by girts or purlins. Supports to the inside flanges are indicated by two close parallel lines on the frame. Two loading combinations have been considered in the analysis and the moment diagrams are given in Fig. 4.2. [The first of these is for a dead plus vertical live loading ($DL + LL$). The second presumes dead plus vertical live loading plus wind loading ($DL + LL + WL$).] The spacing between the frames is taken at 30 ft. The yield stress of the steel is presumed to be 50 ksi.

Solution:

In general, each segment of the frame under each loading condition should be checked. However, some segments can be readily eliminated from consideration by inspection of the unbraced length of the compression flange, and the magnitudes of moment and thrust. Furthermore, the increase of allowable stresses by $\frac{1}{3}$ for the cases with horizontal loads provides additional information for choosing the critical segments. In this example segments 1-2, 2-3, 5-6, 6-7, 9-10, and 10-11 under loading combination $(DL + LL)$ are most likely the critical segments.

Having decided the controlling loading case for each segment, the corresponding maximum stresses are computed:

Axial stresses:* $(DL + LL)$

$$f_{a1} = P_1/A_1 = 76.83/17.87 = 4.30 \text{ ksi}$$

$$f_{a2} = P_2/A_2 = 76.83/25.06 = 3.06 \text{ ksi}$$

$$f_{a3} = P_3/A_3 = 76.83/32.12 = 2.39 \text{ ksi}$$

$$f_{a5} = P_5/A_5 = 82.97/32.12 = 2.58 \text{ ksi}$$

$$f_{a6} = P_6/A_6 = 82.62/30.9 = 2.67 \text{ ksi}$$

$$f_{a7} = P_7/A_7 = 81.76/27.92 = 2.93 \text{ ksi}$$

$$f_{a9} = P_9/A_9 = 78.76/17.82 = 4.42 \text{ ksi}$$

$$f_{a10} = P_{10}/A_{10} = 78.61/18.31 = 4.29 \text{ ksi}$$

$$f_{a11} = P_{11}/A_{11} = 78.47/18.82 = 4.17 \text{ ksi}$$

$$f_{a12} = P_{12}/A_{12} = 78.44/18.92 = 4.14 \text{ ksi}$$

Bending stresses: $(DL + LL)$

$$f_{b2} = M_2/S_2 = 6402/271.9 = 23.54 \text{ ksi}$$

$$f_{b3} = M_3/S_3 = 12693/491.0 = 25.85 \text{ ksi}$$

$$f_{b5} = M_5/S_5 = 13116/491.0 = 26.71 \text{ ksi}$$

$$f_{b6} = M_6/S_6 = 10414/449.8 = 23.15 \text{ ksi}$$

$$f_{b9} = M_9/S_9 = 4746/218.6 = 21.71 \text{ ksi}$$

$$f_{b10} = M_{10}/S_{10} = 5215/233.2 = 22.35 \text{ ksi}$$

$$f_{b11} = M_{11}/S_{11} = 5340/248.3 = 21.5 \text{ ksi}$$

$$f_{b12} = M_{12}/S_{12} = 5323/251.4 = 21.17 \text{ ksi}$$

---

* Axial forces in the various segments are obtained by adding the contributions of all of the forces at the point in question. For example, for "P_1":

$$P_1 = (68.91) (\text{Cos } \theta) + (78.5) (\text{Sin } \theta) = 76.83 \text{ kips}$$

where

$$\theta = \tan^{-1}\left(\frac{x_3 - x_1}{y_3 - y_1}\right) = \tan^{-1}\left(\frac{1.58}{14.87}\right)$$

Shear stress: $(DL + LL)$

$$f_{v1} = V_1/A'_{w1} = 70.73/(14 \times 0.375) = 13.47 \text{ ksi}$$
$$f_{v3} = V_3/A'_{w3} = 70.73/(52 \times 0.375) = 3.63 \text{ ksi}$$

(A) Determine the adequacy of column 1-3:
    (a) Allowable axial stress (AISC Spec. App. D, Sect. D2)
The effective length factor for weak axis is obtained by considering the weak direction as prismatic. Segments 1-2 and 2-3 are continuous spans with the support provided at point 2.

For segment 1-2

$$G_T = \left(\frac{b_T I_0}{L I_T}\right)_y = \frac{7.41 \times 183}{7.54 \times 183} = 0.98 \qquad \text{[Eq. (E-5)]}$$

$G_B = 10$ (AISC recommended value for hinged end)

From the AISC alignment chart in Appendix B (Fig. B-1—sideway prevented) the effective length factor K_y is found to be

$$K_y = 0.855$$

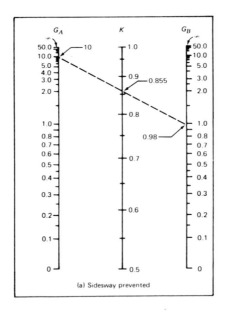

(a) Sideway prevented

Figure B-1

For segment 2-3

$$G_T = 10 \text{ (hinged at end 3)}$$

$$G_B = \left(\frac{b_B I_0}{L I_B}\right)_y = \frac{7.54 \times 183}{7.41 \times 183} = 1.02 \qquad [\text{Eq. (E.6)}]$$

and

$K_y = 0.86$ (AISC alignment chart in Appendix B for sidesway prevented case).

The charts contained in AISC Commentary, Sect. D-2, can be used to
determine the effective length factor K_x. Since the restraining member at
the top of the column is tapered, a modification of the restraining factor G_T
should be made. This has been explained in Appendix E. The following
quantities are needed in order to calculate G_T by using Eq. (E-7) through
Eq. (E-12) of Appendix E. For the equivalent length of the restraining
member (girder 5-12) use Appendix C:

$$\bar{\beta} = L_{8\text{-}12}/L_{5\text{-}12} = (30/55.1) = 0.5$$

$$\bar{\gamma}_1 = d_5/d_8 - 1 = (52/32) - 1 = 0.625$$

$$\bar{\gamma}_2 = d_{12}/d_8 - 1 = (44/32) - 1 = 0.375$$

From Fig. C-5 (Appendix C)

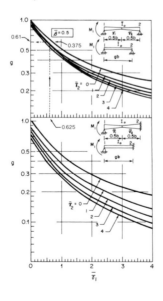

Figure C-5

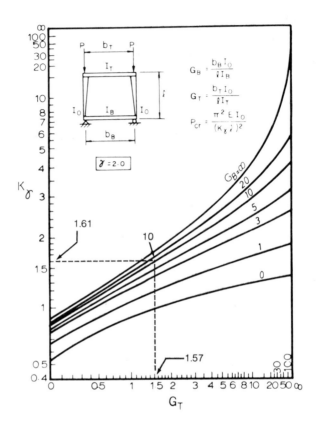

Figure CD 1.5.14

$$g = 0.61$$

For the case of sidesway permitted, (from [Eq. (E-9)]),

$$g_e = 2.0\,g$$

The restraining factor at the top of the column is therefore

$$G_T = \frac{(g_e b)_T I_0}{L I_T} \qquad\qquad \text{[Eq. (E-11)]}$$

$$= \frac{(2.00)\,(0.61)\,(57.03)\,(661.2)}{(16.99)\,(1726)}$$

$$= 1.57$$

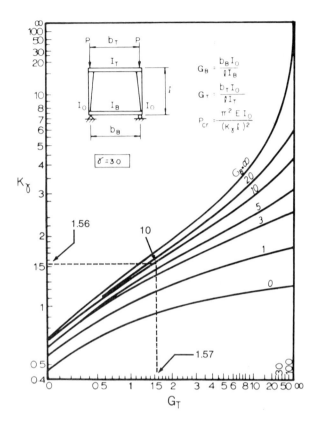

Figure CD 1.5.15

Since the column is hinged at the lower end, use

$$G_B = 10 \text{ (AISC recommended value)}$$

The taper ratio of the column is

$$\gamma_{1\text{-}3} = d_3/d_1 - 1 = (52/14) - 1 = 2.71$$

From the charts in AISC Commentary Sect. D2,

$$K_x = K_\gamma = 1.61 \text{ for } \gamma = 2.0 \text{ (AISC Fig. CD1.5.14)}$$

$$K_\gamma = 1.56 \text{ for } \gamma = 3.0 \text{ (AISC Fig. CD1.5.15)}$$

The effective length factor about the x-axis is estimated to be

$$K_x = 1.58 \text{ for } \gamma = 2.71$$

The slenderness ratios about the weak and strong axes therefore are:

$(KL/r_1)_y = 0.855 \times 7.54 \times 12/3.2 = 24.17$ for *segment 1-2*

$(KL/r_2)_y = 0.86 \times 7.41 \times 12/2.7 = 28.32$ for *segment 2-3*

$(KL/r_1)_x = 1.58 \times 14.95 \times 12/6.08 = 46.62$ for *column 1-3*

The strong-axis, therefore, governs the design. The allowable stress for *column 1-3* can be obtained from the AISC Specification—Table 3-50.

$$F_{a\gamma} = 24.87 \text{ ksi}$$

The axial stress ratios are:

$$f_{a1}/F_{a\gamma} = 4.3/24.87 = 0.173 \text{ for } segment\ 1\text{-}2$$

$$f_{a2}/F_{a\gamma} = 3.06/24.87 = 0.123 \text{ for } segment\ 2\text{-}3$$

(*b*) *Allowable bending stress* (AISC Spec. App. D, Sect. D3) The allowable bending stresses—considering the end restraints provided by the adjacent spans—are calculated as follows:

For segment 1-2, the end restraining factors have been found to be:

$$G_T = 0.98, \quad G_B = 10$$

From Figs. F-1 and F-2 (Appendix F),

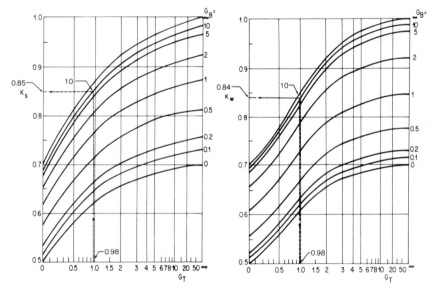

Figure F-1   Figure F-2

$$K_s = 0.85, \quad K_w = 0.84$$

The taper ratio of segment 1-2 is

$$\gamma_{1\text{-}2} = d_2/d_1 - 1 = (33.16/14) - 1 = 1.37$$

$$Ld_1/A_f = 7.54 \times 12 \times 14/(13 \times 0.5) = 194.9$$

$$L/r_{T1} = 7.54 \times 12/3.54 = 25.5$$

The length modification factors are: (AISC App. D, Sect. D3)

$$h_s = 1.0 + 0.023 \, \gamma \sqrt{Ld_1/A_f} = 1.0 + 0.023 \times 1.37 \sqrt{194.9} = 1.44$$

$$h_w = 1.0 + 0.00385 \, \gamma \sqrt{L/r_{T1}} = 1.0 + 0.00385 \times 1.37 \sqrt{25.5} = 1.027$$

From Eqs. (3.38) and (3.37)

$$F_{s\gamma} = F_{b2} = \frac{12,000}{\dfrac{K_s h_s L d_1}{A_f}} = \frac{12,000}{(0.85)\,(1.44)\,(194.9)} = 49.72 \text{ ksi}$$

$$F_{w\gamma} = F_{b1} = \frac{170,000}{\left(\dfrac{K_w h_w L}{r_T}\right)^2} = \frac{170,000}{[(0.84)\,(1.027)\,(25.5)]^2} = 351.3 \text{ ksi}$$

The allowable bending stress for segment 1-2 may be obtained from AISC Appendix D, with $B = 1.0$. From AISC Eq. (D3-2)

$$F_{b\gamma} = \sqrt{F_{s\gamma}^2 + F_{w\gamma}^2} = \sqrt{(49.72)^2 + (351.3)^2}$$

$$= 354.8 \text{ ksi} > \frac{1}{3} F_y$$

Therefore, try the inelastic buckling formula—AISC Eq. (D3-1)

$$F_{b\gamma} = \frac{2}{3}\left[1 - \frac{50}{(6)\,(354.8)}\right] 50 = 32.5 \text{ ksi}$$

Since this value is greater than $0.6\,F_y = 30$ ksi, the permissible value is

$$F_{b\gamma} = 0.6\,F_y = 30 \text{ ksi}$$

For segment 2-3:
   With $G_T = 10$, $G_B = 1.02$, the effective length factors for allowable bending stresses can be found from Appendix F.

$$K_s = 0.86, \quad K_w = 0.85$$

The taper ratio for segment 2-3 is

$$\gamma_{2\text{-}3} = d_3/d_2 - 1 = 52/33.16 - 1 = 0.568$$

$$Ld_2/A_f = 7.41 \times 12 \times 33.16/(13 \times 0.5) = 453.6$$

$$L/r_{T2} = 7.41 \times 12/3.28 = 27.11$$

The length modification factors are obtained from AISC Appendix D, Sect. D3,

$$h_s = 1.0 + 0.023 \times 0.568 \sqrt{453.6} = 1.278$$

$$h_w = 1.0 + 0.00385 \times 0.568 \sqrt{27.11} = 1.011$$

From Eqs. (3.38) and (3.37)

$$F_{s\gamma} = \frac{12{,}000}{\dfrac{K_s h_s Ld_2}{A_f}} = \frac{12{,}000}{(0.86)\,(1.278)\,(453.8)} = 24.07 \text{ ksi}$$

$$F_{w\gamma} = F_{b1} = \frac{170{,}000}{\left(\dfrac{K_w h_w L}{r_T}\right)^2} = \frac{170{,}000}{[(0.84)\,(1.027)\,(25.5)]^2} = 351.3 \text{ ksi}$$

The elastic allowable stress is given by Eq. (D3-2):

$$F_{b\gamma} = \sqrt{F_{s\gamma}^2 + F_{w\gamma}^2} = \sqrt{(24.07)^2 + (313.2)^2} = 314.1 \text{ ksi} > \frac{1}{3} F_y$$

The inelastic allowable stress is given by Eq. (D3-1):

$$F_{b\gamma} = \frac{2}{3}\left[1 - \frac{50}{(6)\,(314.1)}\right] 50 = 32.4 \text{ ksi} > 0.6\, F_y$$

Therefore, the allowable bending stress is

$$F_{b\gamma} = 0.6\, F_y = 30 \text{ ksi}$$

(c)   *Combined axial compression and bending* (AISC Spec. App. D, Sect. D4)

For segment 1-2, $f_{a1}/F_{a\gamma} = 0.173 > 0.15$; thus, both Eq. (D4-1a) and Eq. (D4-1b) must be checked.

$$F_{e\gamma}' = \frac{12\,\pi^2 E}{23\left(\dfrac{KL}{r}\right)_x^2} = \frac{12\pi^2\,(29{,}000)}{23\,(46.62)^2} = 68.7 \text{ ksi} \quad \begin{array}{l}\text{(or from AISC Spec.}\\ \text{Table 9)}\end{array}$$

$$C_m = 0.85 \text{ (sidesway permitted)}$$

Eq. (D4-1a) gives

$$\frac{f_{a1}}{F_{a\gamma}} + \frac{C_m}{\left(1 - \frac{f_{a1}}{F'_{e\gamma}}\right)}\left(\frac{f_{b2}}{F_{b\gamma}}\right) = 0.173 + \frac{0.85}{\left(1 - \frac{4.3}{68.7}\right)}\left(\frac{23.54}{30}\right)$$

$$= 0.884 < 1.0 \qquad \langle O.K. \rangle$$

Eq. (D4-1b) is used to check the combined stresses at point 2. The value of $F_{b\gamma}$ in Eq. (D4-1b) can be replaced by $0.6\,F_y$. However, according to AISC Section 1.10-6, a reduction should be made for web slenderness ratio greater than a certain limit, say $760/\sqrt{F_{b\gamma}}$. The slenderness ratio of the web at *point 2* is

$$\frac{h_2}{t_w} = \frac{32.16}{0.375} = 85.76$$

This value is less than $760/\sqrt{F_{b\gamma}} = 760/\sqrt{30} = 138.7$. Thus,

$$F_{b\gamma} = 0.6\,F_y$$

From Eq. (D4-1b)

$$\frac{f_{a2}}{0.6F_y} + \frac{f_{b2}}{0.6F_y} = \frac{3.06}{30} + \frac{23.54}{30} = 0.886 < 1.0 \qquad \langle O.K. \rangle$$

For segment 2-3, $f_{a2}/F_{a\gamma} = 0.123 < 0.15$. Therefore, Eq. (D4-2) applies.

$$\frac{f_{a2}}{F_{a\gamma}} + \frac{f_{b3}}{F_{b\gamma}} = 0.123 + \frac{25.85}{30} = 0.984 < 1.0 \qquad \langle O.K. \rangle$$

At *point 3*, $h_3/t_w = 51/0.375 = 136 < 760/\sqrt{F_{b\gamma}}$. No reduction of $F_{b\gamma}$ is needed. From Eq. (D4-1b)

$$\frac{f_{a3}}{0.6F_y} + \frac{f_{b3}}{0.6F_y} = \frac{2.39}{30} + \frac{25.85}{30} = 0.941 < 1.0 \qquad \langle O.K. \rangle$$

(d)   *Allowable shear stress* (AISC Spec. Sect. 1.10.5.2)
Assuming that there are no stiffeners placed between *points 1 and 3*, the clear distance between *points 1 and 3* is $a = 14.95 \times 12 = 179.4$ in.
At or near point 1 (use AISC Eq. 1.10-1 or Table 10-50):

$$a/h = 179.4/(14 - 0.375 \times 2) = 13.54 > 1.0$$

$$k = 5.34 + \frac{4.00}{(a/h)^2} = 5.34 + \frac{4.00}{13.54^2} = 5.36$$

$$h/t_w = \frac{14 - 0.375 \times 2}{0.375} = 35.33$$

Try

$$C_v = \frac{190}{h/t_w} \sqrt{\frac{k}{F_y}} = \frac{190}{35.33} \sqrt{\frac{5.36}{50}} = 1.76 > 0.8 \qquad \langle\text{O.K.}\rangle$$

Allowable shear stress at *point 1* is determined by AISC Eq. (1.10-1), F_{v1} = $(F_y/2.89)\ C_v$ = $(50/2.89)\ (1.76)$ = 30.45 ksi, which is greater than 0.4 F_y. Therefore, the allowable shear stress at *point 1* is

$$F_{v1} = 0.4\ F_y = 0.4(50) = 20\ \text{ksi} > f_{v1} = 13.47\ \text{ksi} \qquad \langle\text{O.K.}\rangle$$

At or near *point 3*

$$a/h = 179.4/(52 - 0.375 \times 2) = 3.50 > 1.0$$

$$k = 5.34 + \frac{4.00}{(a/h)^2} = 5.34 + \frac{4.00}{3.5^2} = 5.67$$

$$h/t_w = \frac{52 - 0.375 \times 2}{0.375} = 136.67$$

Try

$$C_v = \frac{45{,}000\ k}{F_y(h/t_w)^2} = \frac{45{,}000 \times 5.67}{50 \times 136.67^2} = 0.273 < 0.8 \qquad \langle\text{O.K.}\rangle$$

The allowable shear stress at point 3 from AISC Eq. (1.10-1), is given by

$$F_{v3} = \frac{F_y}{2.89}\ C_v = \frac{50}{2.89}\ (0.273) = 4.72\ \text{ksi} > f_{v3} = 3.63\ \text{ksi} \qquad \langle\text{O.K.}\rangle$$

(B)   Determine the adequacy of girder 5-12:
    (a)   Allowable axial stress
Since the bottom flange of the girder is not supported at every purlin, weak axis buckling of the compression flange should be checked by using the unsupported flange length. From the moment diagram of Fig. 4.2(a)

$$(L_y)_{5\text{-}6} = 49.3\ \text{in.}$$

$$(L_y)_{6\text{-}7} = 120\ \text{in.}$$

$$(L_y)_{9\text{-}10} = 60\ \text{in.}$$

$$(L_y)_{10\text{-}11} = 60\ \text{in.}$$

For *segments 9-10 and 10-11*, since no lateral support is provided at point 10, these segments are considered to be simply supported segments. The effective length factor for 9-10 and 10-11 is assumed to be $K_y = 1.0$.

For *segments 5-6 and 6-7*, because the compression flange is supported laterally at point 6, the end restraints of these segments may be considered.

Segment 5-6

$$G_T = \left(\frac{b_T I_0}{L I_T}\right)_y = \frac{120 \times 183.3}{49.3 \times 183.3} = 2.43 \qquad [\text{Eq. (E-5)}]$$

$$G_B = 10 \text{ (point 5 hinged)}$$

then, $K_y = 0.92$ (AISC alignment chart in Appendix B for the case of sidesway prevented)

Segment 6-7*

$$G_T = \left(\frac{b_T I_0}{L I_T}\right)_y = \frac{120 \times 183}{120 \times 45.5} = 4.02 \qquad [\text{Eq. (E-5)}]$$

$$G_B = \left(\frac{b_B I_0}{L I_B}\right)_y = \frac{49.3 \times 183.3}{120 \times 183.3} = 0.41 \qquad [\text{Eq. (E-6)}]$$

then $K_y = 0.78$ (AISC alignment chart in Appendix B for the case of sidesway prevented).

To determine the effective length factor for strong axis buckling for *girder 5-12*, certain quantities are needed for calculating G_T and G_B. The restraining member at the upper end of girder 5-12 is the same as girder 5-12 due to frame symmetry. From Appendix C,

$$\bar{\beta} = L_{5\text{-}8}/L_{5\text{-}12} = 25.1/55.1 = 0.5$$

$$\bar{\gamma}_1 = d_{12}/d_8 - 1 = (44/32) - 1 = 0.375$$

$$\bar{\gamma}_1 = d_5/d_8 - 1 = (52/32) - 1 = 0.625$$

$$g = 0.72 \text{ (Fig. C-5 in Appendix C)}$$

$$g_e = 2.0 \text{ } g \text{ for sidesway permitted case [Eq. (E-9)]. Then, from Eq. (E-11)}$$

$$G_T = \left(\frac{g_e b_T I_0}{L I_T}\right)_x = \frac{2 \times 0.72 \times 57.03 \times 1726}{57.03 \times 1726} = 1.44$$

---

* Section properties of segment 7-8 did not appear in the table of Fig. 4.1. $(I_y)_{7\text{-}8}$ is calculated to be 45.5 in.[4]

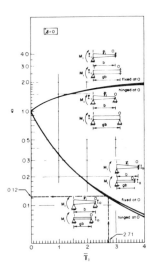

Figure C-3

The restraining member at the lower end of girder 5-12 is column 1-3. For this case,

$$\overline{\beta} = 0$$

$$\overline{\gamma}_1 = d_3/d_1 - 1 = 52/14 - 1 = 2.71$$

$$g = 0.12 \text{ (Fig. C-3)}$$

$$g_e = 2.0 \, g \qquad\qquad\qquad\qquad [\text{Eq. (E-9)}]$$

$$G_B = \left(\frac{g_e b_B I_0}{L I_B}\right)_x \qquad\qquad\qquad [\text{Eq. (E-12)}]$$

$$= \frac{2 \times 0.12 \times 16.99 \times 1726}{57.03 \times 661.2} = 0.202$$

For girder 5-12

$$\beta = 0.5$$

$$\gamma_1 = 0.375$$

$$\gamma_2 = 0.625 \text{ (sidesway permitted)}$$

The effective length factors can be obtained from the curves of Appendix E.

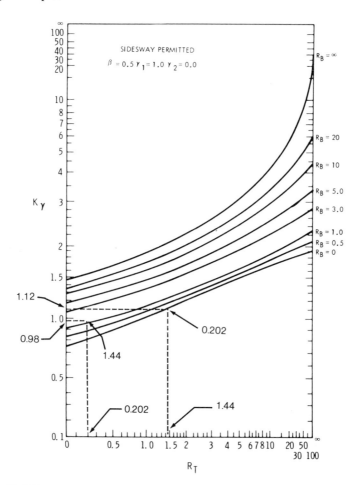

Figure E-4.11

$K_\gamma = 1.12$ for $\gamma_1 = 1.0$, $\gamma_2 = 0.0$ (Fig. E-4.11)

$K_\gamma = 0.98$ for $\gamma_1 = 0.0$, $\gamma_2 = 1.0$ (Fig. E-4.11 with $G_T = 0.202$ and $G_B = 1.44$)

$K_\gamma = 0.90$ for $\gamma_1 = 1.0$, $\gamma_2 = 1.0$ (Fig. E-4.12)

Furthermore, from the alignment chart (Fig. B-1—sideway permitted),

$$K = 1.25 \text{ for } \gamma_1 \text{ and } \gamma_2 = 0$$

By interpolation from the above values,

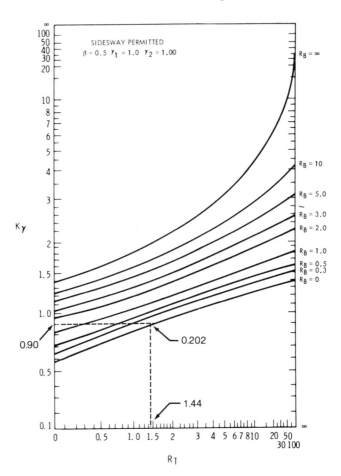

Figure E-4.12

$$K_x = K_\gamma = 1.04 \text{ for } \gamma_1 = 0.375,$$
$$\gamma_2 = 0.625$$

The effective slenderness ratios for strong and weak axes buckling are:

$(KL/r_8)_x = 1.04 \times 55.1 \times 12/11.92 = 57.7$ for girders 5-12

$(KL/r_6)_y = 0.92 \times 49.3/2.43 = 18.66$ for segment 5-6

$(KL/r_7)_y = 0.78 \times 120/2.56 = 36.56$ for segment 6-7

$(KL/r_9)_y = 1.0 \times 60/1.82 = 32.97$ for segment 9-10

$(KL/r_{10})_y = 1.0 \times 60/1.79 = 33.52$ for segment 10-11

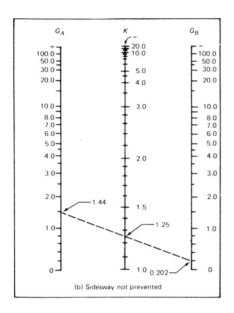

Figure B-1

Thus, the overall strong axis buckling controls. The allowable compression stress for the whole girder is:

$$F_{a\gamma} = 23.11 \text{ ksi (AISC Table 3-50)}$$

(b) *Allowable bending stress* (AISC Spec. App. D, Sect. D3)
By considering the end restraints, the allowable bending stresses for each segment of *girder 5-12* are calculated as follows:

Segment 5-6:

$$G_T = 2.43, \quad G_B = 10 \text{ (same as for axial stress consideration)}$$

$$K_s = 0.92, \quad K_w = 0.93 \text{ (Appendix F)}$$

The taper ratio for *segment 5-6* is

$$\gamma_{5\text{-}6} = (52/48.73) - 1 = 0.067$$

$$Ld_6/A_f = 49.3 \times 48.73/(13 \times 0.5) = 369.6$$

$$L/r_{T6} = 49.3/3.11 = 15.85$$

$$h_s = 1.0 + 0.023 \gamma \sqrt{Ld_6/A_f} = 1.030$$

$$h_w = 1.0 + 0.00385 \gamma\sqrt{L/r_{T6}} = 1.001$$

(When the taper ratio is small, the member can be assumed to be prismatic; that is, $h_s = h_w = 1.0$.) Therefore, from Eqs. (3.38) and (3.37)

$$F_{s\gamma} = \frac{12,000}{\dfrac{K_s h_s L d_6}{A_f}} = \frac{12,000}{(0.92)(1.03)(369.6)} = 34.26 \text{ ksi}$$

$$F_{w\gamma} = \frac{170,000}{\left(\dfrac{K_w h_w L}{r_{T6}}\right)^2} = \frac{170,000}{[(0.93)(1.001)(15.85)]^2} = 780.6 \text{ ksi}$$

The allowable bending stress is

$$F_{b\gamma} = \sqrt{F_{s\gamma}{}^2 + F_{w\gamma}{}^2} = \sqrt{34.26^2 + 780.8^2} = 781.5 \text{ ksi} > \frac{1}{3} F_y$$

$$[\text{Eq. (D3-2)}]$$

or

$$F_{b\gamma} = \frac{2}{3}\left[1 - \frac{50}{(6)(781.5)}\right] 50 = 32.97 \text{ ksi} > 0.6 F_y$$

$$[\text{Eq. (D3-1)}]$$

or

$$F_{b\gamma} = 0.6 F_y = 30 \text{ ksi—Governs}$$

   Segment 6-7:

   $G_T = 4.02$, $G_B = 0.41$ (same as for axial stress consideration)

   $K_s = 0.77$, $K_w = 0.74$ (Appendix F)

   $\gamma_{6\text{-}7} = (48.73/40.78) - 1 = 0.195$

$L d_7 / A_f = 120 \times 40.78/(13 \times 0.5) = 752.8$

$L/r_{T7} = 120/3.19 = 37.61$

   $h_s = 1.0 + 0.023 \times 0.195 \sqrt{752.8} = 1.123$

   $h_w = 1.0 + 0.00385 \times 0.195 \sqrt{37.61} = 1.004$

From Eqs. (3.38) and (3.37):

$$F_{s\gamma} = \frac{12,000}{(0.77)(1.123)(752.8)} = 18.43 \text{ ksi}$$

$$F_{w\gamma} = \frac{17,000}{[(0.74)\ (1.004)\ (37.61)]^2} = 217.7 \text{ ksi}$$

The allowable bending stress is

$$F_{b\gamma} = \sqrt{(18.43)^2 + (217.7)^2} = 218.5 \text{ ksi} > F_y \quad [\text{Eq. (D3-2)}]$$

or

$$F_{b\gamma} = \frac{2}{3}\left[1 - \frac{50}{(6)\ (218.5)}\right](50) = 32.06 \text{ ksi} > 0.6\ F_y \quad [\text{Eq. (D3-1)}]$$

or

$$F_{b\gamma} = 0.6\ F_y = 30 \text{ ksi—Governs}$$

Segment 9-10:

$$\gamma_{9\text{-}10} = (41.59/39.59) - 1 = 0.05$$

$$Ld_9/A_f = 60 \times 39.59/(9.31 \times 0.437) = 583.8$$

$$L/r_{T9} = 60/2.28 = 26.31$$

$$h_s = 1 + 0.023 \times 0.05\ \sqrt{583.8} = 1.027$$

$$h_w = 1 + 0.00385 \times 0.05\ \sqrt{26.31} = 1.001$$

The coefficient B to be multiplied by the allowable bending stress may be determined by using the provision of AISC Sect. D3 (b).

$$B = 1.0 + 0.58\left(1 - \frac{f_{b9'}}{f_{b10}}\right) - 0.7\gamma\left(1 - \frac{f_{b9'}}{f_{b10}}\right) \geq 1.0$$

$$B = 1.0 + 0.58\left(1 - \frac{3931/204}{22.35}\right) - 0.7(0.05)\left(1 - \frac{3931/204}{22.35}\right) = 1.07$$

For

$$F_{s\gamma} = \frac{12,000}{1.027 \times 583.8} = 20.01 \text{ ksi}$$

$$F_{w\gamma} = \frac{170,000}{(1.001 \times 26.31)^2} = 245.1 \text{ ksi}$$

Therefore,

$$F_{b\gamma} = 1.07\ \sqrt{20.01^2 + 245.1^2} = 263 \text{ ksi} > \frac{1}{3}\ F_y \quad [\text{Eq. (D3-2)}]$$

or

$$F_{b\gamma} = \frac{2}{3}\left[1 - \frac{50}{6 \times 263}\right] 50 = 32.3 \text{ ksi} > 0.6 \, F_y \quad [\text{Eq. (D3-1)}]$$

Use $F_{b\gamma}$ = 30 ksi as the allowable bending stress for *segment 9-10*

Segment 10-11:

$$\gamma_{10\text{-}11} = (43.59/41.59) - 1 = 0.05$$

$$Ld_{10}/A_f = 60 \times 41.59/(9.31 \times 0.437) = 613.3$$

$$L/r_{T10} = 60/2.26 = 26.54$$

$$h_s = 1 + 0.023 \times 0.05 \sqrt{613.3} = 1.028$$

$$h_w = 1 + 0.00385 \times 0.05 \sqrt{26.54} = 1.001$$

$$F_{s\gamma} = \frac{12,000}{1.028 \times 613.3} = 19.05 \text{ ksi}$$

$$F_{w\gamma} = \frac{170,000}{(1.001 \times 26.54)^2} = 240.8 \text{ ksi}$$

Since $f_{b10} > f_{b11}$ and $f_{b10} > f_{b9}$, the case is not covered by AISC Sect. D3. Therefore, use $B = 1.0$
  The allowable bending stress is

$$F_{b\gamma} = \sqrt{240.8^2 + 19.05^2} = 241.5 \text{ ksi} > \frac{1}{3} \, F_y \quad [\text{Eq. (D3-2)}]$$

or

$$F_{b\gamma} = \frac{2}{3}\left(1 - \frac{50}{6 \times 241.5}\right) 50 = 32.18 \text{ ksi} > 0.6 \, F_y \quad [\text{Eq. (D3-1)}]$$

or

$$F_{b\gamma} = 0.6 \, F_y = 30 \text{ ksi—Governs}$$

  (c) *Combined axial compression and bending* (AISC Spec. App. D, Sect. D4)
At *point 5* the depth to thickness ratio is

$$\frac{h_5}{t_w} = \frac{51}{0.375} = 136 < \frac{760}{\sqrt{F_b}}; \text{ therefore } F_b = 0.6 \, F_y$$

From Eq. (D4-1)

$$\frac{f_{a5}}{0.6F_y} + \frac{f_{b5}}{0.6F_y} = \frac{2.58}{30} + \frac{26.71}{30} = 0.976 < 1.0 \qquad \langle \text{O.K.} \rangle$$

For *segment 5-6*, $F_{a6}/F_{a\gamma} = 2.58/22.92 = 0.112 < 0.15$; therefore Eq. (D4-2) applies.

$$\frac{f_{a6}}{F_{a\gamma}} + \frac{f_{b5}}{F_{b\gamma}} = 0.112 + \frac{26.71}{30} = 1.00 \qquad \langle \text{O.K.} \rangle$$

For *segment 6-7*, $f_{a7}/F_{a\gamma} = 2.93/23.11 = 0.127 < 0.15$; Eq. (D4-2) applies.

$$\frac{f_{a7}}{F_{a\gamma}} + \frac{f_{b6}}{F_{b\gamma}} = 0.127 + \frac{23.15}{30} = 0.9 < 1.0 \qquad \langle \text{O.K.} \rangle$$

For *segment 9-10*, $f_{a9}/F_{a\gamma} = 4.42/23.11 = 0.191 > 0.15$. Thus, both Eq. (D4-1a) and (D4-1b) apply.

$$C_m = 0.85 \text{ (sidesway permitted)}$$

$$F'_{e\gamma} = 48.55 \text{ (AISC Spec. Table 9)}$$

At *point 10*, $h_{10}/t_w = 40.71/0.25 = 162.8 > 760/\sqrt{F_{b\gamma}} = 138.8$. Therefore, use AISC Eq. (1.10-5) for modified allowable bending stress.

$$F'_{b\gamma} = F_{b\gamma} \left[1.0 - 0.0005 \frac{A_w}{A_f} \left(\frac{h}{t_w} - \frac{760}{\sqrt{F_{b\gamma}}} \right) \right]$$

$$= 30 \left[1.0 - 0.0005 \frac{40.71 \times 0.25}{9.31 \times 0.437} (162.8 - 138.8) \right]$$

$$= 29.1 \text{ ksi}$$

From Eq. (D4-1a)

$$\frac{f_{a9}}{F_{a\gamma}} + \frac{C_m}{\left(1 - \dfrac{f_{a9}}{F'_{e\gamma}} \right)} \left(\frac{f_{b10}}{F'_{b\gamma}} \right) = 0.193 + \frac{0.85}{\left(1 - \dfrac{4.42}{48.55} \right)} \left(\frac{22.35}{29.1} \right)$$

$$= 0.910 < 1.0 \qquad \langle \text{O.K.} \rangle$$

Check Eq. (D4-1b) for point 10,

$$\frac{f_{a10}}{0.6F_y} + \frac{f_{b10}}{F'_{b\gamma}} = \frac{4.29}{30} + \frac{22.35}{29.1} = 0.911 < 1.0 \qquad \langle \text{O.K.} \rangle$$

For segment 10-11:

At *point 11*, $h_{11}/t_w = 42.71/0.25 = 170.8 > 760/\sqrt{F_{b\gamma}} = 138.8$

The modified bending stress is

$$F'_{b\gamma} = 30\left[1.0 - 0.0005\frac{42.71 \times 0.25}{9.31 \times 0.137}(170.8\text{-}138.8)\right] = 28.73 \text{ ksi}$$

[AISC Eq. (1-10-5)]

with

$$f_{a10}/F_{a\gamma} = \frac{4.29}{22.92} = 0.187 > 0.15. \text{ Eq. (D4-1a) gives}$$

$$\frac{f_{a10}}{F_{a\gamma}} + \frac{C_m}{\left(1 - \frac{f_{a10}}{F'_{e\gamma}}\right)}\left(\frac{f_{b11}}{F'_{b\gamma}}\right) = 0.186 + \frac{0.85}{\left(1 - \frac{4.29}{48.55}\right)}\left(\frac{21.5}{28.73}\right)$$

$$= 0.884 < 1.0 \qquad\qquad \langle\text{O.K.}\rangle$$

Check Eq. (D4-1b) for point 11

$$\frac{f_{a11}}{0.6F_y} + \frac{f_{b11}}{F'_{b\gamma}} = \frac{4.17}{30} + \frac{21.5}{28.73} = 0.887 < 1.0 \qquad\qquad \langle\text{O.K.}\rangle$$

At point 12, $h_{12}/t_w = 43.13/0.25 = 172.5 > 760/\sqrt{F_{b\gamma}} = 138.8$

$$F'_{b\gamma} = 30\left[1.0 - 0.0005\frac{43.13 \times 0.75}{9.31 \times 0.437}(172.5 - 138.8)\right]$$

$$= 28.66 \text{ ksi}$$

Eq. (D4-1b) gives

$$\frac{f_{a12}}{0.6F_y} + \frac{f_{b12}}{F'_{b\gamma}} = \frac{4.14}{30} + \frac{21.17}{28.66} = 0.876 < 1.0 \qquad\qquad \langle\text{O.K.}\rangle$$

Example No. 2 (See Fig. 4.3)

In this example, the frame considered in Example No. 1 will be redesigned presuming the use of hot-rolled, I-type shapes. Again, two types of loading combinations are considered. The resulting moment diagrams are shown in Fig. 4.4.

Solution:

From the moment diagrams shown in Fig. 4.4, it is evident that the first loading case $(DL + LL)$ controls the design. Furthermore, segments

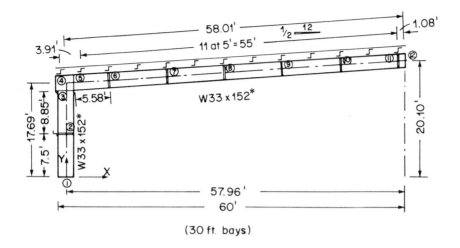

COORDINATES AND SECTION PROPERTIES

Point	1	2	3	4	5	6	7	8	9	10	11	12
X(ft.)	0.00	0.00	0.00	0.00	1.34	6.92	16.91	26.90	36.90	46.89	56.88	57.96
Y(ft.)	0.00	7.50	16.35	17.69	17.75	17.98	18.39	18.81	19.22	19.64	20.06	20.10

*W33 × 152 ($d = 33.5''$, $b_f = 11.565''$, $t_f = 1.055''$, $t_w = 0.635''$
        $A = 44.8$ in.^{2}, $I_x = 8160$ in.^{4}, $S_x = 487.$ in.^{3}, $r_x = 13.5''$
        $I_y = 273$ in.^{4}, $r_y = 2.47''$, $r_T = 2.98''$), $F_y = 50$ ksi.

Figure 4.3. Dimensions and geometry of the frame of Design Example 2.

2-3, 5-6, and 6-7 are most likely to be critical. The maximum stresses in these segments are calculated as follows:

Axial stresses: $(DL + LL)$

$$f_{a2} = P_2/A_2 = 72.36/44.8 = 1.62 \text{ ksi} \quad \text{for segment 2-3}$$

$$f_{a5} = P_5/A_5 = 69.14/44.8 = 1.54 \text{ ksi} \quad \text{for segment 5-6}$$

$$f_{a6} = P_6/A_6 = 68.87/44.8 = 1.54 \text{ ksi} \quad \text{for segment 6-7}$$

Bending stresses: $(DL + LL)$

$$f_{b3} = M_3/S_3 = 13022/487 = 26.74 \text{ ksi} \quad \text{for segment 2-3}$$

$$f_{b5} = M_5/S_5 = 13023/487 = 26.74 \text{ ksi} \quad \text{for segment 5-6}$$

$$f_{b6} = M_6/S_6 = 8858/487 = 18.19 \text{ ksi} \quad \text{for segment 6-7}$$

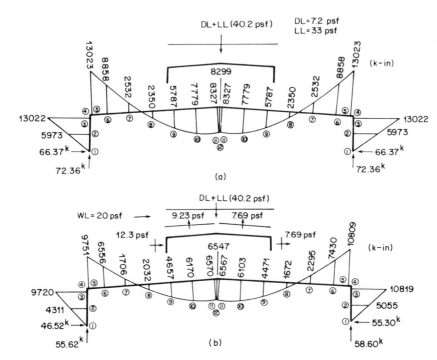

Figure 4.4. Moment diagrams of the frame of Fig. 4.3 due to two sets of loading conditions.

(A)   *Segment 2-3:*

(a)   *Allowable compressive stress*

The adjacent segment 1-2 provides restraint to segment 2-3 for weak-axis buckling. The restraint parameters are given by

$$G_B = \left(\frac{b_B I_0}{LI_B}\right)_y = \frac{7.5 \times 273}{8.85 \times 273} = 0.85 \qquad [\text{Eq. (E-6)}]$$

$$G_T = 10 \ (\text{AISC recommended value for hinged end, 3})$$

The effective length factor for weak axis buckling can be found from AISC alignment chart for the sidesway prevented case.

$$K_y = 0.85$$

For strong axis buckling, the restraining member at the top of the column is girder 5-12:

$$G_T = \left(\frac{g_e b_T I_0}{LI_T}\right)_x = \frac{2 \times 58.01}{17.69} = 6.56 \qquad [\text{Eq. (E-11)}]$$

in which $I_0 = I_T$, $g_e = 2g$ (sidesway permitted) and $g = 1.0$ for prismatic member; $G_B = 10$ (AISC recommended value for hinged end 1). Therefore, the strong axis effective length factor is $K_x = 2.7$ (AISC alignment chart for sidesway permitted case). The slenderness ratios for the strong and weak axes are:

$$(KL/r_1)_x = \frac{2.72 \times 16.35 \times 12}{13.5} = 39.53 \text{ (controls)}$$

$$(KL/r_2)_y = \frac{0.85 \times 8.85 \times 12}{2.47} = 36.54$$

From AISC Spec. Table 3-50, the allowable axial stress for segment 2-3 is:

$$F_a = 25.90 \text{ ksi}$$

(b)   *Allowable bending stress* (AISC Spec. Sect. 1.5.1.4)

By including the end restraints of adjacent segments, the allowable bending stress *for segment 2-3* is obtained as follows:

$$G_T = 10 \text{ (hinged at point 3)}$$

$$G_B = \left(\frac{b_B I_0}{L I_B}\right)_y = \frac{7.5 \times 273}{8.85 \times 273} = 0.85 \qquad [\text{Eq. (E-6)}]$$

From Appendix F, the effective length factors are

$$K_s = 0.84, \quad K_w = 0.82$$

From AISC Spec. Sect. 1.5,

$$C_b = 1.75 - 1.05 \left(\frac{M_2}{M_3}\right) + 0.3 \left(\frac{M_2}{M_3}\right)^2$$

$$= 1.75 - 1.05 \left(\frac{5973}{13{,}022}\right) + 0.3 \left(\frac{5973}{13{,}022}\right)^2$$

$$= 1.33$$

and

$$K_w L/r_7 = 0.82 \times 8.85 \times 12/2.98 = 29.22$$

$$\sqrt{\frac{102 \times 10^3 C_b}{F_y}} = \sqrt{\frac{102{,}000 \times 1.33}{50}} = 51.5 > \frac{K_w L}{r_T}$$

Therefore, the allowable bending stress is

$$F_b = 0.6 \, F_y = 30 \text{ ksi}$$

(c)   *Combined axial compression and bending* (AISC Spec. Sect. 1.6)

For *segment 2-3*, $f_{a2}/F_a = 1.62/25.9 = 0.062 < 0.15$. Therefore, Eq. (1.6-2) applies.

$$\frac{f_{a2}}{F_a} + \frac{f_{b3}}{F_b} = 0.062 + \frac{26.74}{30} = 0.953 < 1.0 \qquad \langle \text{O.K.} \rangle$$

(B)   *Segments 5-6 and 6-7*
      (a)   *Allowable compressive stress*

The effective length factors for weak axis buckling are obtained as follows.

For segment 5-6:

$$G_T = \left(\frac{b_T I_0}{L I_T}\right)_y = \frac{10 \times 273}{5.58 \times 273} = 1.79 \qquad [\text{Eq. (E-5)}]$$

$G_B = 10$ (AISC recommended value for hinged end, 5)

Then $K_y = 0.90$ (AISC alignment chart for sidesway prevented case)

For segment 6-7:

$$G_T = \left(\frac{b_T I_0}{L I_T}\right)_y = \frac{10 \times 273}{10 \times 273} = 1.0 \qquad [\text{Eq. (E-5)}]$$

$$G_B = \left(\frac{b_B I_0}{L I_0}\right)_y = \frac{5.58 \times 273}{10 \times 273} = 0.56 \qquad [\text{Eq. (E-6)}]$$

Then $K_y = 0.74$ (AISC alignment chart for sidesway prevented case) For strong axis buckling (girder 5-12):

$$G_T = \left(\frac{g_e b_T I_0}{L I_T}\right)_x = \frac{2 \times 58.01 \times 8160}{58.01 \times 8160} = 2.0 \quad [\text{Eq. (E-11)}]$$

$$G_B = \left(\frac{g_e b_B I_0}{L I_B}\right)_x = \frac{2 \times 17.69 \times 8160}{58.01 \times 8160} = 0.61 \quad [\text{Eq. (E-12)}]$$

Then $K_x = 1.42$ (AISC alignment chart for sidesway permitted case). The slenderness ratio for the strong and weak axes are:

$$(KL/r_5)_y = \frac{0.9 \times 5.58 \times 12}{2.47} = 24.40 \quad \text{for segment 5-6}$$

$$(KL/r_6)_y = \frac{0.74 \times 10 \times 12}{2.47} = 35.95 \quad \text{for segment 6-7}$$

$$(KL/r_5)_x = \frac{1.42 \times 56.66 \times 12}{13.5} = 71.52 \quad \text{for girder 5-12}$$

Thus, strong-axis buckling controls. The allowable compressive stress is determined from AISC Spec. Table 3-50.

$$F_a = 20.65 \text{ ksi}$$

(b) *Allowable bending stress:*
Including the end restraints of adjacent segments, the allowable bending stress is obtained as follows:

For *segment 5-6:*

$$G_T = 1.79; \quad G_B = 10$$

From Appendix F,

$$K_s = 0.90; \quad K_w = 0.92$$

with

$$C_b = 1.75 - 1.05 \left(\frac{M_6}{M_5}\right) + 0.3 \left(\frac{M_6}{M_5}\right)^2$$

$$= 1.75 - 1.05 \left(\frac{8858}{13{,}023}\right) + 0.3 \left(\frac{8858}{13{,}023}\right)^2$$

$$= 1.17$$

$$K_w L/r_T = 0.92 \times 5.58 \times 12/2.98 = 20.6$$

$$\sqrt{\frac{102 \times 10^3 C_b}{F_y}} = \sqrt{\frac{102 \times 10^3 \times 1.17}{50}}$$

$$= 48.85 > K_w L/r_T$$

Therefore, use

$$F_b = 0.6 \, F_y = 30 \text{ ksi}$$

For *segment 6-7:*

$$G_T = 1.0; \quad G_B = 0.56$$

From Appendix F,

$$K_s = 0.72; \quad K_w = 0.68$$

with

$$C_b = 1.75 - 1.05 \left(\frac{M_7}{M_6}\right) + 0.3 \left(\frac{M_7}{M_6}\right)^2$$

$$= 1.75 - 1.05 \left(\frac{2532}{8858}\right) + 0.3 \left(\frac{2532}{8858}\right)^2$$

$$= 1.47$$

$$K_w L / r_T = 0.68 \times 10 \times 12/2.98 = 27.4$$

$$\sqrt{\frac{102 \times 10^3 \times C_b}{F_y}} = \sqrt{\frac{102 \times 10^3 \times 1.48}{50}}$$

$$= 54.8 > K_w L / r_T$$

Therefore, use

$$F_b = 0.6 \, F_y = 30 \text{ ksi}$$

(c)   *Combined axial compression and bending* (AISC Sect. 1.6)
For *segment 5-6*, $f_{a5}/F_a = 1.54/20.65 = 0.075 < 0.15$; Eq. (1.6-2)
yields:

$$\frac{f_{a5}}{F_a} + \frac{f_{b5}}{F_b} = 0.075 + \frac{26.74}{30} = 0.966 < 1.0 \qquad \langle \text{O.K.} \rangle$$

For *segment 6-7*, $f_{a6}/F_a = 1.54/20.65 = 0.075 < 0.15$; Eq. (1.6-2)
gives:

$$\frac{f_{a6}}{F_a} + \frac{f_{b6}}{F_b} = 0.075 + \frac{18.19}{30} = 0.681 < 1.0 \qquad \langle \text{O.K.} \rangle$$

Example No. 3 (See Fig. 4.5)

The problem is to determine the adequacy of the gable frame shown in Fig.
4.5. The moment diagrams for two types of loading combinations are shown
in Fig. 4.6.

Solution:

In general, all segments of the frame should be checked under every
loading combination. However, by inspecting the moment diagrams,
segments 1-2, 2-3, 6-7, and 7-8 are probably critical under the first
loading combination (*DL + LL*), and segment 9-10 is critical under the

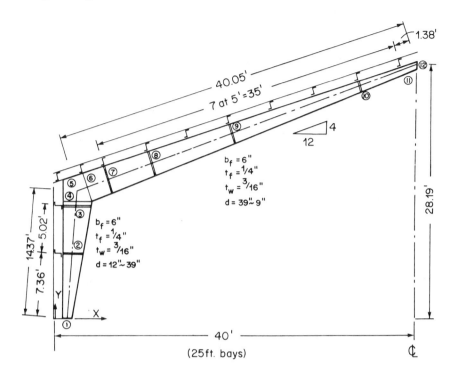

COORDINATES AND SECTION PROPERTIES

Point	1	2	3	4	5	6	7	8	9	10	11	12
X(ft.)	1.21	1.84	2.26	2.33	2.43	3.44	5.86	10.55	19.94	34.02	38.71	40.00
Y(ft.)	0.00	7.33	12.33	13.15	14.32	14.69	15.58	17.31	20.78	25.98	27.71	28.19
d(in.)	12.00	27.06	37.33	39.00	—	39.00	37.02	33.17	25.46	13.91	10.06	9.00
A(in.^{2})	5.16	7.98	9.91	10.22	—	10.22	9.85	9.12	7.68	5.51	4.79	4.59
I_x(in.^{4})	127.4	8319	1811	2017	—	2017	1776	1357	719	178	85.70	67.00
S_x(in.^{3})	21.23	61.48	97.07	103.5	—	103.5	95.89	81.84	56.54	25.54	17.04	14.89
I_y(in.^{4})	8.99	8.97	8.94	9.03	—	9.03	9.03	9.03	9.02	9.01	9.00	9.00
r_T(in.)	1.63	1.42	1.32	1.30	—	1.30	1.32	1.36	1.43	1.58	1.65	1.66

Figure 4.5. Dimensions and geometry of the frame of Design Example 3.

second loading combination ($DL + \frac{1}{2}LL + WL$). The situation for segments 8-9 and 10-11 is not obvious. Therefore, both loading combinations should be checked. Having determined the controlling case for each segment, the maximum stresses are then calculated.

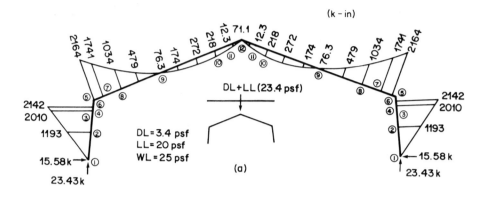

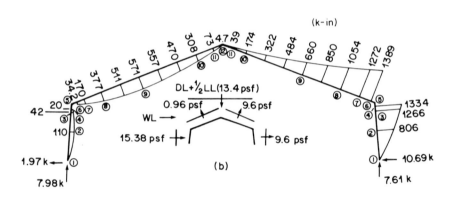

Figure 4.6. Moment diagrams of the frame of Fig. 4.5 due to two sets of loading conditions.

Axial stresses:

$$f_{a1} = P_1/A_1 = 24.7/5.16 = 4.79 \text{ ksi} \quad (DL + LL)$$

$$f_{a2} = P_2/A_2 = 24.7/7.98 = 3.10 \text{ ksi} \quad (DL + LL)$$

$$f_{a3} = P_3/A_3 = 24.7/9.91 = 2.49 \text{ ksi} \quad (DL + LL)$$

$$f_{a4} = P_4/A_4 = 24.7/10.22 = 2.42 \text{ ksi} \quad (DL + LL)$$

$$f_{a6} = P_6/A_6 = 21.9/10.22 = 2.14 \text{ ksi} \quad (DL + LL)$$

$$f_{a7} = P_7/A_7 = 21.4/9.85 = 2.17 \text{ ksi} \quad (DL + LL)$$

$$f_{a8} = P_8/A_8 = 20.5/9.12 = 2.25 \text{ ksi} \quad (DL + LL)$$

$$f_{a9} = P_9/A_9 = 18.6/7.68 = 2.42 \text{ ksi} \quad (DL + LL)$$

$$f_{a9} = P_9/A_9 = 6.8/7.68 = 0.88 \text{ ksi} \quad (DL + \tfrac{1}{2}LL + WL)$$

$$f_{a10} = P_{10}/A_{10} = 5.2/5.51 = 0.94 \text{ ksi} \quad (DL + \tfrac{1}{2}LL + WL)$$

$$f_{a10} = P_{10}/A_{10} = 15.8/5.51 = 2.87 \text{ ksi} \quad (DL + LL)$$

$$f_{a11} = P_{11}/A_{11} = 14.6/4.79 = 3.05 \text{ ksi} \quad (DL + LL)$$

Bending stresses:

$$f_{b2} = M_2/S_2 = 1195/61.48 = 19.44 \text{ ksi} \quad (DL + LL)$$

$$f_{b3} = M_3/S_3 = 2010/97.07 = 20.71 \text{ ksi} \quad (DL + LL)$$

$$f_{b4} = M_4/S_4 = 2142/103.5 = 20.70 \text{ ksi} \quad (DL + LL)$$

$$f_{b6} = M_6/S_6 = 2164/103.5 = 20.91 \text{ ksi} \quad (DL + LL)$$

$$f_{b7} = M_7/S_7 = 174.1/95.89 = 18.16 \text{ ksi} \quad (DL + LL)$$

$$f_{b8} = M_8/S_8 = 1034/81.84 = 12.63 \text{ ksi} \quad (DL + LL)$$

$$f_{b9} = M_9/S_9 = 660/56.54 = 11.67 \text{ ksi} \quad (DL + \tfrac{1}{2}LL + WL)$$

$$f_{10} = M_{10}/S_{10} = 218/25.54 = 8.53 \text{ ksi} \quad (DL + LL)$$

Shear stresses:

$$f_{v1} = V_1/A'_{w1} = 13.53/(12 \times 3/16) = 6.01 \text{ ksi} \quad (DL + LL)$$

$$f_{v4} = V_4/A'_{w4} = 13.53/(39 \times 3/16) = 1.85 \text{ ksi} \quad (DL + LL)$$

(A) *Determine the adequacy of column 1-4:*
   (a) *Allowable compressive stress* (AISC Spec. App. D, Sect. D2)
The effective length factors for weak axis buckling are obtained as follows:

Seg-ment	L_y (ft.)	I_{0y} (in.^{4})	b_{Ty} (ft.)	I_{Ty} (in.^{4})	b_{By} (ft.)	I_{By} (in.^{4})	$G_T = \left(\dfrac{b_T I_0}{LI_T}\right)_y$	$G_B = \left(\dfrac{b_B I_0}{LI_B}\right)_y$	K_y
1-2	7.36	8.99	5.02	8.97	—	—	0.68	10	0.83
2-3	5.02	8.97	—	—	7.36	8.99	10	1.4	0.88

Strong axis effective length factors may be determined from the charts in AISC Commentary Sect. D2.

For restraining member, *girder 6-12,* from Appendix C

$$\bar{\beta} = 0$$

$$\bar{\gamma}_1 = d_6/d_{12} - 1 = (39/9) - 1 = 3.33$$

$$g = 0.092 \text{ (Fig. C-3 in Appendix C)}$$

$$g_e = 2.0g \text{ (sidesway permitted)} \qquad [\text{Eq. (E-9)}]$$

Then

$$G_T = \left(\frac{g_e b_T I_0}{L I_T}\right)_x = \frac{2 \times 0.092 \times 40.05 \times 127.4}{14.37 \times 67.0} = 0.98$$

$$[\text{Eq. (E-11)}]$$

$$G_B = 10 \text{ for pinned end, 1.}$$

The taper ratio for *column 1-4* is

$$\gamma_{1\text{-}4} = d_4/d_1 - 1 = (39/12) - 1 = 2.25$$

From the effective length factors charts in AISC Commentary Sect. D2,

$$K_x = K_\gamma = 1.37 \text{ for } \gamma = 2.0 \text{ (AISC Fig. CD 1.5.14)}$$

$$1.32 \text{ for } \gamma = 3.0 \text{ (AISC Fig. CD 1.5.15)}$$

Then $K_x = 1.36$ for $\gamma = 2.25$

The slenderness ratios for strong and weak axes are:

$$\left(\frac{KL}{r_1}\right)_x = 1.36 \times 12.38 \times 12/4.97 = 40.65 \qquad \textit{for column 1-4}$$

$$\left(\frac{KL}{r_1}\right)_y = 0.83 \times 7.36 \times 12/1.32 = 55.53 \qquad \textit{for segment 1-2}$$

$$\left(\frac{KL}{r_2}\right)_y = 0.88 \times 5.02 \times 12/1.06 = 50.01 \qquad \textit{for segment 2-3}$$

Thus, weak-axis buckling governs. The allowable axial stresses are obtained from AISC Table 3-50.

$$F_{a\gamma} = 23.46 \text{ ksi} \qquad \textit{for segment 1-2}$$

$$F_{a\gamma} = 24.35 \text{ ksi} \qquad \textit{for segment 2-3}$$

(b)   *Allowable bending stress* (AISC Spec. App. D, Sect. D3) Considering the end restraints of adjacent spans, the allowable bending stresses are obtained as follows.

Seg-ment	G_T	G_B	K_s	K_w	L (ft.)	d_0 (in.)	A_f (in.^{2})	r_{T0} (in.)	$\dfrac{Ld_0}{A_f}$	$\dfrac{L}{r_{T0}}$	γ
1-2	0.68	10	0.82	0.8	7.36	12	1.5	1.63	706.6	54.18	1.26
2-3	10	1.46	0.88	0.88	5.02	27.6	1.5	1.42	1087	42.42	0.44

Segment	h_s	h_w	$F_{s\gamma}$ (ksi) = $\dfrac{12 \times 10^3}{K_s h_s Ld_0/A_f}$	$F_{w\gamma}$ (ksi) = $\dfrac{170 \times 10^3}{(K_w h_w L/r_{T0})^2}$	$F_{b\gamma}$ (ksi) Eq. (D3-2)	$F_{b\gamma}$ (ksi) Eq. (D3-1)	Use $F_{b\gamma}$ (ksi)
1-2	1.77	1.012	11.99	88.3	$89.1 > \frac{1}{3}F_y$	$30.21 < 0.6F_y$	30
2-3	1.334	1.011	9.41	119.3	$119.7 > \frac{1}{3}F_y$	$31.0 < 0.6F_y$	30

(c)   *Combined axial compression and bending* (AISC Spec. App. D, Sect. D4)

For *segment 1-2*, $f_{a1}/F_{a\gamma} = 4.79/23.46 = 0.204 > 0.15$; Eq. (D4-1a) applies. For $(KL/r)_x = 40.05$,

$$F'_{e\gamma} = 93.1 \text{ ksi (AISC Spec. Table 9)}$$

Since the column is permitted to sway in its plane,

$$C_m = 0.85$$

At *point 2*,

$$\frac{h_2}{t_w} = \frac{26.56}{0.1875} = 141.6 > \frac{760}{\sqrt{F_{b\gamma}}} = \frac{760}{\sqrt{30}} = 138.8$$

The modified bending allowable stress is calculated from AISC Eq. (1.10-5)

$$F'_{b\gamma} = 30\left[1.0 - 0.0005 \frac{26.56 \times 0.1875}{6 \times 0.25}(141.6 - 138.8)\right]$$

$$= 29.86 \text{ ksi}$$

Therefore, from AISC interaction Eq. (D4-1a),

$$\frac{f_{a1}}{F_{a\gamma}} + \frac{C_m}{\left(1 - \dfrac{f_{a1}}{F'_{e\gamma}}\right)}\left(\frac{f_{b2}}{F'_{b\gamma}}\right) = 0.204 + \frac{0.85}{\left(1 - \dfrac{4.79}{93.1}\right)}\left(\frac{19.44}{29.86}\right)$$

$$= 0.787 < 1.0 \qquad \qquad \langle\text{O.K.}\rangle$$

At *point 2,*

$$F'_{b\gamma} = 29.86 \text{ ksi}$$

From Eq. (D4-1b)

$$\frac{f_{a2}}{0.6F_y} + \frac{f_{b2}}{F'_{b\gamma}} = \frac{3.1}{30} + \frac{19.44}{29.86} = 0.75 < 1.0 \qquad \langle \text{O.K.} \rangle$$

For *segment 2-3,* $f_{a2}/F_{a\gamma} = 3.1/24.35 = 0.127 < 0.15$; Eq. (D4-2) applies. But at *point 3,*

$$\frac{h_3}{t_w} = \frac{36.83}{0.1875} = 196.4 > \frac{760}{\sqrt{F_{b\gamma}}} = \frac{760}{\sqrt{30}} = 138.8$$

AISC Eq. (1.10-5) allows

$$F'_{b\gamma} = 30\left[1.0 - 0.0005 \frac{36.83 \times 0.1875}{6 \times 0.25}(196.4 - 138.8)\right] = 26.02 \text{ ksi}$$

Then,

$$\frac{f_{a2}}{F_{a\gamma}} + \frac{f_{b3}}{F'_{b\gamma}} = 0.127 + \frac{20.71}{26.02} = 0.923 < 1.0 \qquad \langle \text{O.K.} \rangle$$

At *point 3,*

$$F'_{b\gamma} = 26.02 \text{ ksi}$$

From Eq. (D4-1b)

$$\frac{f_{a3}}{0.6F_y} + \frac{f_{b3}}{F'_{b\gamma}} = \frac{2.49}{30} + \frac{20.71}{26.02} = 0.878 < 1.0 \qquad \langle \text{O.K.} \rangle$$

At *point 4:*

$$\frac{h_4}{t_w} = \frac{38.5}{0.1875} = 205.3 > \frac{760}{\sqrt{F_{b\gamma}}} = 138.8$$

$$F'_{b\gamma} = 30[1.0 - 0.0005 \frac{38.5 \times 0.1875}{6 \times 0.25}(205.3 - 138.8)]$$

$$= 25.2 \text{ ksi} \qquad\qquad [\text{AISC Eq. (1.10-5)}]$$

Therefore,

$$\frac{f_{a4}}{0.6F_y} + \frac{f_{b4}}{F'_{b\gamma}} = \frac{2.42}{30} + \frac{20.7}{25.2} = 0.902 < 1.0 \qquad \langle \text{O.K.} \rangle$$

$$[\text{AISC Eq. (D4-1b)}]$$

(*d*) *Allowable shear stress* (AISC Spec. Sect. 1.10.5.2)
The clear distance between transverse stiffeners at points 1 and 4 is

$$a = 13.20 \times 12 = 158.4 \text{ in.}$$

At *point 1* (AISC Eq. 1.10-1 or Table 10-50)

$$a/h = 158.4 \Big/ \left(12 - \frac{3}{16} \times 2\right) = 13.62 > 1.0$$

$$k = 5.34 + \frac{4.00}{(a/h)^2} = 5.34 + \frac{4.00}{13.62^2} = 5.36$$

$$h/t_w = \frac{12 - \frac{3}{16} \times 2}{3/16} = 62$$

Try

$$C_v = \frac{190}{h/t_w} \sqrt{k/F_y} = \frac{190}{62} \sqrt{\frac{5.36}{50}} = 1.004 > 0.8 \qquad \langle \text{O.K.} \rangle$$

The allowable shear stress is obtained from AISC Eq. (1.10-1)

$$F_{v1} = \frac{F_y}{2.89} (C_v) = \frac{50}{2.89} (1.004) = 17.36 \text{ ksi} > f_{v1} = 6.01 \text{ ksi} \quad \langle \text{O.K.} \rangle$$

At point 4:

$$a/h = 158.4 \Big/ \left(39 - \frac{3}{16} \times 2\right) = 4.10 > 1.0$$

$$k = 5.34 + \frac{4.00}{(a/h)^2} = 5.34 + \frac{4.00}{4.1^2} = 5.58$$

$$h/t_w = \frac{39 - (3/16) \times 2}{3/16} = 206$$

Try

$$C_v = \frac{45,000 \, k}{F_y (h/t_w)^2} = \frac{45,000 \times 5.58}{50 \times 206^2} = 0.118 < 0.8 \qquad \langle \text{O.K.} \rangle$$

The allowable shear stress is determined from AISC Eq. (1.10-1)

$$F_{v4} = \frac{F_y}{2.89} (C_v) = \frac{50}{2.89} (0.118) = 2.04 \text{ ksi} > f_{v4} = 1.85 \text{ ksi} \quad \langle \text{O.K.} \rangle$$

(B)   Determine the adequacy of girder 5-12:
     (a)   Allowable compressive stress
The effective length factors for weak axis buckling are obtained as follows:

Segment	L_y (ft.)	I_{0y} (in.⁴)	b_{Ty} (ft.)	I_{Ty} (in.⁴)	b_{By} (ft.)	I_{By} (in.⁴)	$G_T = \left(\dfrac{b_T I_0}{L I_T}\right)_y$	$G_B = \left(\dfrac{b_B I_0}{L I_B}\right)_y$	K_y
6-7	2.58	9.03	5	9.03	—	—	1.94	10	0.9
7-8	5	9.03	10	9.02	2.58	9.03	2	0.52	0.77
8-9	10	9.02	15	9.01	5	9.03	1.5	0.5	0.75
9-10	15	9.01	6.38	9.00	10	9.02	0.42	0.67	0.69
10-11	5	9.00	—	—	—	—	—	—	1.0

To determine the strong axis effective length of *girder 6-12*, the following quantities of adjacent segments are necessary.
     For adjacent girder at point 12.

$$\bar{\beta} = 1.0$$

$$\bar{\gamma}_2 = d_6/d_{12} - 1 = (39/9) - 1 = 3.33$$

$$g = 0.41 \text{ (Fig. C-7 in Appendix C)}$$

$$g_e = 2g \text{ for sidesway permitted [Eq. (E-9)]}$$

$$G_T = \left(\frac{g_e b_T I_0}{L I_T}\right)_x = \frac{2 \times 0.41 \times 40.05 \times 67.0}{40.05 \times 67.0} = 0.82$$

$$[\text{Eq. (E-11)}]$$

For column 1-5

$$\bar{\beta} = 0$$

$$\bar{\gamma}_1 = d_4/d_1 - 1 = (39/12) - 1 = 2.25$$

$$g = 0.15 \text{ (Fig. C-3 in Appendix C)}$$

$$g_e = 2g \text{ [Eq. (E-9)]}$$

$$G_B = \left(\frac{g_e b_B I_0}{L I_B}\right)_x = \frac{2 \times 0.15 \times 14.37 \times 67.0}{40.05 \times 127.4} = 0.057 \quad [\text{Eq. (E-12)}]$$

and

$$\gamma_{6\text{-}12} = 3.33$$

From the charts in AISC Commentary Sect. D2

$$K_x = K_\gamma = 0.82 \quad \text{for } \gamma = 3.0 \quad [\text{AISC Fig. CD1.5.15}]$$

$$K_x = 0.78 \quad \text{for } \gamma = 4.0 \quad [\text{AISC Fig. CD1.5.16}]$$

Therefore,

$$K_x = 0.81 \quad \text{for } \gamma = 3.33$$

The slenderness ratios for weak and strong axes are:

$$\left(\frac{KL}{r_7}\right)_y = \frac{0.9 \times 258 \times 12}{0.96} = 29.02 \qquad \textit{for segment 6-7}$$

$$\left(\frac{KL}{r_8}\right)_y = \frac{0.77 \times 5 \times 12}{0.99} = 46.67 \qquad \textit{for segment 7-8}$$

$$\left(\frac{KL}{r_9}\right)_y = \frac{0.75 \times 10 \times 12}{1.08} = 83.33 \qquad \textit{for segment 8-9}$$

$$\left(\frac{KL}{r_{10}}\right)_y = \frac{0.69 \times 15 \times 12}{1.28} = 97.03 \qquad \textit{for segment 9-10}$$

$$\left(\frac{KL}{r_{11}}\right)_y = \frac{1.0 \times 5 \times 12}{1.37} = 43.80 \qquad \textit{for segment 10-11}$$

$$\left(\frac{KL}{r_{12}}\right)_x = \frac{0.81 \times 38.97 \times 12}{3.82} = 99.16 \qquad \textit{for segment 6-12}$$

The strong axis buckling controls for all segments. The allowable axial stress is

$$F_{a\gamma} = 14.9 \text{ ksi} \qquad (\text{AISC Table 3-50})$$

Since segment 9-10 is considered under the second loading combination $(DL + \frac{1}{2}LL + WL)$, the allowable stress can be increased by $1/3$ according to AISC Spec. 1.5.6. Therefore,

$$F_{a\gamma} = 14.9 \times \frac{4}{3} = 19.86 \text{ ksi} \qquad \textit{for segment 9-10}$$

(b)   *Allowable bending stress* (AISC Spec. App. D, Sect. D3) Considering the end restraints by the adjacent spans, the allowable bending stresses are obtained as follows:

Seg- ment	G_T	G_B	K_s	K_w	L (ft.)	d_0 (in.)	A_f (in.²)	r_{T0} (in.)	$\dfrac{Ld_0}{A_f}$	$\dfrac{L}{r_{T0}}$	γ	B
6-7	1.94	10	0.91	0.92	2.58	37.02	1.5	1.32	76.41	23.45	0.05	—
7-8	2	0.52	0.76	0.73	5	33.17	1.5	1.36	1327.	44.1	0.116	—
8-9	1.5	0.5	0.74	0.71	10	25.46	1.5	1.43	2037.	83.9	0.303	—
9-10	0.42	0.67	0.67	0.62	15	13.91	1.5	1.58	1669.	113.9	0.83	—
10-11	—	—	1.0	1.0	5	10.06	1.5	1.65	402.4	36.4	0.38	1.0

Seg- ment	h_s	h_w	$F_{s\gamma}$ (ksi) = $\dfrac{12 \times 10^3}{K_s h_s L d_0/A_f}$	$F_{w\gamma}$ (ksi) = $\dfrac{170 \times 10^3}{(K_w h_w L/r_{T0})^2}$	$F_{b\gamma}$ (ksi) Eq. (D3-2)	$F_{b\gamma}$ (ksi) Eq. (D3-1)	Use $F_{b\gamma}$ (ksi)
6-7	1.032	1.001	15.22	364.5	$364.8 > \dfrac{1}{3} F_y$	$32.57 > 0.6 F_y$	30
7-8	1.097	1.003	10.85	163.0	$163.4 > \dfrac{1}{3} F_y$	$31.63 > 0.6 F_y$	30
8-9	1.314	1.010	6.06	46.95	$47.34 > \dfrac{1}{3} F_y$	$27.5 < 0.6 F_y$	27.5
9-10	1.780	1.034	5.71	31.88	$32.39 > \dfrac{1}{3} F_y$	$24.75 < 0.6 F_y$	24.75
10-11	1.175	1.009	25.38	126.0	$128.5 > \dfrac{1}{3} F_y$	$31.2 > 0.6 F_y$	30

An increase of 1/3, therefore, of the stress for segment 9-10 is permitted due to wind load.

$$F_{b\gamma} = 24.75 \times 4/3 = 33 \text{ ksi} \qquad [\text{AISC Spec. 1.5.6}]$$

(c) *Combined axial compression and bending* (AISC Spec. App. D, Sect. D4)

At *point 6:*

$$\frac{h_6}{t_w} = \frac{38.5}{0.1875} = 205.3 > \frac{760}{\sqrt{F_b}} = \frac{760}{\sqrt{30}} = 138.8$$

From AISC Eq. (1.10-5), the modified allowable bending stress is

$$F'_{b\gamma} = F_{b\gamma} \left[1.0 - 0.0005 \frac{A_w}{A_f} \left(\frac{h}{t_w} - \frac{760}{\sqrt{F_{b\gamma}}} \right) \right]$$

$$= 30 \left[1.0 - 0.0005 \frac{38.5 \times 0.1875}{6 \times 0.75} (205.3 - 138.8) \right]$$

$$= 25.2 \text{ ksi}$$

AISC Eq. (D4-1b) gives

$$\frac{f_{a6}}{0.6F_y} + \frac{f_{b6}}{F'_{b\gamma}} = \frac{2.14}{30} + \frac{20.91}{25.2} = 0.9 < 1.0 \qquad \langle \text{O.K.} \rangle$$

Segment 6-7:

$$f_{a7}/F_{a\gamma} = 2.17/14.9 = 0.146 < 0.15$$

Since

$$F'_{b\gamma} = 25.2 \text{ ksi}$$

Eq. (D4-2) gives

$$\frac{f_{a7}}{F_{a\gamma}} + \frac{f_{b6}}{F'_{b\gamma}} = \frac{2.17}{14.9} + \frac{20.91}{25.2} = 0.975 < 1.0 \qquad \langle \text{O.K.} \rangle$$

Segment 7-8:
At point 7,

$$\frac{h_7}{t_w} = \frac{36.52}{0.1875} = 194.8 > \frac{760}{\sqrt{F_{b\gamma}}} = \frac{760}{\sqrt{30}} = 138.8$$

AISC Eq. (1.10-5) gives

$$F'_{b\gamma} = 30\left[1.0 - 0.0005 \frac{36.52 \times 0.1875}{6 \times 0.25}(194.8 - 138.8)\right]$$

$$= 26.17 \text{ ksi}$$

with

$$f_{a8}/F_{a\gamma} = 2.25/14.9 = 0.151 > 0.15, \ F'_{e\gamma} = 15.19 \text{ ksi (AISC Table 9)}$$

Eq. (D4-1a) gives

$$\frac{f_{a8}}{F_{a\gamma}} + \frac{C_m}{\left(1 - \frac{f_{a8}}{F'_{e\gamma}}\right)}\left(\frac{f_{b7}}{F'_{b\gamma}}\right) = 0.151 + \frac{0.85}{\left(1 - \frac{2.25}{15.19}\right)}\left(\frac{18.16}{26.17}\right)$$

$$= 0.841 < 1.0 \qquad \langle \text{O.K.} \rangle$$

Segment 8-9:
At *point 8,*

$$\frac{h_8}{t_w} = \frac{32.67}{0.1875} = 174.2 > \frac{760}{\sqrt{F_b}} = \frac{760}{\sqrt{27.5}} = 144.9$$

AISC Eq. (1.10-5) gives

$$F'_{b\gamma} = 27.5 \left[1 - 0.0005 \frac{32.67 \times 0.1875}{6 \times 0.25} (174.2 - 144.9) \right]$$

$$= 25.8 \text{ ksi}$$

with $f_{a9}/F_{a\gamma} = 2.42/14.9 = 0.162 > 0.15$
Eq. (D4-1a) yields

$$\frac{f_{a9}}{F_{a\gamma}} + \frac{C_m}{\left(1 - \dfrac{f_{a9}}{F'_{e\gamma}}\right)} \left(\frac{f_{b8}}{F'_{b\gamma}}\right) = 0.162 + \frac{0.85}{\left(1 - \dfrac{2.42}{15.19}\right)} \left(\frac{12.63}{25.8}\right)$$

$$= 0.657 < 1.0 \qquad\qquad \langle\text{O.K.}\rangle$$

Segment 9-10:

$$\text{Since } \frac{h_9}{t_w} = \frac{24.96}{0.1875} = 133 < \frac{760}{\sqrt{F_{b\gamma}}} = \frac{1760}{\sqrt{24.75}} = 152.7$$

$$F'_b = F_b = 33 \text{ ksi}$$

with $f_{a10}/F_{a\gamma} = 0.94/19.89 = 0.047 < 0.15$
AISC Eq. (D4-2) gives

$$\frac{f_{a10}}{F_{a\gamma}} + \frac{f_{b9}}{F'_{b\gamma}} = 0.047 + \frac{11.67}{33} = 0.401 < 1.0 \qquad\qquad \langle\text{O.K.}\rangle$$

Segment 10-11

$$f_{a11}/F_{a\gamma} = 3.05/14.9 = 0.205 > 0.15$$

Eq. (D4-1a) gives

$$\frac{f_{a11}}{F_{a\gamma}} + \frac{C_m}{\left(1 - \dfrac{f_{a11}}{F'_{e\gamma}}\right)} \left(\frac{f_{b11}}{F'_{b\gamma}}\right) = 0.205 + \frac{0.85}{\left(1 - \dfrac{3.05}{15.19}\right)} \left(\frac{853}{30}\right)$$

$$= 0.507 < 1.0 \qquad\qquad \langle\text{O.K.}\rangle$$

Example No. 4 (See Fig. 4.7)

The rigid frame with an interior column is shown in Fig. 4.7. The spacing between frames is taken at 25 ft. Two kinds of loading combinations are considered. The moment diagrams are shown in Figs. 4.8. The yield stress of the steel is presumed to be 50 ksi. Determine the adequacy of column 1-3 and girder 5-12.

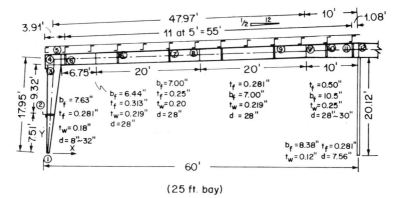

(25 ft. bay)

COORDINATES AND SECTION PROPERTIES

Point	1	2	3	4	5	6	7	8	9	10	11	12
X(ft.)	0.00	0.45	1.00	1.07	2.28	2.91	22.91	27.91	42.92	52.91	57.91	59.00
Y(ft.)	0.00	7.50	16.80	17.92	17.97	18.00	18.83	19.03	19.86	19.99	20.10	20.12
d(in.)	8.00	18.71	32.00	—	28.00	28.00	28.00	28.00	28.00	29.96	32.46	33.00
A(in.^{2})	5.62	7.55	9.96	—	10.02	10.02	9.00	9.00	9.96	17.74	18.36	18.49
I_x(in.^{4})	70.14	453.8	1546	—	1147	1147	1020	1020	1133	2784	3330	3455
S_x(in.^{3})	17.53	48.51	96.62	—	81.93	81.93	72.86	72.86	80.93	185.8	205.2	209.4
I_y(in.^{4})	20.75	20.81	20.93	—	13.95	13.95	14.29	14.29	16.06	95.50	96.50	96.51
r_T(in.)	2.10	1.97	1.84	—	1.52	1.52	1.64	1.64	1.65	2.73	2.71	2.71

Figure 4.7. Dimensions and geometry of the frame of Design Example 4.

Solution:

From the moment diagrams in Fig. 4.8, it is readily concluded that the first loading case controls the design. The maximum stresses are computed as follows:

Axial stresses: $(DL + LL)$

$$f_{a1} = P_1/A_1 = 30.28/5.62 = 5.39 \text{ ksi}$$

$$f_{a2} = P_2/A_2 = 30.28/7.55 = 4.01 \text{ ksi}$$

$$f_{a3} = P_3/A_3 = 30.28/9.96 = 3.04 \text{ ksi}$$

$$f_{a5} = P_5/A_5 = 12.35/10.02 = 1.23 \text{ ksi}$$

$$f_{a6} = P_6/A_6 = 12.3/10.02 = 1.23 \text{ ksi}$$

$$f_{a7} = P_7/A_7 = 11.42/9.00 = 1.27 \text{ ksi}$$

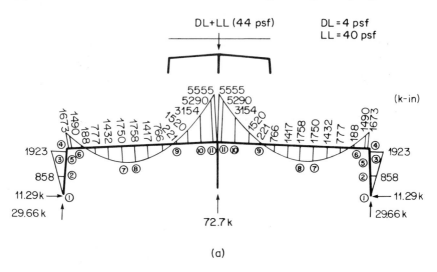

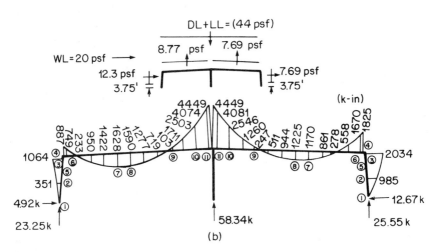

Figure 4.8. Moment diagrams of the frame of Fig. 4.7 due to two sets of loading conditions.

$$f_{a8} = P_8/A_8 = 11.19/9.00 = 1.24 \text{ ksi}$$

$$f_{a9} = P_9/A_9 = 10.68/9.96 = 1.07 \text{ ksi}$$

$$f_{a10} = P_{10}/A_{10} = 10.67/17.74 = 0.58 \text{ ksi}$$

$$f_{a11} = P_{11}/A_{11} = 10.56/18.36 = 0.575 \text{ ksi}$$

$$f_{a12} = P_{12}/A_{12} = 10.53/18.49 = 1.57 \text{ ksi}$$

Bending stresses $(DL + LL)$

$$f_{b2} = M_2/S_2 = 858/48.5 = 17.68 \text{ ksi}$$

$$f_{b3} = M_3/S_3 = 1923/96.6 = 19.90 \text{ ksi}$$

$$f_{b5} = M_5/S_5 = 1673/81.9 = 20.42 \text{ ksi}$$

$$f_{b6} = M_6/S_6 = 1490/81.9 = 18.19 \text{ ksi}$$

$$f_{b8} = M_8/S_8 = 1758/72.86 = 24.13 \text{ ksi}$$

$$f_{b10} = M_{10}/S_{10} = 3154/185.8 = 16.97 \text{ ksi}$$

$$f_{b11} = M_{11}/S_{11} = 5290/205.1 = 25.78 \text{ ksi}$$

$$f_{b12} = M_{12}/S_{12} = 5555/209.4 = 26.53 \text{ ksi}$$

(A) *Determine the adequacy of column 1-3*

    (a) *Allowable compressive stress* (AISC Spec. App. D, Sect. D2) The effective length factors for weak axis buckling are obtained by considering the end restraints for each segment. They are summarized in the following table.

Segment	L_y (ft.)	I_{0y} (in.^{4})	b_{Ty} (ft.)	I_{Ty} (in.^{4})	b_{By} (ft.)	I_{By} (in.^{4})	$G_T = \left(\dfrac{b_T I_0}{LI}\right)_y$	$G_B = \left(\dfrac{b_B I_0}{LI_B}\right)_y$	K_y
1-2	7.51	20.78	9.32	20.87	—	—	1.23	10	0.87
2-3	9.32	20.87	—	—	7.51	20.78	10	0.81	0.84

For strong axis buckling, the restraining member (girder 5-12) can be conservatively taken as a prismatic member with $I_x = 1020$ in.^{4}. Then

$$G_T = \frac{g_e b_T I_0}{L I_T} = \frac{2 \times 57.97 \times 70.14}{17.95 \times 1020} = 0.44 \qquad \text{[Eq. (E-11)]}$$

$$G_B = 10 \qquad \text{(AISC recommended value for hinged end)}$$

From the charts in AISC Commentary Sect. D2, for the taper ratio $\gamma_{1\text{-}3} = (32/8) - 1 = 3$,

$$K_x = K_\gamma = 1.0 \qquad \text{(Fig. CD1.5.15)}$$

The slenderness ratios for the strong and weak axes are:

$$\left(\frac{KL}{r_1}\right)_x = 1.0 \times 16.83 \times 12/3.53 = 57.21 \qquad \textit{for column 1-3}$$

$$\left(\frac{KL}{r_1}\right)_y = 0.87 \times 7.51 \times 12/1.92 = 40.8 \qquad \textit{for segment 1-2}$$

$$\left(\frac{KL}{r_2}\right)_y = 0.84 \times 9.32 \times 12/1.66 = 56.6 \qquad \textit{for segment 2-3}$$

Therefore, strong axis buckling controls and the allowable compressive stress is:

$$F_{a\gamma} = 23.18 \text{ ksi} \qquad \text{(AISC Table 3-50)}$$

(*b*)   *Allowable bending stress* (AISC Spec. App. D, Sect. D3) Considering the end restraints of the adjacent segments, the allowable bending stresses are calculated as follows:

Segment	G_T	G_B	K_s	K_w	L (in.)	d_0 (in.)	A_f (in.^{2})	r_{T0} (in.)	$\dfrac{L d_0}{A_f}$	$\dfrac{L}{r_{T0}}$	γ
1-2	1.23	10	0.88	0.87	90.12	8.00	2.14	2.10	336.2	42.9	1.34
2-3	10	0.81	0.84	0.82	111.8	18.71	2.14	1.97	977	56.7	0.71

Segment	h_s	h_w	$F_{s\gamma} \text{ (ksi)} = \dfrac{12 \times 10^3}{K_s h_s L d_0 / A_f}$	$F_{w\gamma} \text{ (ksi)} = \dfrac{170 \times 10^3}{(K_w h_w L / r_{T0})^2}$	$F_{b\gamma}$ (ksi) Eq. (D3-2)	$F_{b\gamma}$ (ksi) Eq. (D3-1)	Use $F_{b\gamma}$ (ksi)
1-2	1.565	1.034	25.92	114.1	$117 > \frac{1}{3} F_y$	$31.0 > 0.6 F_y$	30
2-3	1.510	1.020	9.68	75.6	$76.2 > \frac{1}{3} F$	$29.7 < 0.6 F_y$	29.7

(*c*)   *Combined axial compression and bending* (AISC Spec. App. D, Sect. D4)
For *segment 1-2*, $f_{a1}/F_{a\gamma} = 5.39/23.18 = 0.232 > 0.15$. Eq. (D4-1a) applies.

$$F'_{e\gamma} = 45.63 \text{ ksi} \qquad \text{(AISC Spec. Table 9)}$$

$$C_m = 0.85 \qquad \text{(sidesway permitted)}$$

At *point 2*, $h_2/t_w = 100.8 < 760/\sqrt{F_{b\gamma}} = 138.8$; hence, $F_{b\gamma} = 30$ ksi

$$\frac{f_{a1}}{F_{a\gamma}} + \frac{C_m}{\left(1 - \dfrac{f_{a1}}{F'_{e\gamma}}\right)}\left(\frac{f_{b2}}{F'_{b\gamma}}\right) = 0.232 + \frac{0.85}{\left(1 - \dfrac{5.39}{45.63}\right)}\left(\frac{17.68}{30}\right)$$

$$= 0.8 < 1.0 \qquad \langle \text{O.K.} \rangle$$

Check Eq. (D4-1b) at point 2,

$$\frac{f_{a2}}{0.6F_y} + \frac{f_{b2}}{0.6F_y} = \frac{4.01 + 17.68}{30} = 0.723 < 1.0 \qquad \langle \text{O.K.} \rangle$$

For *segment 2-3*,
  Since

$$\frac{h_3}{t_w} = 174.6 > 760/\sqrt{F_{b\gamma}} = 138.8, \text{ AISC Eq. (1.10-5) gives}$$

$$F'_{b\gamma} = F_{b\gamma}\left[1.0 - 0.0005 \frac{A_w}{A_f}\left(\frac{h}{t_w} - \frac{760}{\sqrt{F_{b\gamma}}}\right)\right]$$

$$= 30[1.0 - 0.0005 \frac{31.44 \times 0.18}{7.63 \times 0.281}(174.6 - 138.8)]$$

$$= 28.58 \text{ ksi}$$

With

$$f_{a2}/F_{a\gamma} = 4.01/23.18 = 0.173 > 0.15. \text{ Eq. (D4-1a) yields}$$

$$\frac{f_{a2}}{F_{a\gamma}} + \frac{C_m}{\left(1 - \dfrac{f_{a2}}{F'_{e\gamma}}\right)}\left(\frac{f_{b3}}{F'_{b\gamma}}\right) = 0.173 + \frac{0.85}{\left(1 - \dfrac{4.01}{45.63}\right)}\left(\frac{19.9}{28.58}\right)$$

$$= 0.822 < 1.0 \qquad \langle \text{O.K.} \rangle$$

Check Eq. (D4-1b) at point 3,

$$\frac{f_{a3}}{0.6F_y} + \frac{f_{b3}}{F'_{b\gamma}} = \frac{3.04}{30} + \frac{19.9}{28.58} = 0.797 < 1.0 \qquad \langle \text{O.K.} \rangle$$

(B)   Determine the adequacy of girder 5-12
   (a)   Allowable compressive stress:
Including the end restraints for each segment, the effective length factors for weak axis buckling are determined as shown in the following table.

Seg-ment	L_y (ft.)	I_{0y} (in.^{4})	b_{Ty} (ft.)	I_{Ty} (in.^{4})	b_{By} (ft.)	I_{By} (in.^{4})	$G_T = \left(\dfrac{b_T I_0}{L I_T}\right)_y$	$G_B = \left(\dfrac{b_B I_0}{L I_B}\right)_y$	K_y
6-6′	10	13.95	10	14.29	0.63	13.95	0.97	0.063	0.64
7-8	5	14.29	—	—	—	—	—	—	1.0
9-10	10	55	5	96	10	16.06	0.29	3.42	0.75
10-11	5	96	2.16	96.5	10	55	0.43	3.49	0.78

To determine the effective length factor for strong axis buckling of girder 5-12, the following considerations are made in calculating G_T and G_B.

At point 12 of girder 5-12, the rotational restraint is determined by considering the adjacent member as prismatic. Since the interior column provides vertical support at point 12, it is reasonable to assume that the girder is sidesway prevented. Thus, from Eq. (E-7) $g_e = 0.67\, g$. For

$$\overline{\beta} = 0, \quad \overline{\gamma}_1 = 0$$

and $g = 1.0$ (Fig. C-3 in Appendix C)

$$G_T = \frac{g_e b_T I_0}{L I_T} = 0.67 \qquad \text{[Eq. (E-11)]}$$

At the lower end of girder 5-12 (column 1-3)

$$\overline{\beta} = 0$$

$$\overline{\gamma}_1 = 3$$

$$g = 0.11 \text{ (Fig. C.3 in Appendix C)}$$

$$g_e = 0.67g \text{ (sidesway prevented)} \qquad \text{[Eq. (E-7)]}$$

Then,

$$G_B = \frac{g_e b_B I_0}{L I_B} = \frac{0.67 \times 0.11 \times 17.95 \times 1020}{57.97 \times 70.14} = 0.33 \quad \text{[Eq. (E-12)]}$$

From the alignment chart of the AISC Spec. for the case of sidesway prevented, the effective length factor is

$$K_x = 0.68$$

The slenderness ratios for strong and weak axes are:

$$\left(\frac{KL}{r_8}\right)_x = 0.68 \times 56.75 \times 12/10.64 = 43.52 \qquad \textit{for strong axis}$$

$$\left(\frac{KL}{r_6}\right)_y = 0.64 \times 10 \times 12/1.18 = 65.08 \qquad \textit{for segment 6-6'}$$

$$\left(\frac{KL}{r_7}\right)_y = 1.0 \times 5 \times 12/1.26 = 47.62 \qquad \textit{for segment 7-8}$$

$$\left(\frac{KL}{r_9}\right)_y = 0.75 \times 10 \times 12/1.27 = 70.87 \qquad \textit{for segment 9-10}$$

$$\left(\frac{KL}{r_{10}}\right)_y = 0.78 \times 5 \times 12/2.32 = 20.17 \qquad \textit{for segment 10-11}$$

Thus, strong axis governs the design of segment 10-11.

$$F_{a\gamma} = 25.33 \text{ ksi} \qquad \text{(AISC Table 3-50)}$$

and the weak axis controls the other segments.

$$(F_{a\gamma})_{6-6'} = 21.83 \text{ ksi}$$

$$(F_{a\gamma})_{7-8} = 24.72 \text{ ksi} \qquad \text{(AISC Table 3-50)}$$

$$(F_{a\gamma})_{9-10} = 20.77 \text{ ksi}$$

(b) *Allowable bending stress* (AISC Spec. Sect. 1.5.1.4)
Segment 6-6':
Since this segment has a change in cross-sectional properties, some approximations are made by using the equations in AISC Spec. Sect. 1.5.1.4.
For $G_T = 0.97$, $G_B = 0.063$

$$K_s = 0.63, \quad K_w = 0.61 \qquad \text{(charts in Appendix F)}$$

Therefore

$$K_w L/r_{T6} = 0.61 \times 120/1.52 = 48.16$$

$$f_{b6'} = 777/72.86 = 10.66 \text{ ksi}$$

$$f_{b6'}/f_{b6} = 10.66/18.19 = 0.586$$

and

$$C_b = 1.75 - 1.05 \left(\frac{f_{b6'}}{f_{b6}}\right) + 0.3 \left(\frac{f_{b6'}}{f_{b6}}\right)^2$$

$$= 2.47 > 2.3, \quad \text{Use } C_b = 2.3$$

Since

$$\sqrt{\frac{102 \times 10^3 C_b}{F_y}} = 68.5 > K_w L/r_{T6},$$

$$F_b = 0.6\, F_y = 30 \text{ ksi} \qquad \text{[AISC Sect. 1.5.1.4]}$$

Segment 7-8:

$$L/r_{T7} = 5 \times 12/1.64 = 36.6$$

For

$$f_{b7} = f_{b8},$$

$$C_b = 1.0$$

$$\sqrt{\frac{102 \times 10^3\, C_b}{F_y}} = 45.1 > L/r_{T7} = 36.6$$

Thus, $F_b = 30$ ksi. $\qquad\qquad$ [AISC Sect. 1.5.1.4]

Segment 9-10:

Segment 9-10 may be conservatively taken as a prismatic segment.

$$G_T = 0.29, \quad G_B = 3.42$$

$$K_s = 0.73, \quad K_w = 0.71 \qquad \text{(charts in Appendix F)}$$

Then $K_w L/r_{T9} = 0.7 \times 120/1.65 = 51.63$

$$f_{b9'} = 1520/80.9 = 18.78 \text{ ksi} > f_{b10} = 16.97 \text{ ksi}$$

$$C_b = 1.0 \qquad \text{(see AISC Spec. Sect. 1.5.1.4.6a)}$$

$$\sqrt{\frac{102 \times 10^3 C_b}{F_y}} = 45.1 < K_w L/r_{T9}$$

$$\sqrt{\frac{510 \times 10^3 C_b}{F_y}} = 101 > K_w L/r_{T9}$$

Eq. (1.5-6a) applies

$$F_{b\gamma} = \left[\frac{2}{3} - \frac{F_y (K_w L/r_{T9})^2}{1530 \times 10^3 C_b}\right] F_y$$

$$= \left[\frac{2}{3} - \frac{50\,(51.63)^2}{1530 \times 10^3}\right] 50 = 28.98 \text{ ksi}$$

$$F_{b\gamma} = \frac{12 \times 10^3 C_b}{K_s L d_9/A_f} = \frac{12,000}{0.73 \times 120 \times 28/(7 \times 0.281)} = 9.6 \text{ ksi}$$

$$\text{[Eq. (3.33b)]}$$

Use $F_b = 28.98$ ksi

Segment 10-11: (AISC Spec. App. D, Sect. D3)

$$G_T = 0.43, \quad G_B = 3.49$$

$$K_s = 0.75, \quad K_w = 0.73 \qquad \text{(Appendix F)}$$

The taper and slenderness ratios for segment 10-11 are

$$\gamma_{10\text{-}11} = (32.46/29.96) - 1 = 0.083$$

$$Ld_{10}/A_f = 60 \times 29.96/(10.5 \times 0.5) = 342.4$$

$$L/r_{T10} = 60/2.73 = 21.98$$

The length modification factors are:

$$h_s = 1 + 0.023 \times 0.083 \sqrt{342.4} = 1.035$$

$$h_w = 1 + 0.00385 \times 0.083 \sqrt{21.98} = 1.001$$

Therefore,

$$F_{s\gamma} = \frac{12,000}{0.75 \times 1.035 \times 342.4} = 45.15 \text{ ksi} \qquad [\text{Eq. (3.38)}]$$

$$F_{w\gamma} = \frac{170,000}{(0.73 \times 1.001 \times 21.98)^2} = 659.0 \text{ ksi} \qquad [\text{Eq. (3.37)}]$$

The allowable bending stress is given by

$$F_{b\gamma} = \sqrt{45.15^2 + 659^2} = 660.5 \text{ ksi} > \frac{1}{3} F_y \quad [\text{Eq. (D3-2)}]$$

or

$$F_{b\gamma} = \frac{2}{3}\left(1 - \frac{50}{6 \times 660.5}\right) 50 = 32.9 \text{ ksi} > 0.6F_y \quad [\text{Eq. (D3-1)}]$$

or

$$F_{b\gamma} = 0.6F_y = 30 \text{ ksi—Governs}$$

(c) *Combined axial compression and bending:*
At *point 5,* $h_5/t_w = 27.37/0.219 = 125 < 760/\sqrt{0.6F_y} = 138.7$
Eq. (1.6.1b) in AISC Spec. Sect. 1.6 gives

$$\frac{f_{a5}}{0.6F_y} + \frac{f_{b5}}{0.6F_y} = \frac{1.23 + 20.42}{30} = 0.72 < 1.0 \qquad \langle\text{O.K.}\rangle$$

For *segment 6-6'*, $f_{a6}/F_{a\gamma} = 1.23/21.83 = 0.056 < 0.15$. AISC Eq. (1.6-2) gives:

$$\frac{f_{a6}}{F_{a\gamma}} + \frac{f_{b6}}{F_{b\gamma}} = 0.056 + \frac{18.19}{30} = 0.66 < 1.0 \qquad \langle\text{O.K.}\rangle$$

For *segment 7-8*, $f_{a7}/F_{a\gamma} = 1.27/24.72 = 0.051 < 0.15$.
   AISC Eq. (1.6-2) gives:

$$\frac{f_{a7}}{F_{a\gamma}} + \frac{f_{b8}}{F_{b\gamma}} = 0.051 + \frac{24.13}{30} = 0.855 < 1.0 \qquad \langle\text{O.K.}\rangle$$

For *segment 9-10*, $f_{a9}/F_{a\gamma} = 1.07/20.77 = 0.051 < 0.15$.
   AISC Eq. (1.6-2) gives,

$$\frac{f_{a9}}{F_{a\gamma}} + \frac{f_{b9'}}{F_{b\gamma}} = 0.051 + \frac{18.78}{28.98} = 0.699 < 1.0 \qquad \langle\text{O.K.}\rangle$$

For *segment 10-11*, $f_{a10}/F_{a\gamma} = 0.575/25.33 = 0.023 < 0.15$.
   AISC Eq. (D4-2) gives,

$$\frac{f_{a10}}{F_{a\gamma}} + \frac{f_{b11}}{F_{b\gamma}} = 0.023 + \frac{25.78}{30} = 0.882 < 1.0 \qquad \langle\text{O.K.}\rangle$$

At *point 12*, $h_{12}/t_w = 29/0.25 = 116 < 760/\sqrt{0.6F_y}$. AISC Eq. (1.6-1b) gives

$$\frac{f_{a12}}{0.6F_y} + \frac{f_{b12}}{0.6F_y} = \frac{0.57 + 26.53}{30} = 0.903 < 1.0 \qquad \langle\text{O.K.}\rangle$$

Example No. 5 (See Fig. 4.9)

This frame is basically the same as that of example 1, except that the bracing of the columns is removed and a larger inside flange of the columns is to be used. This is shown in Fig. 4.9. The columns will be checked by using Appendix G. Only one loading combination is considered in this example. The moment diagram is shown in Fig. 4.10.

Solution:

   The axial stress at the smaller end of the column is

$$f_{a1} = P_1/A_1 = 76.87/19.2 = 4.00 \text{ ksi}$$

   To find the compressive bending stress of the inside flange at the larger end, the distance from centroid to the outer fiber of the compression flange

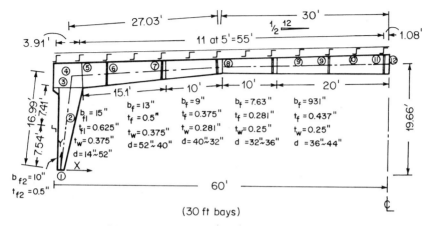

COORDINATES AND SECTION PROPERTIES

Point	1	2	3	4	5	6	7	8*	9	10	11	12
X(ft.)	0.00	0.79	1.58	1.80	3.65	7.75	17.73	28.75	47.73	52.73	57.73	58.75
Y(ft.)	0.00	7.50	14.87	16.89	17.03	17.34	18.08	18.91	19.38	19.51	19.63	19.66
d(in.)	14.00	33.16	52.00	—	52.00	48.73	40.78	32.00	39.59	41.59	43.59	44.00
A(in.²)	19.20	—	33.45	—	32.12	30.90	27.92	12.15	17.82	18.31	18.82	18.92
I_x(in.⁴)	667.3	—	13211	—	12765	10960	7241	1726	4328	4851	5412	5531
S_x(in.³)	—	—	—	—	491.0	449.8	355.1	107.9	218.6	233.3	248.3	251.4
I_y(in.⁴)	217.5	—	217.7	—	183.3	183.3	18.33	20.8	58.8	58.8	58.8	58.8
r_T(in.)	4.15	—	3.74	—	3.07	3.11	3.19	1.74	2.28	2.25	2.24	2.24

*Smaller values of section properties of both sides. F_y = 50 ksi.

Figure 4.9. Dimensions and geometry of the frame of Design Example 5.

should be obtained first. This distance is $\bar{d}_3 = 22.68''$. Then the compressive bending stress at the larger end is

$$f_{b3} = M_3 \times \bar{d}_3/I_{x3} = 12708 \times 22.68/13211 = 21.81 \text{ ksi}$$

(A)   Allowable compressive stress
The Charts in AISC Commentary Sect. D2 may be used to determine the effective length factor, K_x.
As obtained in Example 1, $g = 0.61$ and $g_e = 2g$. Then

$$G_T = \left(\frac{g_e b_T I_0}{L I_T}\right)_x = \frac{2 \times 0.61 \times 57.03 \times 667.3}{16.99 \times 1726}$$

$$= 1.58 \qquad\qquad\qquad [\text{Eq. (E-11)}]$$

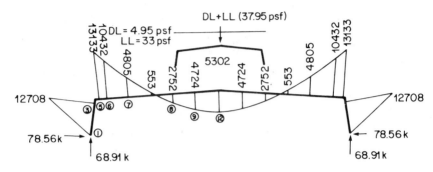

Figure 4.10. Moment diagram of the frame of Fig. 4.9.

And $G_B = 10$ for hinged end

From the charts in AISC Commentary Sect. D2

$$K_x = K_\gamma = 1.62 \text{ for } \gamma = 2.0 \qquad \text{(AISC Fig. CD1.5.14)}$$

$$K_\gamma = 1.58 \text{ for } \gamma = 3.0 \qquad \text{(AISC Fig. CD1.5.15)}$$

Then $K_x = 1.60$ for $\gamma = 2.71$

For weak axis buckling, $K_y = 1.0$

The slenderness ratios for both axes are

$$(KL/r_1)_y = 1 \times 14.95 \times 12/3.37 = 53.23$$

$$(KL/r_1)_x = 1.6 \times 14.95 \times 12/5.90 = 48.65$$

The allowable axial stress for weak axis buckling can be determined from the charts in Appendix G.

Column 1-3 has properties as follows:

$$\gamma = 2.71$$

$$\rho = \frac{b_2 t_2}{b_1 t_1} = \frac{10 \times 0.5}{15 \times 0.625} = 0.533$$

$$\frac{b_2/t_2}{b_1/t_1} = \frac{10/0.5}{15/0.625} = 0.833$$

and

$$\frac{KL}{r_{y0}} = 53.23$$

From Fig. G-1.3 of Appendix G, for $\gamma = 2$, $(b_2/t_2)/(b_1/t_1) = 1.0$ and $KL/r_{y0} = 53.23$, there is obtained

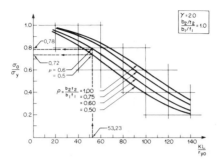

Figure G-1.3

$$\sigma_a = 0.78 \ \sigma_y \text{ for } \rho = 0.6$$

$$\sigma_a = 0.72 \ \sigma_y \text{ for } \rho = 0.5$$

By interpolation,

$$(\sigma_a)_1 = 0.74 \ \sigma_y \text{ for } \rho = 0.533, \frac{b_2/t_2}{b_1/t_1} = 1.0$$

From Fig. G-1.4, for $\gamma = 2$, $(b_2/t_2)/(b_1/t_1) = 0.5$ and $KL/r_{yo} = 53.23$,

$$\sigma_a = 0.655 \ \sigma_y \text{ for } \rho = 0.6$$

$$\sigma_a = 0.57 \ \sigma_y \text{ for } \rho = 0.5$$

Then

$$(\sigma_a)_2 = 0.60 \ \sigma_y \text{ for } \rho = 0.533, \frac{b_2/t_2}{b_1/t_1} = 0.5$$

Based on the values of $(\sigma_a)_1$ and $(\sigma_a)_2$ it is possible to determine a value of σ_a for $\gamma = 2.0$, $\rho = 0.533$ and $(b_2/t_2)/(b_1/t_1) = 0.833$; that is,

$$(\sigma_a)_3 = 0.693 \ \sigma_y$$

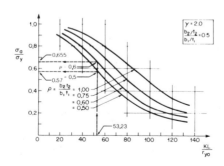

Figure G-1.4

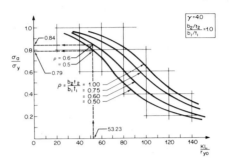

Figure G-1.5

Using this same procedure, the value of σ_a for $\gamma = 4.0$, $\rho = 0.533$ and $(b_2/t_2)/(b_1/t_1) = 0.833$ may be estimated; $(\sigma_a)_4 = 0.745\ \sigma_y$ (Figs. G-1.5 and G-1.6).

Again, by interpolation,

$$\sigma_a = 0.711\ \sigma_y \text{ for } \gamma = 2.71,\ \rho = 0.533,\ \frac{b_2/t_2}{b_1/t_1} = 0.833$$

Therefore, the allowable axial stress for weak axis buckling finally can be estimated:

$$F_{ay} = (0.711\ \sigma_y)\ (FS) = 0.711 \times 50 \times 0.6 = 21.33 \text{ ksi}$$

For strong axis, the allowable axial stress can be found in AISC Table 3-50.

$$F_{ax} = 24.56 > F_{ay}$$

Thus, weak-axis controls, and

$$F_a = 21.33 \text{ ksi}$$

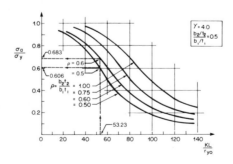

Figure G-1.6

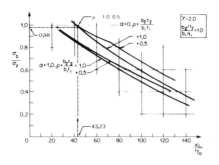

Figure G-2.3

(B)   Allowable compressive bending stress:
The allowable compressive bending stress can be obtained from Fig. G-2.1–G-2.3 in Appendix G. The following quantities should first be determined.

For *column 1-3*

$$\gamma = 2.71$$

$$\alpha = 0 \text{ (moment gradient)}$$

$$\rho = 0.533$$

$$L/r_{T0} = \frac{14.95 \times 12}{4.15} = 43.23$$

From Fig. G-2.3 $[\gamma = 2, (b_2/t_2)/(b_1/t_1) = 1.0, \alpha = 0,$ and $L/r_{T0} = 43.23]$

$$\sigma_b = 0.98 \ \sigma_y \text{ for } \rho = 0.5 \text{ and } 1.0$$

Thus $(\sigma_b)_1 = 0.98 \ \sigma_y$ for $\rho = 0.533$, $\gamma = 2$, $(b_2/t_2)/(b_1/t_1) = 1.0$

And, from Fig. G-2.4 ($\gamma = 2$,

$$\frac{b_2/t_2}{b_1/t_1} = 0.5, \alpha = 0, \text{ and } L/r_{T0} = 43.23)$$

$$\sigma_b = 0.96 \ \sigma_y \text{ for } \rho = 0.5$$

$$\sigma_b = 0.95 \ \sigma_y \text{ for } \rho = 1.0$$

Then $(\sigma_b)_2 = 0.959 \ \sigma_y$ for $\rho = 0.533$, $\gamma = 2$,

$$\frac{b_2/t_2}{b_1/t_1} = 0.5$$

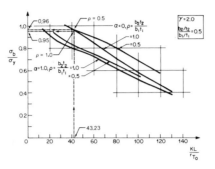

Figure G-2.4

Based on the values of $(\sigma_b)_1$ and $(\sigma_b)_2$

$$(\sigma_b)_3 = 0.973 \; \sigma_y \text{ for } \gamma = 2.0, \; \rho = 0.533, \; \frac{b_2/t_2}{b_1/t_1} = 0.833$$

Using the same procedure, the value of σ_b for $\gamma = 4$, $\rho = 0.533$, $\alpha = 0$, and $(b_2/t_2)/(b_1/t_1) = 0.833$ can be obtained. (Figs. G-2.5 and G-2.6.)

$$(\sigma_b)_4 = 0.902 \; \sigma_y$$

Interpolating, there is obtained

$$\sigma_b = 0.948 \; \sigma_y \text{ for } \gamma = 2\,71,$$

$$\rho = 0.533 \text{ and } \frac{b_2/t_2}{b_1/t_1} = 0.833$$

Therefore, the allowable bending stress is given by

$$F_{b\gamma} = \sigma_b(FS) = 0.948 \times 50 \times 0.6 = 28.44 \text{ ksi}$$

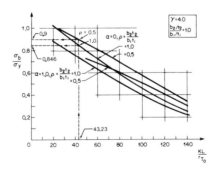

Figure G-2.5

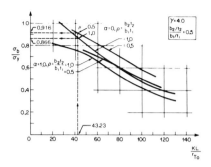

Figure G-2.6

It is necessary to check the width-thickness ratios of the flanges of the column according to AISC Spec. Sect. 1.9:

$$\frac{b_1/2}{t_1} = \frac{10/2}{0.5} = 10 < \frac{95}{\sqrt{F_y}} = 13.4 \qquad \langle \text{O.K.} \rangle$$

$$\frac{b_2/2}{t_2} = \frac{15/2}{0.625} = 12 < \frac{95}{\sqrt{F_y}} \qquad \langle \text{O.K.} \rangle$$

Checking the width-thickness ratio of the web at the larger end according to AISC Sect. 1.10.6,

$$\frac{h_w}{t_w} = \frac{52 - 0.5 - 0.625}{0.375} = 135.6 < \frac{760}{\sqrt{F_{b\gamma}}} = \frac{760}{\sqrt{28.44}} = 142.5$$

(c) *Combined compression and bending*

The interaction equation for tapered columns with unequal flanges subjected to combined bending and axial force is given by: (see Chapter 3)

$$\frac{f_{a0}}{F_a} + \xi \frac{f_{bL}}{F_b} = 1.0 \qquad \text{[Eq. (G-1)]}$$

in which ξ can be obtained from Fig. G-3.1 through G-3.6 in Appendix G.

For *column 1-3*,

$$\gamma = 2.71$$

$$\frac{b_2/t_2}{b_1/t_1} = 0.833$$

$$\rho = 0.533$$

$$KL/r_{y0} = 53.23$$

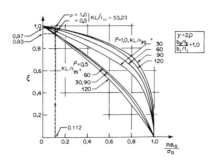

Figure G-3.3

and

$$f_{a1}/\sigma_a = \frac{4}{0.711 \times 50} = 0.112$$

From Fig. G-3.3 [$\gamma = 2$, $(b_2/t_2)/(b_1/t_1) = 1.0$, $f_a/\sigma_a = 0.112$ and $KL/r_{y0} = 53.23$]

$$\xi = 0.97 \text{ for } \rho = 1.0$$

$$\xi = 0.93 \text{ for } \rho = 0.5$$

Then

$$(\xi)_1 = 0.933 \text{ for } \rho = 0.533, \gamma = 2, \text{ and } \frac{b_2/t_2}{b_1/t_1} = 1.0$$

From Fig. G-3.4

$$\left(\gamma = 2, \frac{b_2/t_2}{b_1/t_1} = 0.5, \frac{f_a}{\sigma_a} = 0.112 \text{ and } \frac{KL}{r_{y0}} = 53.23\right)$$

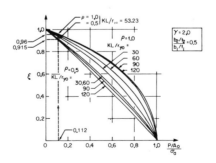

Figure G-3.4

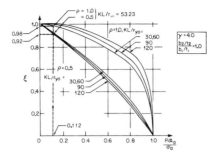

Figure G-3.5

$$\xi = 0.96 \quad \text{for } \rho = 1.0$$
$$\xi = 0.915 \text{ for } \rho = 0.5$$

Then

$$(\xi)_2 = 0.918 \text{ for } \rho = 0.533, \gamma = 2, \text{ and } \frac{b_2/t_2}{b_1/t_1} = 0.5$$

Based on the values of $(\xi)_1$ and $(\xi)_2$, we may estimate the value of the moment modification factor, ξ.

$$(\xi)_3 = 0.928 \text{ for } \rho = 0.533, \gamma = 2, \text{ and } \frac{b_2/t_2}{b_i/t_1} = 0.833$$

With the same procedure, a value of ξ can be determined from Figs. G-3.5 and G-3.6.

$$(\xi)_4 = 0.917 \text{ for } \rho = 0.533, \gamma = 4 \text{ and } \frac{b_2/t_2}{b_1/t_1} = 0.833$$

Then, by interpolation,

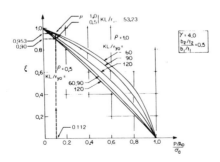

Figure G-3.6

$$\xi = 0.924 \text{ for } \rho = 0.533, \gamma = 2.71 \text{ and } \frac{b_2/t_2}{b_1/t_1} = 0.833$$

Therefore, the interaction equation (Eq. G-1) yields

$$\frac{f_{a0}}{F_a} + \xi \frac{f_{bL}}{F_b} = \frac{4.0}{21.33} + 0.924 \left(\frac{21.81}{28.44} \right) = 0.896 < 1.0 \quad \langle O.K. \rangle$$

Example No. 6 (See Fig. 4.11)

The portal frame of an industrial building—defined in Fig. 4.11—is designed for two types of loading conditions. The moment diagrams are shown in Fig. 4.12. The yield stress of the steel is presumed to be 50 ksi. Both outside and inside flanges of the columns and girders are supported laterally by girts or purlins as indicated.

The purpose of this example is to illustrate the design procedure described in Chapter 3, Sect. 3.5, and to compare the design with that resulting from the AISC provisions.

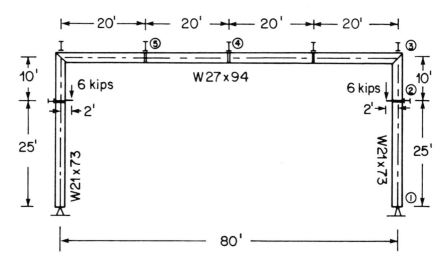

$F_y = 50$ ksi.
W21 × 73 ($A = 21.5$ in.^{2}, $I_x = 1600$ in.^{4}, $S_x = 151$ in.^{3}, $r_x = 8.64$ in.,
$I_y = 70.6$ in.^{4}, $r_y = 1.81$ in., $r_T = 2.16$ in., $d/A_f = 3.46$ in.$^{-1}$,
$d = 21.24$ in., $J = 3.02$ in.^{4})
W27 × 94 ($A = 27.7$ in.^{2}, $I_x = 3270$ in.^{4}, $S_x = 243$ in.^{3}, $r_x = 10.9$ in.,
$I_y = 124$ in.^{4}, $r_y = 2.12$ in., $r_T = 2.56$ in., $d/A_f = 3.61$ in.$^{-1}$,
$d = 26.91$ in., $J = 4.06$ in.^{4})

Figure 4.11. Dimensions and geometry of the frame of Design Example 6.

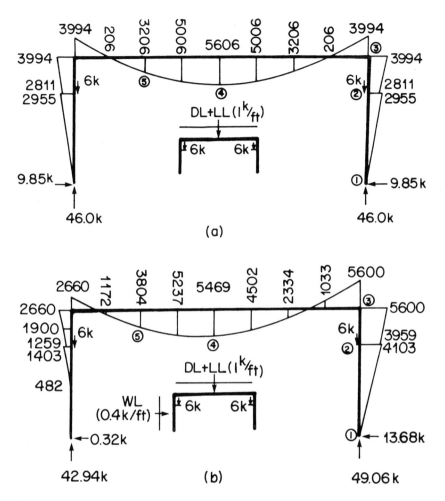

Figure 4.12. Moment diagrams of the frame of Fig. 4.11.

Solution:

To determine the adequacy of the chosen sections, three critical segments 1-2, 2-3, and 4-5 are examined. The maximum stresses of these segments are calculated as follows:

Axial stresses:

$$f_{a2} = P_2/A_2 = 49.06/21.5 = 2.28 \text{ ksi} \qquad (DL + LL + WL)$$

$$f_{a3} = P_3/A_3 = 43.06/21.5 = 2.00 \text{ ksi} \qquad (DL + LL + WL)$$

$$f_{a4} = P_4/A_4 = 13.68/27.7 = 0.49 \text{ ksi} \qquad (DL + LL)$$

Bending stresses:

$$f_{b2} = M_2/S_2 = 4103/151 = 27.17 \text{ ksi} \qquad (DL + LL + WL)$$

$$f_{b3} = M_3/S_3 = 5600/151 = 37.08 \text{ ksi} \qquad (DL + LL + WL)$$

$$f_{b4} = M_4/S_4 = 5606/243 = 23.07 \text{ ksi} \qquad (DL + LL)$$

(A)   *Determine the adequacy of column 1-3 $(DL + LL + WL)$*
    (a)   *Allowable compressive stress:*

For *strong axis*, points 1 and 3 are assumed to be braced. The restraining factors are obtained as follows:

$$G_3 = \left(\frac{b_T I_0}{L I_T}\right)_x = \frac{80 \times 1600}{35 \times 3270} = 1.12 \qquad [\text{Eq. (E-5)}]$$

$$G_1 = 10 \quad (\text{AISC recommended value for hinged end})$$

From the AISC alignment chart for the case of sidesway permitted, $K_x = 1.9$. Therefore,

$$(KL/r_3)_x = 1.9 \times 35 \times 12/8.64 = 92.36$$

The allowable axial stress for strong axis buckling is determined from AISC Specification Table 3-50.

$$F_{ax} = 16.42 \text{ ksi}$$

An increase of 1/3 (AISC Spec. 1.5.6) when wind loads are included gives $F_{ax} = 16.42 \times 4/3 = 21.89$ ksi for column 1-3.

For *weak axis*, both segments 1-2 and 2-3 are restrained at point 2. For *segment 1-2*

$$G_2 = \left(\frac{b_T I_0}{L I_T}\right)_y = \frac{10 \times 70.6}{25 \times 70.6} = 0.4 \qquad [\text{Eq. (E-5)}]$$

$$G_1 = 10$$

$K_y = 0.79$ (AISC alignment chart for the case of sidesway prevented)

Hence

$$(KL/r_2)_y = 0.79 \times 25 \times 12/1.81 = 130.9$$

and

$$F_{ay} = 8.72 \text{ ksi} \quad (\text{AISC Spec. Table 3-50})$$

An increase of 1/3 for including wind load gives

$$F_{ay} = 8.72 \times 4/3 = 11.63 \text{ ksi} \qquad (\text{AISC Spec. 1.5.6})$$

For *segment 2-3:*

$$\text{Use } K_y = 1.0$$

The weak axis effective slenderness ratio is

$$(KL/r_3)_y = 1.0 \times 10 \times 12/1.81 = 66.3$$
$$F_{ay} = 21.65 \text{ ksi} \qquad (\text{AISC Spec. Table 3-50})$$

Therefore, the allowable axial stress is

$$F_{ay} = 21.65 \times 4/3 = 28.83 \text{ ksi} \qquad (\text{AISC Spec. 1.5.6})$$

(b)   *Allowable bending stress:*
For strong axis bending, $0.6F_y$ is used as the allowable bending stress Based on AISC Spec. 1.5.6, $F_{bx} = 0.6F_y \times 4/3 = 0.8F_y = 40$ ksi.

For weak axis, the end restraints from adjacent spans are considered. The end restraining factors are the same as those determined under allowable compressive stress.

For *segment 1-2:*

$$G_2 = 0.4, \quad G_1 = 10$$

From Figs. F.1 and F.2 of Appendix F, the end restraining factors are:

$$K_s = 0.78, \quad K_w = 0.75$$

Based on the formulas of Chapter 3,

$$C_b = 1.75 \qquad [\text{Eq. (3.34b)}]$$

$$F_{b1} = \frac{170{,}000C_b}{\left(\dfrac{K_wL}{r_T}\right)^2} = \frac{170{,}000 \times 1.75}{\left(\dfrac{0.75 \times 25 \times 12}{2.16}\right)^2} = 27.42 \text{ ksi}$$

$$[\text{Eq. (3.33a)}]$$

and

$$F_{b2} = \frac{12{,}000C_b}{K_sLd/A_f} = \frac{12{,}000 \times 1.75}{0.78 \times 25 \times 12 \times 3.46} = 25.93 \text{ ksi}$$

$$[\text{Eq. (3.33b)}]$$

Therefore, the allowable bending stress is given by:

$$F_b = \sqrt{F_{b1}{}^2 + F_{b2}{}^2} = \sqrt{27.42^2 + 25.93^2} = 37.74 \text{ ksi}$$
$$[\text{Eq. (3.31)}]$$

This value is greater than $\frac{1}{3}F_y$, therefore, lateral buckling takes place in the inelastic range. In such a case Eq. (3.32) governs.

It is to be noted that Eq. (3.32) was developed under the assumption that the maximum compressive residual stress is equal to $0.3F_y$. On the other hand, the same formula developed for tapered members assumed a magnitude of $\frac{1}{2}F_y$ for the maximum compressive residual stress. This later formula is given by Eq. (D3-1) of the AISC specifications (Appendix D). Since AISC (D3-1) is more conservative, it is used to determine the allowable bending stress.

$$F_b = \frac{2}{3}\left(1 - \frac{F_y}{6\sqrt{F_{b1}{}^2 + F_{b2}{}^2}}\right)F_y = \frac{2}{3}\left(1 - \frac{50}{6 \times 37.74}\right)50 = 25.97 \text{ ksi}$$

From AISC 1.5.6.

$$F_b = 25.97 \times 4/3 = 34.63 \text{ ksi for segment 1-2}$$

For *segment 2-3:*

$$G_3 = 10, \quad G_2 = \frac{25 \times 70.6}{10 \times 70.6} = 2.5$$

From Figs. F-1 and F-2 of Appendix F, the effective length factors for lateral buckling are given by

$$K_s = 0.92, \quad K_w = 0.93$$

with

$$C_b = 1.75 - 1.05\left(\frac{3959}{5600}\right) + 0.3\left(\frac{3959}{5600}\right)^2 = 1.16 \quad [\text{Eq. (3.34a)}]$$

Then

$$F_{b1} = \frac{170,000C_b}{\left(\dfrac{K_wL}{r_T}\right)^2} = \frac{170,000 \times 1.16}{\left(\dfrac{0.93 \times 10 \times 12}{2.16}\right)^2} = 73.87 \text{ ksi} \quad [\text{Eq. (3.33a)}]$$

$$F_{b2} = \frac{12,000C_b}{K_sLd/A_f} = \frac{12,000 \times 1.16}{0.92 \times 10 \times 12 \times 3.46} = 36.44 \text{ ksi}$$
$$[\text{Eq. (3.33b)}]$$

and

$$F_b = \sqrt{F_{b1}{}^2 + F_{b2}{}^2} = \sqrt{73.87^2 + 36.44^2} = 82.37 \text{ ksi}$$
$$[\text{Eq. (3.31)}]$$

Use AISC Eq. (D3-1)

$$F_b = \frac{2}{3}\left[1 - \frac{F_y}{6\sqrt{F_{b1}{}^2 + F_{b2}{}^2}}\right] F_y = \frac{2}{3}\left[1 - \frac{50}{6 \times 82.37}\right] 50$$

$$= 29.96 \text{ ksi} < 0.6\,F_y = 30 \text{ ksi}$$

With load combination including the wind load, (AISC Spec. 1.5.6), the allowable bending stress is given by:

$$F_b = 29.96 \times 4/3 = 39.95 \text{ ksi for segment 2-3}$$

(c) *Combined axial compression and bending*
For strong axis, AISC Spec. Eq. (1.6-1a) is used for *column 1-3:*

$$F_e' = 17.50 \text{ ksi} \qquad \text{(AISC Spec. Table 9)}$$

$$C_m = 0.85 \qquad \text{(sidesway permitted)}$$

AISC Eq. (1.6-1a) gives

$$\frac{f_{a2}}{F_{ax}} + \frac{C_m}{\left(1 - \dfrac{f_{a2}}{F_e'}\right)}\left(\frac{f_{b3}}{0.8F_y}\right) = \frac{2.28}{21.89} + \frac{0.85}{\left(1 - \dfrac{2.28}{17.5}\right)}\left(\frac{37.08}{40}\right)$$

$$= 1.01 \doteq 1.0 \qquad \langle\text{O.K.}\rangle$$

For weak axis Eq. (3.35) is used for segments 1-2 and 2-3.
For *segment 1-2,*

$$\left(\frac{KL}{r_2}\right)_y = 130.9 > 100$$

From Eq. (3.36),

$$\xi = 1 - 0.5\left(\frac{f_{a2}}{F_{ay}}\right) = 1 - 0.5\left(\frac{2.28}{11.63}\right) = 0.90$$

Eq. (3.35) gives

$$\frac{f_{a2}}{F_{ay}} + \xi\frac{f_{b2}}{F_b} = \frac{2.28}{11.63} + 0.9\left(\frac{27.17}{34.63}\right) = 0.902 < 1.0 \qquad \langle\text{O.K.}\rangle$$

For *segment 2-3:*

$$\left(\frac{KL}{r_3}\right)_y = 66.3 < 100$$

$$\xi = 1.0 \qquad\qquad [\text{Eq. (3.36)}]$$

Eq. (3.35) gives

$$\frac{f_{a3}}{F_{ay}} + \xi\frac{f_{b3}}{F_b} = \frac{2.0}{28.83} + \frac{37.08}{39.95} = 0.997 < 1.0 \qquad \langle\text{O.K.}\rangle$$

(B) *Determine the adequacy of segment 4-5 of the girder* $(DL + LL)$. Since the axial stress of segment 4-5 is negligibly small, only the bending stress is checked. Considering end restraints at points 4 and 5, the allowable bending stress of segment 4-5 is determined as follows:

$$G_4 = G_5 = \left(\frac{b_1 I_0}{L I_1}\right)_y = \frac{20 \times 124}{20 \times 124} = 1 \qquad [\text{Eq. (E-5)}]$$

$$K_s = 0.76, \quad K_w = 0.73 \qquad\qquad (\text{Appendix F})$$

$$C_b = 1.75 - 1.05\left(\frac{3206}{5606}\right) + 0.3\left(\frac{3206}{5606}\right)^2 = 1.25 \quad [\text{Eq. (3.34a)}]$$

$$F_{b1} = \frac{170,000C_b}{\left(\frac{K_w L}{r_{T4}}\right)^2} = \frac{170,000 \times 1.25}{(0.73 \times 240/2.56)^2} = 45.37 \text{ ksi} \qquad [\text{Eq. (3.33a)}]$$

$$F_{b2} = \frac{12,000C_b}{K_s L d/A_f} = \frac{12,000 \times 1.25}{0.76 \times 240 \times 3.61} = 22.78 \text{ ksi} \quad [\text{Eq. (3.33b)}]$$

and

$$F_b = \sqrt{F_{b1}^2 + F_{b2}^2} = \sqrt{45.37^2 + 22.78^2} = 50.77 \text{ ksi} \quad [\text{Eq. (3.31)}]$$

The value is greater than $1/3 \, F_y$. Use AISC Eq. (D3-1),

$$F_b = \frac{2}{3}\left[1 - \frac{F_y}{6\sqrt{F_{b1}^2 + F_{b2}^2}}\right]F_y = \frac{2}{3}\left[1 - \frac{50}{6 \times 50.77}\right]50$$

$$= 27.86 \text{ ksi} > f_{b4} = 23.07 \text{ ksi} \quad \langle\text{O.K.}\rangle$$

(C) *In this section, the adequacy of column 1-3 and segment 4-5 is checked using the AISC formulas.*
   (a) *Column 1-3* $(DL + LL + WL)$

(i) Allowable axial stress

The allowable axial stress for strong axis buckling is

$$F_{ax} = 21.89 \text{ ksi for } (KL/r)_x = 92.36$$

For weak axis, the effective length factor is assumed to be 1.0. Then

$$(KL/r_2)_y = 1 \times 25 \times 12/1.81 = 165.7 \qquad \text{for segment 1-2}$$

$$(KL/r_3)_y = 1 \times 10 \times 12/1.81 = 66.3 \qquad \text{for segment 2-3}$$

Therefore, for *segment 1-2*, weak axis controls.

$$F_a = 5.44 \text{ ksi} \qquad \text{(AISC Table 3-50)}$$

For combined wind loading (AISC Spec. 1.5.6), an increase of 1/3 is permitted.

$$F_a = 5.44 \times 4/3 = 7.25 \text{ ksi}$$

For segment 2-3, strong axis controls, and $F_a = 21.89$ ksi.

(ii) Allowable bending stress

For *segment 1-2*

$$L/r_T = 25 \times 12/2.16$$

$$= 138.8 > \sqrt{\frac{510{,}000C_b}{F_y}} = \sqrt{\frac{510{,}000 \times 1.75}{50}} = 133.6$$

From AISC Eq. (1.5-6b)

$$F_{b1} = \frac{170 \times 10^3 C_b}{(L/r_T)^2} = \frac{170{,}000 \times 1.75}{138.8^2} = 15.44 \text{ ksi}$$

And from AISC Eq. (1.5-7)

$$F_{b2} = \frac{12{,}000C_b}{Ld/A_f} = \frac{12{,}000 \times 1.75}{25 \times 12 \times 3.46} = 20.23 \text{ ksi} < 0.6F_y$$

However, from the commentary of the AISC Spec. (Sect. 1.5.1.4.5), AISC Eqs. (1.5-6a) and (1.5-6b) may be found, including both St. Venant's and warping torsion, using an equivalent radius of gyration, r_{Te}.

$$r_{Te}{}^2 = \frac{I_y}{2S_x} \sqrt{d^2 + \frac{0.156 \, L^2 J}{I_y}}$$

$$= \frac{70.6}{2 \times 151} \sqrt{21.24^2 + \frac{0.156 \times 300^2 \times 3.02}{70.6}} = 7.58$$

$$r_{Te} = 2.75$$

$$L/r_{Te} = 300/2.75 = 109.1 < \sqrt{\frac{510,000C_b}{F_y}} = 133.6$$

From AISC Eq. (1.5-6a),

$$F_{b3} = \left[\frac{2}{3} - \frac{F_y(L/r_{Te})^2}{1530 \times 10^3 C_b}\right] F_y = \left[\frac{2}{3} - \frac{50(109.1)^2}{1530 \times 10^3 \times 1.75}\right] 50$$

$$= 22.22 \text{ ksi} < 0.6F_y$$

F_{b3} is chosen, and is increased by $1/3$ according to AISC Spec. 1.5.6. The allowable bending stress for segment 1-2 is given by

$$F_b = 22.22 \times 4/3 = 29.63 \text{ ksi}$$

For *segment 2-3*

$$F_b = \frac{12,000C_b}{Ld/A_f} = \frac{12,000 \times 1.16}{10 \times 12 \times 3.46} = 33.52 \text{ ksi} > 0.6F_y$$

$$[\text{AISC Eq. (1.5-7)}]$$

Use

$$F_b = 0.6F_y \times 4/3 = 40 \text{ ksi}$$

(iii)   Combined stresses:
   For *segment 1-2,* AISC Eq. (1.6-1a) gives

$$\frac{f_{a2}}{F_a} + \frac{C_m}{\left(1 - \frac{f_{a2}}{F_e'}\right)}\left(\frac{f_{b2}}{F_b}\right) = \frac{2.28}{7.25} + \frac{0.85}{\left(1 - \frac{2.28}{17.5}\right)}\left(\frac{27.17}{29.63}\right)$$

$$= 1.22 > 1.0 \qquad \langle \text{N.G.} \rangle$$

For *segment 2-3,* AISC Eq. (1.6-1a) gives

$$\frac{f_{a3}}{F_a} + \frac{C_m}{\left(1 - \frac{f_{a3}}{F_e'}\right)}\left(\frac{f_{b3}}{F_b}\right) = \frac{2.0}{21.89} + \frac{0.85}{\left(1 - \frac{2.0}{17.5}\right)}\left(\frac{37.08}{40}\right)$$

$$= 0.98 < 1.0 \qquad \langle \text{O.K.} \rangle$$

   (b)   *Segment 4-5 (DL + LL)*
Since the small axial stress is neglected, only bending is considered

$$L/r_T = 240/2.56$$

$$= 93.97 < \sqrt{\frac{510,000 C_b}{F_y}} = \sqrt{\frac{510,000 \times 1.25}{50}} = 112.9$$

From AISC Eq. (1.5-6a)

(i) $F_b = \left[\frac{2}{3} - \frac{F_y (L/r_T)^2}{1530 \times 10^3 C_b}\right] F_y$

$$= \left[\frac{2}{3} - \frac{50 \times 93.75^2}{1530 \times 10^3 \times 1.25}\right] 50 = 21.84 \text{ ksi}$$

From AISC Eq. (1.5-7)

(ii) $F_b = \dfrac{12,000 C_b}{Ld/A_f} = \dfrac{12,000 \times 1.25}{240 \times 3.61} = 17.31 \text{ ksi}$

The equivalent radius of gyration from AISC Commentary Sect. 1.5.1.4.5 is determined as follows:

$$r_{Te}^2 = \frac{I_y}{2S_x} \sqrt{d^2 + \frac{0.156 \, L^2 J}{I_y}}$$

$$= \frac{124}{2 \times 243} \sqrt{26.91^2 + \frac{0.156 \times 240^2 \times 4.06}{124}} = 8.14$$

hence

$$r_{Te} = 2.85 \text{ in.}$$

For

$$L/r_{Te} = 84.11 < \sqrt{\frac{510,000 C_b}{F_y}} = 112.9, \text{ AISC Eq. (1.5-6a) gives}$$

(iii) $F_b = \left[\frac{2}{3} - \frac{F_y (L/r_{Te})^2}{1530 \times 10^3 C_b}\right] F_y$

$$= \left[\frac{2}{3} - \frac{50 \times 84.11^2}{1530 \times 10^3 \times 1.25}\right] 50 = 24.08 \text{ ksi} < 0.6 F_y$$

Use

$$F_b = 24.08 \text{ ksi} > f_{b4} = 23.07 \text{ ksi} \qquad \langle \text{O.K.} \rangle$$

Chapter Five

References

SPECIFICATIONS

1. American Institute of Steel Construction, "Specification for the Design, Fabrication and Erection of Structural Steel for Buildings, with Commentary," Nov. 1, 1978, New York, NY.
2. Metal Building Manufacturers Association, "Metal Building Systems Manual," 1981, Cleveland, OH.

STRUCTURAL ANALYSIS

3. Cook, R. D., "Concepts and Applications of Finite Element Analysis," John Wiley & Sons, 1974.
4. Ketter, R. L., Lee, G. C., and Prawel, S. P., "Structural Anslysis and Design," McGraw-Hill Book Co., 1979.

TAPERED MEMBERS

5. Amirikian, A., "Wedge-Beam Framing," *Trans. ASCE,* Vol. 117, 1952, p. 596.
6. Appl, F. M. and Smith, J. O., "Buckling of Inelastic Tapered Pin-Ended Columns," ASCE *J. Engng. Mech. Div.,* Vol. 94, EM2, April 1968.
7. Boley, B. A., "On the Accuracy of the Bernouilli-Euler Theory for Beams of Variable Section," *J. Appl. Mech.,* Vol 30, Sept. 1963, pp. 373-378.
8. Butler, D. J. and Anderson, G. B., "The Elastic Buckling of Tapered Beam-Columns," *Weld. J. Res. Suppl.,* Vol. 42, No. 1, Jan. 1963.
9. Butler, D. J., "Elastic Buckling Tests on Laterally and Torsionally Braced Tapered I-Beams," *Weld. J. Res. Suppl.,* Vol. 45, No. 1, Jan. 1966.
10. Culver, C. G. and Preg, S. M. Jr., "Elastic Stability of Tapered Beam-Columns," ASCE *J. Struct. Div.,* Vol. 94, ST2, Feb. 1968, pp. 455-470.
11. Falby, W. W. and Lee, G. C., "Tension-Field Design of Tapered Webs," *AISC Engng. J.,* Vol. 13, No. 1, Jan. 1976.
12. Fogel, C. M. and Ketter, R. L., "Elastic Strength of Tapered Columns," ASCE *J. Struct. Div.,* Vol. 88, ST6, Oct. 1962, Proc. 3301, pp. 67-106.
13. Gere, J. M. and Carter, W. O., "Critical Buckling Loads for Tapered Columns," ASCE *J. Struct. Div.,* Vol. 88, ST1, Feb. 1962, Proc. 3045, pp. 1-11.
14. Girijavallabhan, C. V., "Buckling Loads of Nonuniform Columns," ASCE *J. Struct. Div.,* Vol. 95, ST11, Nov. 1969, pp. 2419-2431.
15. Hsu, T. L. and Lee, G. C., "Design of Bean Columns with Lateral-Torsional End Restraints," Dept. of Civil Engineering Research Rept., SUNY/Buffalo, 1979.

16. B. J. Johnston, editor, "Guide to Stability Design Criteria for Metal Structures," Structural Stability Research Council, John Wiley & Sons, Inc., 1976.
17. Krefeld, W. J., Butler, D. J., and Anderson, G. B., "Welded Cantilever Wedge Beams," *Weld. J. Res. Suppl.,* Vol. 38, No. 3, March 1959.
18. Krishnamurthy, N., "A Fresh Look at Bolted End-Plate Behavior and Design," *AISC Engng. J.,* 2nd quarter, 1978.
19. Krishnamurthy, N., Huang, H., Jeffery, P., and Avery, L., "Analytical M-ϕ Curves for End-Plate Connections," ASCE *J. Struct. Div.,* Vol. 105, ST1, Jan. 1979.
20. Lee, G. C. and Szabo, B. A., "Torsional Response of Tapered I-Girders," ASCE *J. Struct. Div..* Vol. 93, ST5, Oct. 1967, pp. 233–252.
21. Lee, G. C., Chen, Y. C., and Hsu, T. L., "Allowable Axial Stress of Restrained Multi-Segment, Tapered Roof Girders," *Weld. Res. Council Bull.,* No. 248, May 1979.
22. Lee, G. C., Morrell, M. L., and Ketter, R. L., "Design of Tapered Members," *Weld. Res. Council Bull.,* No. 173, June 1972.
23. Lee, G. C. and Morrell, M. L., "Stability of Space Frames Composed of Thin-Walled Structures," *Proc.* ASCE Struct. Engng. Conf., Cincinnati, OH, 1974.
24. Lee, G. C. and Morrell, M. L., "Applications of AISC Design Provisions for Tapered Members," *AISC Engng. J.,* Vol. 12, No. 1, Jan. 1975.
25. Lee, G. C. and Hsu, T. L., "Design of Tapered Columns with Unequal Flanges," Dept. of Civil Engng. Research Report, SUNY/Buffalo, 1979.
26. Lee, G. C., Morrell, M. L., and Ketter, R. L., "Residual Stresses in Tapered I-Shapes," Civil Engng. Research Rept., SUNY/Buffalo, 1979.
27. Lee, G. C., Sawada, Y., and Hsu, T-L., "Lateral Buckling of Roof Girders under Negative Bending," Dept. of Civil Engng. Research Rept., SUNY/Buffalo, 1979.
28. Lee, L. H. N., "On the Lateral Buckling of a Tapered Narrow Rectangular Beam," *J. Appl. Mech.,* Vol. 26, Sept. 1959, pp. 457–458.
29. Morrell, M. L. and Lee, G. C., "Allowable Stresses for Web-Tapered Beams with Lateral Restraints," *Weld. Res. Council Bull.,* No. 192, Feb. 1974.
30. Prawel, S. P. Jr., Morrell, M. L., and Lee, G. C., "Bending and Buckling Strength of Tapered Members," *Weld. Res. J. Suppl.,* Feb. 1974. p. 75–S.
31. Tuma, J. J. and Munshi, R. K., "Advanced Structural Analysis," *Schaum's Outline of Theory and Problems,* McGraw-Hill Book Co., 1971.

Appendix A

Instructions and Listings for a Finite Element Computer Program for the Analysis of Two-Dimensional Frame Structures

This computer program was developed by E. Wilson and W. Doherty, and was published in September 1967 as part of the SESM PROGRAMS of the University of California, Berkeley under the title "Analysis of Two-Dimensional Frame Structures". It is reprinted here with the permission of Professor E. Wilson of the Department of Civil Engineering of the University of California at Berkeley.

SESM PROGRAMS
University of California
Berkeley

Identification

ANALYSIS OF TWO-DIMENSIONAL FRAME STRUC-
TURES—Programmed by E. Wilson and W. Doherty, September
1967.

Description

Joint deflections, member end forces and joint reactions are determined
for plane frames which may be subjected to joint loads, joint displacements and member loads. Supports may be rigid or linearly elastic.
Members may be non-prismatic. Member-to-joint connections may be
flexible (partially rigid).

Use

Each nodal point (joint) of the structure is given a unique identification number starting with one. Similarly, each element (member) is identified.

Two right-handed orthogonal cartesian coordinate systems are used.

1. Global system (X, Y, Z). An arbitrary point is chosen as the origin such that the structure lies in the X–Y plane. Joint displacements and reactions are output in global coordinates.

2. Local system (x, y, z). Each element has a local coordinate system used only for the direction of the coordinate axes. The x axis is directed along the centroidal axis from Node I to Node J (see "Element Data Cards"). The global Z and local z axes have the same direction. The local x and z axes define the direction of the local y axis. Member end forces are output in the local coordinate directions.

Input

A series of punched cards in the following order numerically define the structure to be analyzed.

a) Identification card (78H)

   Columns 1 to 78 contain information to be printed with the results as a heading.

b) Control card (6I5)

Columns		
	1– 5	Number of elements (no maximum)
	6–10	Number of nodal points (1000 maximum)
	11–15	Number of materials (10 maximum)
	16–20	Number of element geometric property cards (200 maximum)
	21–25	Number of elastic support cards (40 maximum)
	26–30	Number of fixed end force cards (40 maximum)

c) Material property cards (I5,2F10.0)

Columns		
	1– 5	Material identification—any number from 1 to 10

    Columns   6–15   Young's Modulus
               16–25   Poisson's Ratio—may be left blank if shear de-
                        formations are not to be included in analysis

d) Elastic support cards (I5,3F10.0)—Optional

    Columns   1– 5   Identification—any number from 1 to 40
               6–15   *SX—X* component of elastic joint restraint
               16–25   *SY—Y* component of elastic joint restraint
               26–35   *SZ—Z* component of elastic joint restraint

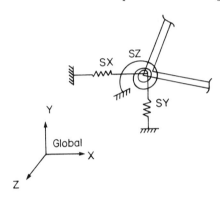

Each unique set of values of spring constants which may appear at any
joint in the structure is given an identification number. The elastic stiffness coefficients are then associated with this number. Any of *SX, SY*
or *SZ* may be left blank. When elastic supports are included in the
analysis "Elastic Foundation Reactions" are printed with the results.

e) Geometric property cards (I5,3F10.0)

    Columns   1– 5   Identification—any number from 1 to 200
               6–15   Axial area
               16–25   Shear area (optional)
               26–35   Moment of inertia

One card is required for each unique set of properties. Shear area is included only if shear deformations are to be included in the analysis. For
non-prismatic members the axial area becomes the effective area and
the moment of inertia is a reference value. For non-prismatic members
shear deformation calculations are computed as if member were prismatic with the specified effective shear area.

f) Fixed-end force cards (I5,6F10.0)—Optional

Columns	1– 5	Identification—any number from 1 to 40
	6–15	S1
	16–25	S2
	26–35	S3
	36–45	S4
	46–55	S5
	56–65	S6

Fixed-end forces are input in local coordinates. *Note* that the values given are literally *fixed-end* forces. Corrections due to hinges or rollers are performed within the program. For non-prismatic structures and flexible connections a table of frame constants is helpful.

g) Nodal point data cards (2I5,5F10.0,2I5)

Columns	1– 5	Identification—nodal point number
	6–10	Joint code
	11–20	Global X coordinate
	21–30	Global Y coordinate
	31–40	Applied joint force or displacement in Global X direction (X boundary condition)
	41–50	Applied joint force or displacement in Global Y direction (y boundary condition)
	51–60	Applied joint moment or rotation about Global Z direction (Z boundary condition)
	61–65	Elastic support identification number corresponding to this joint if applicable, otherwise blank.
	66–70	Optional parameter causing automatic generation of nodal point data reducing required input.

This option is described below under a separate heading. If option is not used, leave blank.

The joint code is a three digit number composed of ones and/or zeros. A *one* denotes a displacement boundary condition (known joint displacement component, unknown applied joint force component) and a *zero* (blank) is a force boundary condition. The 1st, 2nd, and 3rd digits refer to the X, Y, and Z boundary conditions respectively.

Example

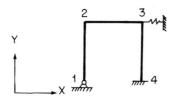

Joint Code	
1	110
2	000
3	000
4	111

h) Element data cards (6I5,I10,I5,3F10.0)

Columns   1– 5   Identification—element number

             6–10   Identification—Node I

          11–15   Identification—Node J

          16–20   Material identification number

          21–25   Geometric properties identification number

          26–30   Fixed-end forces identification number

          31–40   Element code

          41–45   Optional parameter causing automatic generation of element data reducing required inputs. This option is described below under a separate heading. If option is not used, leave blank.

          46–55   *KIJ*—Relative flexural stiffness of End *I* when End *J* is fully fixed.

          56–65   *KJI*—Relative flexural stiffness of End *J* when End *I* is fully fixed.

          66–75   *CIJ*—Flexural carry-over from End *I* to End *J*.

Columns 46 to 75 may be left blank for prismatic members with fully rigid or fully released components of force transferred from member to joint.

The maximum allowable difference in the nodal point identification numbers for any element is 24.

The identification numbers in Columns 16 to 30 correspond to the identification number in C, E, and F above.

The element code is a six-digit number composed of ones and/or zeros (blanks). The first digit corresponds to member end force 1 in the following diagram. The second digit refers to force 2, etc.

If any of the above 6-member forces is known to be zero (e.g., hinge) and if, in addition, the member end displacement differs from the joint displacement, the digit corresponding to that force is a *one*, otherwise it is left blank.

Example

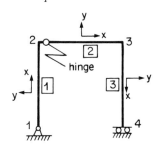

Element	Node I	Node J	Code
1	1	2	not applicable (blank)
2	2	3	00100
3	3	4	not applicable (blank)

Note that element code is in local coordinate system.

Since Joint 1 has same rotation as End *I* rotation of member ① no element code is used. Similar comments apply to joint 4.

An element code number is required for member ② since member rotation at End *I* differs from joint 2 rotation.

The flexural stiffness *KIJ* and *KJI* are defined as

$$KIJ = \frac{M_I}{EI/L}$$

$$KJI = \frac{M_J}{EI/L}$$

where E = Young's Modulus

     I = Reference moment of inertia

    L = Member length

   M_I = Moment at End I when rotation at End I is unity and that at End J is zero

   M_J = Moment at End J when rotation at End J is unity and that at End I is zero

The carry-over factor CIJ is from End I to End J. KIJ, KJI, and CIJ may be taken directly from a handbook. The carry-over factor from End J to End I is calculated in the program.

Note that if a shear area is specified, the values of KIJ, KJI, and CIJ are modified in the program to account for shear deformation as if the member were prismatic.

Automatic Nodal Point Data Generation

Only the nodal point data cards for the first and last node need to given as input when the nodes occur equally spaced on a straight line;

If   1) Each nodal point number is one greater than the previous number in the series,

and the   i) Joint code number

            ii) Applied joint loads and displacements (boundary conditions)

           iii) Elastic support identification number

           2a) are the same for each nodal point in the series

or   2b) are all zero for each point in the series except for the first which may have any values of i, ii, and iii.

    The generator option is left blank in Case 2a) and has a *one* in Column 70 for Case 2b).

Automatic Element Data Generation

If a series of elements occurs in which each element number NE_i is one greater than the previous number NE_{i-1}

$$i.e., NE_i = NE_{i-1} + 1$$

only the element data card for the first element in the series need be given as input.

If   1) The end nodal point numbers NI_i and NJ_i are obtained from the previous element and nodal point numbers by adding a constant k

$$\text{i.e., } NI_i = NI_{i-1} + k$$

$$Nj_i = NJ_{i-1} + k$$

and the   i) material identification number
            ii) geometric property identification number
           iii) fixed-end force identification number
           iv) element code
            v) stiffness and carry-over coefficients

are the same for each element in the series.

The generator option is the value of k and if left blank is taken to be one. The element data card for the last element in the structure must always be given.

```
      PROGRAM FRAME2                                              2FRAM    1
    1 (INPUT,OUTPUT,TAPE 5=INPUT,TAPE 6=OUTPUT,TAPE 1,TAPE 2)     2FRAM    2
      COMMON / PARAM /                                            2FRAM    3
    1     HED(13),NUMEL,NUMNP,NEQ,NUMSPR                          2FRAM    4
      COMMON / MATARG /                                          2FRAM    5
    1     E(10),G(10)                                              2FRAM    6
      COMMON / ELEARG /                                          2FRAM    7
    1     SF(6),LM(6),         SA(6,6),ASA(6,6),T(3,3),          2FRAM    8
    2     NBLK,NEL,NI,NJ,                                        2FRAM    9
    3     S(6,6),RF(6),JK(3)                                      2FRAM   10
      COMMON                                                      2FRAM   11
    1     MBAND,NN,NUMBLK,NPSTP(1000),SP(40,3),BCF(3000),         2FRAM   12
    2     BC(3000),X(1000),Y(1000),KODE(1000),SFT(40,6),         2FRAM   13
    3     COAX(200),COAY(200),COAAZ(200)                         2FRAM   14
C                                                                 2FRAM   15
C     FOR THIS PROGRAM NN MUST BE A MULTIPLE OF 3 AND MUST EQUAL THE 2FRAM 16
C     NUMBER OF COLUMNS IN THE DIMENSIONED MATRIX A              2FRAM   17
C                                                                 2FRAM   18
      NN=75                                                       2FRAM   19
C                                                                 2FRAM   20
C     READ AND PRINT CONTROL DATA                                2FRAM   21
C                                                                 2FRAM   22
    1 READ  (5,1000) HED,NUMEL,NUMNP,NUMMAT,NUMETP,NUMSPR,NUMFIX 2FRAM   23
      WRITE (6,2000) HED,NUMEL,NUMNP,NUMMAT,NUMETP,NUMSPR,NUMFIX 2FRAM   24
      IF((NUMEL.EQ.0).OR.(NUMNP.EQ.0).OR.(NUMMAT.EQ.0).OR.(NUMETP.EQ.0))2FRAM 25
    1 GO TO 2                                                     2FRAM   26
      GO TO 3                                                     2FRAM   27
    2 WRITE (6,2012)                                              2FRAM   28
      CALL EXIT                                                   2FRAM   29
    3 CONTINUE                                                    2FRAM   30
C                                                                 2FRAM   31
C     READ AND PRINT MATERIAL PROPERTY DATA                      2FRAM   32
C                                                                 2FRAM   33
      WRITE (6,2001)                                              2FRAM   34
      DO 10 I=1,NUMMAT                                            2FRAM   35
      READ  (5,1001) N,E(N),G(N)                                 2FRAM   36
      WRITE (6,2002) N,E(N),G(N)                                 2FRAM   37
   10 G(N)=0.5*E(N)/(1.0+G(N))                                   2FRAM   38
C                                                                 2FRAM   39
C     READ AND PRINT STIFFNESS OF ELASTIC SUPPORTS               2FRAM   40
C                                                                 2FRAM   41
      IF(NUMSPR .EQ. 0) GO TO 50                                 2FRAM   42
      WRITE (6,2007)                                              2FRAM   43
      DO 40 I=1,NUMSPR                                            2FRAM   44
      READ  (5,1003) N,(SP(N,J),J=1,3)                           2FRAM   45
   40 WRITE (6,2008) N,(SP(N,J),J=1,3)                           2FRAM   46
   50 CONTINUE                                                    2FRAM   47
C                                                                 2FRAM   48
C     READ AND PRINT GEOMETRIC PROPERTIES OF COMMON ELEMENTS.    2FRAM   49
C                                                                 2FRAM   50
      WRITE (6,2003)                                              2FRAM   51
      DO 30 I=1,NUMETP                                            2FRAM   52
      READ  (5,1002) N,COAX(N),COAY(N),COAAZ(N)                  2FRAM   53
      IF((COAX(N).NE.0.0).AND. (COAAZ(N).NE.0.0)) GO TO 20       2FRAM   54
      WRITE (6,2013)                                              2FRAM   55
      CALL EXIT                                                   2FRAM   56
   20 WRITE (6,2004) N,COAX(N),COAY(N),COAAZ(N)                  2FRAM   57
   30 CONTINUE                                                    2FRAM   58
C                                                                 2FRAM   59
C     READ AND PRINT FIXED END FORCES IN LOCAL COORDINATES       2FRAM   60
C                                                                 2FRAM   61
      IF(NUMFIX .EQ. 0) GO TO 56                                 2FRAM   62
      WRITE (6,2010)                                              2FRAM   63
      DO 55 I=1,NUMFIX                                            2FRAM   64
      READ  (5,1005) N,(SFT(N,J),J=1,6)                          2FRAM   65
   55 WRITE (6,2011) N,(SFT(N,J),J=1,6)                          2FRAM   66
   56 CONTINUE                                                    2FRAM   67
C                                                                 2FRAM   68
C     READ AND PRINT NODAL POINT DATA. GENERATE MISSING INPUT.   2FRAM   69
C                                                                 2FRAM   70
      WRITE (6,2005)                                              2FRAM   71
      L=0                                                         2FRAM   72
   60 READ  (5,1004) N,KODE(N),X(N),Y(N),BC(3*N-2),BC(3*N-1),BC(3*N), 2FRAM 73
    1 NPSTP(N),ITAG                                              2FRAM   74
      NL=L+1                                                      2FRAM   75
      IF (L.EQ.0) GO TO 70                                       2FRAM   76
```

```
        ZX=N-L                                              2FRAM 77
        DX=(X(N)-X(L))/ZX                                   2FRAM 78
        DY=(Y(N)-Y(L))/ZX                                   2FRAM 79
     70 L=L+1                                               2FRAM 80
        IF(N-L) 100,90,80                                   2FRAM 81
     80 CONTINUE                                            2FRAM 82
        X(L)=X(L-1)+DX                                      2FRAM 83
        Y(L)=Y(L-1)+DY                                      2FRAM 84
        I=3*L                                               2FRAM 85
        IF(NTAG.EQ. 1) GO TO 82                             2FRAM 86
        BC(I-2)=BC(I-5)                                     2FRAM 87
        BC(I-1)=BC(I-4)                                     2FRAM 88
        BC(I)  =BC(I-3)                                     2FRAM 89
        NPSTP(L)=NPSTP(L-1)                                 2FRAM 90
        KODE(L)=KODE(L-1)                                   2FRAM 91
        GO TO 70                                            2FRAM 92
     82 BC(I-2)=0.0                                         2FRAM 93
        BC(I-1)=0.0                                         2FRAM 94
        BC(I)  =0.0                                         2FRAM 95
        NPSTP(L)=0                                          2FRAM 96
         KODE(L)=0                                          2FRAM 97
        GO TO 70                                            2FRAM 98
     90 WRITE (6,2006) (K,KODE(K),X(K),Y(K),BC(3*K-2),BC(3*K-1),BC(3*K),  2FRAM 99
       1 NPSTP(K),K=NL,N)                                   2FRAM100
        NTAG=ITAG                                           2FRAM101
        IF(NUMNP-N) 100,110,60                              2FRAM102
    100 WRITE (6,2009) N                                    2FRAM103
        CALL EXIT                                           2FRAM104
    110 CONTINUE                                            2FRAM105
C                                                           2FRAM106
C       FORM STIFFNESS FOR EACH ELEMENT                     2FRAM107
C                                                           2FRAM108
        REWIND 1                                            2FRAM109
        REWIND 2                                            2FRAM110
        CALL ELSTIF                                         2FRAM111
C                                                           2FRAM112
C       ADD ELEMENT STIFFNESS TO STRUCTURE STIFFNESS IN BLOCKS  2FRAM113
C                                                           2FRAM114
        CALL STIFF                                          2FRAM115
C                                                           2FRAM116
C       SOLVE FOR DISPLACEMENTS                             2FRAM117
C                                                           2FRAM118
        REWIND 2                                            2FRAM119
        CALL BANSOL                                         2FRAM120
C                                                           2FRAM121
C       SOLVE FOR ELEMENT END FORCES AND STRUCTURE REACTIONS  2FRAM122
C                                                           2FRAM123
        REWIND 1                                            2FRAM124
        CALL FORCE                                          2FRAM125
C                                                           2FRAM126
        GO TO 1                                             2FRAM127
C                                                           2FRAM128
   1000 FORMAT(13A6/6I5)                                    2FRAM129
   1001 FORMAT(I5,2F10.0)                                   2FRAM130
   1002 FORMAT(I5,3F10.0)                                   2FRAM131
   1003 FORMAT(I5,3F10.0)                                   2FRAM132
   1004 FORMAT(2I5,5F10.0,2I5)                              2FRAM133
   1005 FORMAT(I5,6F10.0)                                   2FRAM134
   2000 FORMAT(1H1,13A6//                                   2FRAM135
       1 34H NUMBER OF ELEMENTS               =I6/         2FRAM136
       2 34H NUMBER OF NODAL POINTS           =I6/         2FRAM137
       3 34H NUMBER OF MATERIALS              =I6/         2FRAM138
       4 34H NUMBER OF ELEMENT TYPES          =I6/         2FRAM139
       5 34H NUMBER OF ELASTIC SUPPORT TYPES =I6/          2FRAM140
       6 34H NUMBER OF FIXED END FORCE TYPES =I6////)      2FRAM141
   2001 FORMAT(50H1MATERIAL     YOUNG S        POISSON S   2FRAM142
       1      /50H             MODULUS         RATIO       )2FRAM143
   2002 FORMAT(1H ,I5,3X,F12.0,F14.5)                      2FRAM144
   2003 FORMAT(1H1/                                        2FRAM145
       1    60H ELEMENT      AXIAL        SHEAR     MOMENT OF  2FRAM146
       2   /60H  TYPE        AREA         AREA      INERTIA  )2FRAM147
   2004 FORMAT(1H ,I5,3X,3F12.3)                           2FRAM148
   2005 FORMAT(1H1,                                        2FRAM149
       1    39H                 NODAL COORDINATES         2FRAM150
       2    47H        BOUNDARY CONDITIONS        ELASTIC SUPPORT//  2FRAM151
       3    10H NODE CODE,7X,1HX,11X,1HY,11X,1HX,11X,1HY,11X,1HZ,10X,4HTYPE)2FRAM152
```

```
2006 FORMAT(1H ,I4,I5,5F12.3,I9)                                          2FRAM153
2007 FORMAT(1H1/                                                          2FRAM154
   1  60H              SPRING CONSTANTS OF ELASTIC SUPPORTS             /2FRAM155
   2 /60H          LINEAR          LINEAR          ROTATIONAL          /2FRAM156
   3  60H  TYPE STIFFNESS  X    STIFFNESS  Y    STIFFNESS  Z          )2FRAM157
2008 FORMAT(1H ,I4,3F16.3)                                                2FRAM158
2009 FORMAT(26HONODAL POINT CARD ERROR N= I5)                            2FRAM159
2010 FORMAT(1H1/                                                          2FRAM160
   1  60H                    FIXED END FORCES IN LOCAL COORDINATES    /2FRAM161
   2 /44H   TYPE     AXIAL I     SHEAR I     MOMENT I                   2FRAM162
   3   36H          AXIAL J     SHEAR J     MOMENT J)                   2FRAM163
2011 FORMAT(1H ,I5,2X,6F12.3)                                            2FRAM164
2012 FORMAT (50HOPROBLEMS COMPLETED OR CONTROL CARD ERROR             )2FRAM165
2013 FORMAT(1H0/                                                         2FRAM166
   1  60H AXIAL AREA OR FLEXURAL INERTIA CANNOT BE SPECIFIED AS ZERO.)2FRAM167
     STOP                                                               2FRAM168
     END                                                                2FRAM169
     SUBROUTINE ELSTIF                                                  ELSTI   1
     COMMON / PARAM /                                                   ELSTI   2
   1      HED(13),NUMEL,NUMNP,NEQ,NUMSPR                                ELSTI   3
     COMMON / MATARG /                                                  ELSTI   4
   1      E(10),G(10)                                                   ELSTI   5
     COMMON / ELEARG /                                                  ELSTI   6
   1      SF(6),LM(6),          SA(6,6),ASA(6,6),T(3,3),               ELSTI   7
   2      NBLK,NEL,NI,NJ,                                               ELSTI   8
   3      S(6,6),RF(6),JK(3)                                            ELSTI   9
     COMMON                                                             ELSTI  10
   1      MBAND,NN,NUMBLK,NPSTP(1000),SP(40,3),BCF(3000),              ELSTI  11
   2      BC(3000),X(1000),Y(1000),KODE(1000),SFT(40,6),              ELSTI  12
   3      COAX(200),COAY(200),COAAZ(200)                               ELSTI  13
C                                                                       ELSTI  14
     DIMENSION IDISP(6)                                                ELSTI  15
C    INITIALIZATION                                                    ELSTI  16
C                                                                       ELSTI  17
     NEQ=3*NUMNP                                                       ELSTI  18
     NUMBLK=(NEQ-1)/NN+1                                               ELSTI  19
     MBAND=0                                                           ELSTI  20
     NNN=NUMBLK*NN                                                     ELSTI  21
     DO 5 I=1,NNN                                                      ELSTI  22
   5 BCF(I)=0.0                                                        ELSTI  23
C                                                                       ELSTI  24
     DO 10 I=1,6                                                       ELSTI  25
     S(I,1)=0.0                                                        ELSTI  26
     S(4,I)=0.0                                                        ELSTI  27
  10 S(I,4)=0.0                                                        ELSTI  28
     T(3,3)=1.0                                                        ELSTI  29
     DO 20 I=1,2                                                       ELSTI  30
     T(3,I)=0.0                                                        ELSTI  31
  20 T(I,3)=0.0                                                        ELSTI  32
C                                                                       ELSTI  33
C    STORE APPLIED JOINT FORCES IN BCF(NEQ). SET ROWS                  ELSTI  34
C    CORRESPONDING TO DISPLACEMENT BOUNDARY CONDITIONS TO ZERO.        ELSTI  35
C                                                                       ELSTI  36
     DO 70 N=1,NUMNP                                                   ELSTI  37
     KD=100                                                            ELSTI  38
     I=3*N-2                                                           ELSTI  39
     KK=KODE(N)                                                        ELSTI  40
     DO 70 K=1,3                                                       ELSTI  41
     IF(KK-KD) 40,50,50                                                ELSTI  42
  40 BCF(I)=BC(I)                                                      ELSTI  43
     GO TO 60                                                          ELSTI  44
  50 BCF(I)=0.0                                                        ELSTI  45
     KK=KK-KD                                                          ELSTI  46
  60 I=I+1                                                             ELSTI  47
  70 KD=KD/10                                                          ELSTI  48
C                                                                       ELSTI  49
C    READ AND PRINT ELEMENT DATA. GENERATE MISSING INPUT.             ELSTI  50
C                                                                       ELSTI  51
     WRITE (6,4000)                                                    ELSTI  52
     L=0                                                               ELSTI  53
 400 KKK=0                                                             ELSTI  54
     READ  (5,3000) INEL,INI,INJ,IMAT,IMEL,IMFIX,INELK,INC,ASIJ,ASJI, ELSTI  55
   1      ACIJ                                                         ELSTI  56
     IF( INC .EQ. 0)     INC=1                                         ELSTI  57
     IF( ASIJ .EQ. 0.)   ASIJ=4.0                                     ELSTI  58
     IF( ASJI .EQ. 0.)   ASJI=4.0                                     ELSTI  59
```

```
          IF( ACIJ .EQ. 0.)  ACIJ=0.5                           ELSTI 60
      401 L=L+1                                                  ELSTI 61
          KKK=KKK+1                                              ELSTI 62
          ML=INEL-L                                             ELSTI 63
          IF(ML) 402,403,404                                    ELSTI 64
      402 WRITE (6,4003) INEL                                   ELSTI 65
          CALL EXIT                                            ELSTI 66
C                                                               ELSTI 67
      403 NEL=INEL                                              ELSTI 68
          NI   =INI                                             ELSTI 69
          NJ   =INJ                                             ELSTI 70
          MATTYP=IMAT                                           ELSTI 71
          MELTYP=IMEL                                           ELSTI 72
          MFIX  =IMFIX                                          ELSTI 73
          NELKOD=INELK                                          ELSTI 74
          SIJ=ASIJ                                              ELSTI 75
          SJI=ASJI                                              ELSTI 76
          CIJ=ACIJ                                              ELSTI 77
          GO TO 405                                             ELSTI 78
C                                                               ELSTI 79
      404 NEL=INEL-ML                                           ELSTI 80
          NI   =IN+KKK*INCR                                     ELSTI 81
          NJ   =JN+KKK*INCR                                     ELSTI 82
          MATTYP=IMATT                                          ELSTI 83
          MELTYP=IMELT                                          ELSTI 84
          MFIX  =IFIX                                           ELSTI 85
          NELKOD=INEK                                           ELSTI 86
          SIJ=BSIJ                                              ELSTI 87
          SJI=BSJI                                              ELSTI 88
          CIJ=BCIJ                                              ELSTI 89
      405 CONTINUE                                              ELSTI 90
C                                                               ELSTI 91
          WRITE (6,4001) NEL,NI,NJ,MATTYP,MELTYP,NELKOD,MFIX,SIJ,SJI,CIJ  ELSTI 92
C                                                               ELSTI 93
C         DETERMINE NUMERICALLY GREATEST OF NI AND NJ           ELSTI 94
C         DETERMINE BANDWIDTH.                                  ELSTI 95
C                                                               ELSTI 96
          IF(NJ-NI) 71,72,73                                    ELSTI 97
       71 NL=NJ                                                 ELSTI 98
          NG=NI                                                 ELSTI 99
          GO TO 74                                              ELSTI100
       72 WRITE (6,4004) NEL                                    ELSTI101
          CALL EXIT                                            ELSTI102
       73 NL=NI                                                 ELSTI103
          NG=NJ                                                 ELSTI104
       74 MM=3*(1+NG-NL)                                        ELSTI105
          IF (MM .GT. NN  ) GO TO 77                            ELSTI106
          IF (MM .GT. MBAND) MBAND=MM                           ELSTI107
          GO TO 78                                              ELSTI108
       77 WRITE (6,4006) NEL                                    ELSTI109
          CALL EXIT                                            ELSTI110
C                                                               ELSTI111
       78  AX= COAX(MELTYP)                                     ELSTI112
           AY= COAY(MELTYP)                                     ELSTI113
          AAZ=COAAZ(MELTYP)                                     ELSTI114
C                                                               ELSTI115
          DX=X(NJ)-X(NI)                                        ELSTI116
          DY=Y(NJ)-Y(NI)                                        ELSTI117
          DL=SQRT(DX*DX+DY*DY)                                  ELSTI118
          IF(DL) 75,75,76                                       ELSTI119
       75 WRITE (6,4005) NEL                                    ELSTI120
          CALL EXIT                                            ELSTI121
       76 COSA=DX/DL                                            ELSTI122
          SINA=DY/DL                                            ELSTI123
C                                                               ELSTI124
C                                                               ELSTI125
C         DETERMINE IF SHEAR DEFORMATIONS ARE TO BE INCLUDED.   ELSTI126
C                                                               ELSTI127
          SHF=0.0                                               ELSTI128
          IF(AY .NE. 0.0) SHF=6.*E(MATTYP)*AAZ/(G(MATTYP)*AY*DL*DL)  ELSTI129
          COMM=E(MATTYP)*AAZ/DL                                 ELSTI130
          SHEF=0.5*(2.+SHF)/(1.+2.*SHF)                         ELSTI131
          COMM=COMM*SHEF                                        ELSTI132
          SIJ=SIJ*COMM                                          ELSTI133
          SJI=SJI*COMM                                          ELSTI134
          CIJ=(CIJ-0.5*SHF)/(1.+0.5*SHF)                        ELSTI135
```

```
      CJI=CIJ*SIJ/SJI                                               ELSTI136
C                                                                   ELSTI137
                                                                    ELSTI138
      DO 80 I=1,6                                                   ELSTI139
   80 SF(I)=0.0                                                     ELSTI140
C                                                                   ELSTI141
      IF(MFIX .EQ. 0) GO TO 100                                     ELSTI142
C                                                                   ELSTI143
      DO 90 I=1,6                                                   ELSTI144
   90 SF(I)=SFT(MFIX,I)                                             ELSTI145
  100 CONTINUE                                                      ELSTI146
C                                                                   ELSTI147
C     FORM GLOBAL TO LOCAL COORDINATE TRANSFORMATION.               ELSTI148
C                                                                   ELSTI149
      T(1,1)= COSA                                                  ELSTI150
      T(1,2)= SINA                                                  ELSTI151
      T(2,1)=-SINA                                                  ELSTI152
      T(2,2)= COSA                                                  ELSTI153
C                                                                   ELSTI154
C     FORM ELEMENT STIFFNESS IN LOCAL COORDINATES                  ELSTI155
C                                                                   ELSTI156
      S(1,1)= AX*E(MATTYP)/DL                                       ELSTI157
      S(4,1)=-S(1,1)                                                ELSTI158
      S(3,2)= SIJ*(1.+CIJ)/DL                                       ELSTI159
      S(6,2)= SJI*(1.+CJI)/DL                                       ELSTI160
      S(2,2)= (S(3,2)+S(6,2))/DL                                    ELSTI161
      S(5,2)=-S(2,2)                                                ELSTI162
      S(3,3)= SIJ                                                   ELSTI163
      S(6,3)= CIJ*SIJ                                               ELSTI164
      S(5,3)=-(S(3,3)+S(6,3))/DL                                    ELSTI165
      S(4,4)= S(1,1)                                                ELSTI166
      S(5,5)=-S(5,2)                                                ELSTI167
      S(6,5)=-S(6,2)                                                ELSTI168
      S(6,6)= SJI                                                   ELSTI169
      DO 110 I=1,5                                                  ELSTI170
      M=I+1                                                         ELSTI171
      DO 110 J=M,6                                                  ELSTI172
  110 S(I,J)=S(J,I)                                                 ELSTI173
C                                                                   ELSTI174
C     MODIFY ELEMENT STIFFNESS AND ELEMENT FIXED END FORCES FOR KNOWN ELSTI175
C     ZERO MEMBER END FORCES.                                       ELSTI176
C                                                                   ELSTI177
      IF(NELKOD .EQ. 0) GO TO 145                                  ELSTI178
      KK=NELKOD                                                     ELSTI179
      KD=100000                                                     ELSTI180
      DO 140 I=1,6                                                  ELSTI181
      IF(KK-KD) 140,120,120                                         ELSTI182
  120 SII=S(I,I)                                                    ELSTI183
      SFI=SF(I)                                                     ELSTI184
      DO 125 N=1,6                                                  ELSTI185
  125 SA(1,N)=S(I,N)                                                ELSTI186
      DO 130 M=1,6                                                  ELSTI187
      COF=S(M,I)/SII                                                ELSTI188
      SF(M)=SF(M)-COF*SFI                                           ELSTI189
      DO 130 N=1,6                                                  ELSTI190
  130 S(M,N)=S(M,N)-COF*SA(1,N)                                     ELSTI191
      KK=KK-KD                                                      ELSTI192
  140 KD=KD/10                                                      ELSTI193
C                                                                   ELSTI194
C     OBTAIN SA(6,6) RELATING ELEMENT END FORCES (LOCAL) AND JOINT  ELSTI195
C     DISPLACEMENTS (GLOBAL).                                       ELSTI196
C                                                                   ELSTI197
  145 DO 150 I=1,6                                                  ELSTI198
      DO 150 J=1,3                                                  ELSTI199
      SA(I,J)  =0.0                                                 ELSTI200
      SA(I,J+3)=0.0                                                 ELSTI201
      DO 150 K=1,3                                                  ELSTI202
      IF(T(K,J) .EQ. 0.0) GO TO 150                                 ELSTI203
      SA(I,J)  =SA(I,J)  +S(I,K)  *T(K,J)                           ELSTI204
      SA(I,J+3)=SA(I,J+3)+S(I,K+3)*T(K,J)                           ELSTI205
  150 CONTINUE                                                      ELSTI206
C                                                                   ELSTI207
C     OBTAIN ELEMENT STIFFNESS ASA(6,6) AND FIXED END FORCES RF(6) IN ELSTI208
C     GLOBAL COORDINATES.                                           ELSTI209
C                                                                   ELSTI210
      DO 160 I=1,3                                                  ELSTI211
      DO 160 J=1,6
```

```
         ASA(I,J)  =0.0                                              ELSTI212
         ASA(I+3,J)=0.0                                             ELSTI213
         DO 160 K=1,3                                               ELSTI214
         IF(T(K,I) .EQ. 0.0) GO TO 160                              ELSTI215
         ASA(I+3,J)=ASA(I+3,J)+T(K,I)*SA(K+3,J)                     ELSTI216
         ASA(I,J)  =ASA(I,J)  +T(K,I)*SA(K,J)                       ELSTI217
 160  CONTINUE                                                      ELSTI218
         DO 165 I=1,3                                               ELSTI219
         RF(I)  =0.0                                                ELSTI220
         RF(I+3)=0.0                                                ELSTI221
         DO 165 J=1,3                                               ELSTI222
         IF(T(J,I) .EQ. 0.0) GO TO 165                              ELSTI223
         RF(I)  =RF(I)  -T(J,I)*SF(J)                               ELSTI224
         RF(I+3)=RF(I+3)-T(J,I)*SF(J+3)                             ELSTI225
 165  CONTINUE                                                      ELSTI226
C                                                                   ELSTI227
C        FORM LOCAL LOCATION MATRIX FOR ELEMENT                     ELSTI228
C                                                                   ELSTI229
         DO 170 M=1,3                                               ELSTI230
         J=M-3                                                      ELSTI231
         LM(M)=3*NI+J                                               ELSTI232
 170  LM(M+3)=3*NJ+J                                                ELSTI233
C                                                                   ELSTI234
C        MODIFY GLOBAL STIFFNESS AND BOUNDARY CONDITIONS FOR KNOWN JOINT  ELSTI235
C        DISPLACEMENTS AND FOR FIXED END FORCES.                    ELSTI236
C                                                                   ELSTI237
         JK(1)=KODE(NI)                                             ELSTI238
         JK(2)=KODE(NJ)                                             ELSTI239
         DO 178 N=1,2                                               ELSTI240
         KD=100                                                     ELSTI241
         KK=JK(N)                                                   ELSTI242
         DO 178 M=1,3                                               ELSTI243
         I=3*(N-1)+M                                                ELSTI244
         IF (KK-KD) 176,177,177                                     ELSTI245
 176  IDISP (I)=0                                                   ELSTI246
         GO TO 178                                                  ELSTI247
 177  IDISP(I)=1                                                    ELSTI248
         KK=KK-KD                                                   ELSTI249
 178  KD=KD/10                                                      ELSTI250
         DO 240 N=1,2                                               ELSTI251
         KD=100                                                     ELSTI252
         KK=JK(N)                                                   ELSTI253
         DO 240 M=1,3                                               ELSTI254
         I=3*(N-1)+M                                                ELSTI255
         II=LM(I)                                                   ELSTI256
         IF(KK-KD) 180,190,190                                      ELSTI257
C                                                                   ELSTI258
C          1. FIXED END FORCES                                      ELSTI259
C                                                                   ELSTI260
 180  BCF(II)=BCF(II)+RF(I)                                         ELSTI261
         GO TO 240                                                  ELSTI262
C                                                                   ELSTI263
C          2. DISPLACEMENT BOUNDARY CONDITION                       ELSTI264
C                                                                   ELSTI265
 190  DISP=BC(II)                                                   ELSTI266
         DO 230 K=1,6                                               ELSTI267
         JJ=LM(K)                                                   ELSTI268
         IF(JJ-II) 200,210,200                                      ELSTI269
 200  CONTINUE                                                      ELSTI270
         IF (IDISP(K).EQ.1) GO TO 220                               ELSTI271
         BCF(JJ)=BCF(JJ)-ASA(K,I)*DISP                              ELSTI272
         GO TO 220                                                  ELSTI273
 210  BCF(JJ)=BCF(JJ)+DISP                                          ELSTI274
 220  ASA(I,K)=0.0                                                  ELSTI275
 230  ASA(K,I)=0.0                                                  ELSTI276
         ASA(I,I)=1.0                                               ELSTI277
         KK=KK-KD                                                   ELSTI278
 240  KD=KD/10                                                      ELSTI279
C                                                                   ELSTI280
C        STORE ELEMENT INFORMATION ON TAPE 1                        ELSTI281
C                                                                   ELSTI282
         NBLK=3*(NL-1)/NN+1                                         ELSTI283
         WRITE (1) (SF(I),I=1,97)                                   ELSTI284
C                                                                   ELSTI285
         IF(NUMEL-NEL) 402,500,260                                  ELSTI286
 260  CONTINUE                                                      ELSTI287
```

```
         IF (ML) 402,270,401                               ELSTI288
  270  IN   =INI                                           ELSTI289
       JN   =INJ                                           ELSTI290
       IMATT=IMAT                                          ELSTI291
       IMELT=IMEL                                          ELSTI292
       IFIX =IMFIX                                         ELSTI293
       INEK =INELK                                         ELSTI294
       INCR =INC                                           ELSTI295
       BSIJ=ASIJ                                           ELSTI296
       BSJI=ASJI                                           ELSTI297
       BCIJ=ACIJ                                           ELSTI298
       GO TO 400                                           ELSTI299
  500 RETURN                                               ELSTI300
C                                                          ELSTI301
 3000 FORMAT(6I5,I10,I5,3F10.0)                            ELSTI302
 4000 FORMAT(1H1/                                          ELSTI303
    1  60H ELEMENT  NODE  NODE  MATERIAL  ELEMENT  ELEMENT  FIXED END ELSTI304
    2  60H        RELATIVE STIFFNESS   CARRY OVER          ELSTI305
    3 /60H          I      J      TYPE     TYPE     CODE   FORCE TYPE ELSTI306
    4  60H         KIJ          KJI        FACTOR          )ELSTI307
 4001 FORMAT(1H ,I5,I7,I6,I8,I10,I11,I8,6X,2F10.5,F11.5)   ELSTI308
 4003 FORMAT(36HOELEMENT CARD ERROR, ELEMENT NUMBER= I6)   ELSTI309
 4004 FORMAT(1H ,31HNODAL POINT NUMBERS FOR ELEMENT,I5,36HARE IDENTICAL.ELSTI310
    1 EXECUTION TERMINATED.)                               ELSTI311
 4005 FORMAT(8HOELEMENT,I5,39H HAS ZERO LENGTH. EXECUTION TERMINATED.) ELSTI312
 4006 FORMAT(50HO MAX. NODAL POINT DIFFERENCE EXCEEDED FOR MEMBER      ELSTI313
    1  I5,50HO EXECUTION TERMINATED.                       )ELSTI314
      END                                                  ELSTI315
      SUBROUTINE STIFF                                     STIFF   1
      COMMON / PARAM /                                     STIFF   2
    1      HED(13),NUMEL,NUMNP,NEQ,NUMSPR                  STIFF   3
      COMMON / ELEARG /                                    STIFF   4
    1      SF(6),LM(6),        SA(6,6),ASA(6,6),T(3,3),    STIFF   5
    2      NBLK,NEL,NI,NJ,                                 STIFF   6
    3      S(6,6),RF(6),JK(3)                              STIFF   7
      COMMON                                               STIFF   8
    1      MBAND,NN,NUMBLK,NPSTP(1000),SP(40,3),BCF(3000), STIFF   9
    2      B(150),A(150,75)                                STIFF  10
C                                                          STIFF  11
C     INITIALIZATION                                       STIFF  12
C                                                          STIFF  13
      NN2=2*NN                                             STIFF  14
      NNH=NN/3                                             STIFF  15
      DO 10 I=1,NN2                                        STIFF  16
      DO 10 J=1,MBAND                                      STIFF  17
   10 A(I,J)=0.0                                           STIFF  18
C                                                          STIFF  19
C     FORM EQUILIBRIUM EQUATIONS IN BLOCKS                 STIFF  20
C                                                          STIFF  21
C         1. ADD ELEMENT STIFFNESS TO STRUCTURE STIFFNESS. STIFF  22
C                                                          STIFF  23
      DO 50 NB=1,NUMBLK                                    STIFF  24
      REWIND 1                                             STIFF  25
      NBN=NNH*(NB-1)                                       STIFF  26
      NBB=NN*(NB-1)                                        STIFF  27
      DO 30 N=1,NUMEL                                      STIFF  28
      READ  (1) (SF(I),I=1,97)                             STIFF  29
      IF(NBLK.NE.NB) GO TO 30                              STIFF  30
      DO 20 I=1,6                                          STIFF  31
      II=LM(I)                                             STIFF  32
      IJ=II-NBB                                            STIFF  33
      DO 20 J=1,6                                          STIFF  34
      JJ=LM(J)-II+1                                        STIFF  35
      IF( JJ .LE. 0 ) GO TO 20                             STIFF  36
      A(IJ,JJ)=A(IJ,JJ)+ASA(I,J)                           STIFF  37
   20 CONTINUE                                             STIFF  38
   30 CONTINUE                                             STIFF  39
C                                                          STIFF  40
C         2. ADD STIFFNESS OF ELASTIC FOUNDATION TO STRUCTURE STIFFNESS. STIFF  41
C                                                          STIFF  42
      IF ( NUMSPR .EQ. 0 ) GO TO  37                       STIFF  43
      DO 36 J=1,NNH                                        STIFF  44
      I=J+NBN                                              STIFF  45
      IF (I .GT. NUMNP) GO TO 37                           STIFF  46
      MSPR=NPSTP(I)                                        STIFF  47
      IF (MSPR .EQ. 0)  GO TO 36                           STIFF  48
```

```
            DO 35 K=1,3                                             STIFF 49
            KJ=3*(J-1)+K                                            STIFF 50
         35 A(KJ,1)=A(KJ,1)+SP(MSPR,K)                              STIFF 51
         36 CONTINUE                                                STIFF 52
      C                                                             STIFF 53
      C        3. STORE EQUATION BLOCK ON TAPE                      STIFF 54
      C                                                             STIFF 55
         37 JF=3*NBN+1                                              STIFF 56
            JL=JF+NN-1                                              STIFF 57
            WRITE (2) (BCF(J),J=JF,JL),((A(K,M),M=1,MBAND),K=1,NN)  STIFF 58
            IF(NB.EQ.NUMBLK) GO TO 60                               STIFF 59
      C                                                             STIFF 60
      C        4. SHIFT TERMS CONTRIBUTING TO NEXT BLOCK.           STIFF 61
      C                                                             STIFF 62
            DO 40 K=1,NN                                            STIFF 63
            KK=K+NN                                                 STIFF 64
            DO 40 M=1,MBAND                                         STIFF 65
            A(K,M)=A(KK,M)                                          STIFF 66
         40 A(KK,M)=0.0                                             STIFF 67
         50 CONTINUE                                                STIFF 68
      C                                                             STIFF 69
         60 RETURN                                                  STIFF 70
            END                                                     STIFF 71
            SUBROUTINE BANSOL                                       BANSL  1
            COMMON                                                  BANSL  2
           1        MM,NN,NUMBLK,NPSTP(1000),SP(40,3),RE(3000),     BANSL  3
           2        B(150),A(150,75)                                BANSL  4
      C                                                             BANSL  5
            NL=NN+1                                                 BANSL  6
            NH=NN+NN                                                BANSL  7
            NB=0                                                    BANSL  8
            GO TO 150                                               BANSL  9
      C***************************************************************BANSL 10
      C    REDUCE EQUATIONS BY BLOCKS                               BANSL 11
      C***************************************************************BANSL 12
      C                                                             BANSL 13
      C    1. SHIFT BLOCK OF EQUATIONS                              BANSL 14
      C                                                             BANSL 15
        100 NB=NB+1                                                 BANSL 16
            DO 125 N=1,NN                                           BANSL 17
            NM=NN+N                                                 BANSL 18
            B(N)=B(NM)                                              BANSL 19
            B(NM)=0.0                                               BANSL 20
            DO 125 M=1,MM                                           BANSL 21
            A(N,M)=A(NM,M)                                          BANSL 22
        125 A(NM,M)=0.0                                             BANSL 23
      C                                                             BANSL 24
      C    2. READ NEXT BLOCK OF EQUATIONS INTO CORE                BANSL 25
      C                                                             BANSL 26
            IF (NUMBLK-NB) 150,200,150                              BANSL 27
        150 READ (2) (B(N),N=NL,NH),((A(N,M),M=1,MM),N=NL,NH)       BANSL 28
            IF (NB) 200,100,200                                     BANSL 29
      C                                                             BANSL 30
      C    3. REDUCE BLOCK OF EQUATIONS                             BANSL 31
      C                                                             BANSL 32
        200 DO 300 N=1,NN                                           BANSL 33
            IF (A(N,1)) 225,300,225                                 BANSL 34
        225 B(N)=B(N)/A(N,1)                                        BANSL 35
            DO 275 L=2,MM                                           BANSL 36
            IF (A(N,L)) 230,275,230                                 BANSL 37
        230 C=A(N,L)/A(N,1)                                         BANSL 38
            I=N+L-1                                                 BANSL 39
            J=0                                                     BANSL 40
            DO 250 K=L,MM                                           BANSL 41
            J=J+1                                                   BANSL 42
        250 A(I,J)=A(I,J)-C*A(N,K)                                  BANSL 43
            B(I)=B(I)-A(N,L)*B(N)                                   BANSL 44
            A(N,L)=C                                                BANSL 45
        275 CONTINUE                                                BANSL 46
        300 CONTINUE                                                BANSL 47
      C                                                             BANSL 48
      C    4. WRITE BLOCK OF REDUCED EQUATIONS ON TAPE 1            BANSL 49
      C                                                             BANSL 50
            IF (NUMBLK-NB) 375,400,375                              BANSL 51
        375 WRITE (1) (B(N),(A(N,M),M=2,MM),N=1,NN)                 BANSL 52
            GO TO 100                                               BANSL 53
```

```
C**********************************************************************BANSL 54
C      BACK-SUBSTITUTION                                               BANSL 55
C**********************************************************************BANSL 56
  400 DO 450 M=1,NN                                                    BANSL 57
      N=NN+1-M                                                         BANSL 58
      DO 425 K=2,MM                                                    BANSL 59
      L=N+K-1                                                          BANSL 60
  425 B(N)=B(N)-A(N,K)*B(L)                                            BANSL 61
      NM=N+NN                                                          BANSL 62
      B(NM)=B(N)                                                       BANSL 63
  450 A(NM,NB)=B(N)                                                    BANSL 64
      NB=NB-1                                                          BANSL 65
      IF (NB) 475,500,475                                              BANSL 66
  475 BACKSPACE 1                                                      BANSL 67
      READ (1) (B(N),(A(N,M),M=2,MM),N=1,NN)                           BANSL 68
      BACKSPACE 1                                                      BANSL 69
      GO TO 400                                                        BANSL 70
C**********************************************************************BANSL 71
C      ORDER UNKNOWNS IN B ARRAY                                       BANSL 72
C**********************************************************************BANSL 73
  500 K=0                                                              BANSL 74
      DO 600 NB=1,NUMBLK                                               BANSL 75
      DO 600 N=1,NN                                                    BANSL 76
      NM=N+NN                                                          BANSL 77
      K=K+1                                                            BANSL 78
  600 B(K)=A(NM,NB)                                                    BANSL 79
C                                                                      BANSL 80
      RETURN                                                           BANSL 81
      END                                                              BANSL 82
      SUBROUTINE FORCE                                                 FORCE  1
      COMMON / PARAM /                                                 FORCE  2
     1      HED(13),NUMEL,NUMNP,NEQ,NUMSPR                             FORCE  3
      COMMON / ELEARG /                                                FORCE  4
     1      SF(6),LM(6),        SA(6,6),ASA(6,6),T(3,3),               FORCE  5
     2      NBLK,NEL,NI,NJ,                                            FORCE  6
     3      S(6,6),RF(6),SPF(3)                                        FORCE  7
      COMMON                                                           FORCE  8
     1      MM,NN,NUMBLK,NPSTP(1000),SP(40,3),RE(3000),                FORCE  9
     2      B(150),A(150,75)                                           FORCE 10
C                                                                      FORCE 11
C      INITIALIZATION                                                  FORCE 12
C                                                                      FORCE 13
      DO 10 N=1,NEQ                                                    FORCE 14
   10 RE(N)=0.0                                                        FORCE 15
C                                                                      FORCE 16
C      PRINT DISPLACEMENTS                                             FORCE 17
C                                                                      FORCE 18
      WRITE (6,8000)                                                   FORCE 19
      WRITE (6,8001) (M,B(3*M-2),B(3*M-1),B(3*M),M=1,NUMNP)            FORCE 20
C                                                                      FORCE 21
C      DETERMINE ELASTIC FOUNDATION REACTIONS, PRINT AND STORE         FORCE 22
C      CONTRIBUTION TO APPLIED JOINT LOADS IN RE(NEQ)                  FORCE 23
C                                                                      FORCE 24
      IF(NUMSPR .EQ. 0) GO TO 3                                        FORCE 25
      WRITE (6,8006)                                                   FORCE 26
      DO 2 N=1,NUMNP                                                   FORCE 27
      MSPR=NPSTP(N)                                                    FORCE 28
      IF(MSPR .EQ. 0) GO TO 2                                          FORCE 29
      DO 1 K=1,3                                                       FORCE 30
      KK=3*(N-1)+K                                                     FORCE 31
      SPF(K)=-SP(MSPR,K)*B(KK)                                         FORCE 32
    1 RE(KK)=RE(KK)-SPF(K)                                             FORCE 33
      WRITE (6,8005) N,(SPF(K),K=1,3)                                  FORCE 34
    2 CONTINUE                                                         FORCE 35
    3 CONTINUE                                                         FORCE 36
C                                                                      FORCE 37
C      DETERMINE MEMBER END FORCES AND PRINT                           FORCE 38
C                                                                      FORCE 39
      WRITE (6,8002)                                                   FORCE 40
      DO 30 N=1,NUMEL                                                  FORCE 41
      READ  (1) (SF(I),I=1,97)                                         FORCE 42
      DO 25 I=1,6                                                      FORCE 43
      RF(I)=0.0                                                        FORCE 44
      DO 20 J=1,6                                                      FORCE 45
      JJ=LM(J)                                                         FORCE 46
   20 RF(I)=RF(I)+SA(I,J)*B(JJ)                                        FORCE 47
```

```
   25 RF(I)=RF(I)+SF(I)                                                     FORCE 48
      WRITE (6,8003) NEL,(RF(I),I=1,6)                                      FORCE 49
C                                                                          FORCE 50
C     OBTAIN CONTRIBUTION OF ELEMENT END FORCES TO APPLIED JOINT LOADS     FORCE 51
C     AND STORE IN RE(NEQ).                                                FORCE 52
C                                                                          FORCE 53
      DO 30 I=1,3                                                          FORCE 54
      II=LM(I)                                                             FORCE 55
      III=LM(I+3)                                                          FORCE 56
      DO 30 J=1,3                                                          FORCE 57
      RE(II)=RE(II)+T(J,I)*RF(J)                                           FORCE 58
   30 RE(III)=RE(III)+T(J,I)*RF(J+3)                                       FORCE 59
C                                                                          FORCE 60
C     PRINT APPLIED JOINT LOADS                                            FORCE 61
C                                                                          FORCE 62
      WRITE (6,8004)                                                       FORCE 63
      WRITE (6,8005) (M,RE(3*M-2),RE(3*M-1),RE(3*M),M=1,NUMNP)             FORCE 64
C                                                                          FORCE 65
 8000 FORMAT(1H1/                                                          FORCE 66
    1  60H JOINT    X-DISPLACEMENT     Y-DISPLACEMENT        Z-ROTATION )FORCE 67
 8001 FORMAT(1H ,I4,3F18.5)                                                FORCE 68
 8002 FORMAT(1H1/                                                          FORCE 69
    1  60H                                       MEMBER END FORCES    /FORCE 70
    2  56H ELEMENT     AXIAL I     SHEAR I    MOMENT I     AXIAL J        FORCE 71
    3  60H      SHEAR J    MOMENT J                                   )FORCE 72
 8003 FORMAT(1H ,I5,2X,6F12.3)                                             FORCE 73
 8004 FORMAT(1H1/                                                          FORCE 74
    1  60H               APPLIED JOINT LOADS AND REACTIONS         /FORCE 75
    2  60H NODE         FORCE X        FORCE Y        MOMENT Z      )FORCE 76
 8005 FORMAT(1H ,I5,3F15.3)                                                FORCE 77
 8006 FORMAT(1H1/                                                          FORCE 78
    1  60H                 ELASTIC FOUNDATION REACTIONS            /FORCE 79
    2  60H NODE         FORCE X        FORCE Y        MOMENT Z      )FORCE 80
      RETURN                                                               FORCE 81
      END                                                                  FORCE 82
```

Appendix B

Selected AISC Specification Design Formulas (Part I)—For Prismatic Members

SECTION 1.5 ALLOWABLE STRESSES

Except as provided in Sects. 1.6, 1.7, 1.10, 1.11, 1.16.4, and in Part 2, all components of the structure shall be so proportioned that the stress, in kips per square inch, shall not exceed the following values, except as rounded off in Appendix A. See Appendix D for allowable stresses for web-tapered members.

1.5.1 Structural Steel

1.5.1.1 Tension

Except for pin-connected members, F_t shall not exceed $0.60F_y$ on the gross area nor $0.50F_u$ on the effective net area.

For pin-connected members: $F_t = 0.45F_y$ on the net area.

For tension on threaded parts: See Table 1.5.2.1

1.5.1.2 Shear

1.5.1.2.1 Except as provided in Sects. 1.5.1.2.2 and 1.10.5.2, on the cross-sectional area effective in resisting shear:

$$F_v = 0.40F_y$$

The effective area in resisting shear of rolled and fabricated shapes may be taken as the overall depth times the web thickness.

1.5.1.2.2 At beam end connections where the top flange is coped, and in similar situations where failure might occur by shear along a plane through the fasteners, or by a combination of shear along a plane through the fasteners plus tension along a perpendicular plane, on the area effective in resisting tearing failure:

$$F_v = 0.30 F_u$$

The effective area is the minimum net failure surface, bounded by the bolt holes.

1.5.1.3 Compression

1.5.1.3.1 On the gross section of axially loaded compression members whose cross sections meet the provisions of Sect. 1.9, when Kl/r, the largest effective slenderness ratio of any unbraced segment as defined in Sect. 1.8, is less than C_c:

$$F_a = \frac{\left[1 - \frac{(Kl/r)^2}{2C_c^2} \right] F_y}{\frac{5}{3} + \frac{3(Kl/r)}{8C_c} - \frac{(Kl/r)^3}{8C_c^3}} \qquad (1.5\text{-}1)$$

where

$$C_c = \sqrt{\frac{2\pi^2 E}{F_y}}$$

1.5.1.3.2 On the gross section of axially loaded compression members, when Kl/r exceeds C_c:

$$F_a = \frac{12\pi^2 E}{23(Kl/r)^2} \qquad (1.5\text{-}2)$$

1.5.1.4 Bending

1.5.1.4.1 Tension and compression on extreme fibers of compact hot-rolled or built-up members (except hybrid girders and members of A514 steel) symmetrical about, and loaded in, the plane of their minor axis and meeting the requirements of this section:

$$F_b = 0.66 F_y$$

In order to qualify under this section, a member must meet the following requirements:

1. The flanges shall be continuously connected to the web or webs.
2. The width-thickness ratio of unstiffened projecting elements of the compression flange, as defined in Sect. 1.9.1.1, shall not exceed $65/\sqrt{F_y}$.
3. The width-thickness ratio of stiffened elements of the compression flange, as defined in Sect. 1.9.2.1, shall not exceed $190/\sqrt{F_y}$.
4. The depth-thickness ratio of the web or webs shall not exceed the value given by Formula (1.5-4a) or (1.5-4b), as applicable.

The Design of Single Story Rigid Frames

TABLE 3-50

ALLOWABLE STRESS

FOR COMPRESSION MEMBERS OF 50 KSI SPECIFIED YIELD STRESS STEEL

Main and Secondary Members Kl/r not over 120						Main Members[b] Kl/r 121 to 200				Secondary Members[a,b] l/r 121 to 200			
$\dfrac{Kl}{r}$	F_a (ksi)	$\dfrac{Kl}{r}$	F_a (ksi)	$\dfrac{Kl}{r}$	F_a (ksi)	$\dfrac{Kl}{r}$	F_a (ksi)	$\dfrac{Kl}{r}$	F_a (ksi)	$\dfrac{l}{r}$	F_{as} (ksi)	$\dfrac{l}{r}$	F_{as} (ksi)
1	29.94	41	25.69	81	18.81	121	10.20	161	5.76	121	10.25	161	7.25
2	29.87	42	25.55	82	18.61	122	10.03	162	5.69	122	10.13	162	7.20
3	29.80	43	25.40	83	18.41	123	9.87	163	5.62	123	10.02	163	7.16
4	29.73	44	25.26	84	18.20	124	9.71	164	5.55	124	9.91	164	7.12
5	29.66	45	25.11	85	17.99	125	9.56	165	5.49	125	9.80	165	7.08
6	29.58	46	24.96	86	17.79	126	9.41	166	5.42	126	9.70	166	7.04
7	29.50	47	24.81	87	17.58	127	9.26	167	5.35	127	9.59	167	7.00
8	29.42	48	24.66	88	17.37	128	9.11	168	5.29	128	9.49	168	6.96
9	29.34	49	24.51	89	17.15	129	8.97	169	5.23	129	9.40	169	6.93
10	29.26	50	24.35	90	16.94	130	8.84	170	5.17	130	9.30	170	6.89
11	29.17	51	24.19	91	16.72	131	8.70	171	5.11	131	9.21	171	6.85
12	29.08	52	24.04	92	16.50	132	8.57	172	5.05	132	9.12	172	6.82
13	28.99	53	23.88	93	16.29	133	8.44	173	4.99	133	9.03	173	6.79
14	28.90	54	23.72	94	16.06	134	8.32	174	4.93	134	8.94	174	6.76
15	28.80	55	23.55	95	15.84	135	8.19	175	4.88	135	8.86	175	6.73
16	28.71	56	23.39	96	15.62	136	8.07	176	4.82	136	8.78	176	6.70
17	28.61	57	23.22	97	15.39	137	7.96	177	4.77	137	8.70	177	6.67
18	28.51	58	23.06	98	15.17	138	7.84	178	4.71	138	8.62	178	6.64
19	28.40	59	22.89	99	14.94	139	7.73	179	4.66	139	8.54	179	6.61
20	28.30	60	22.72	100	14.71	140	7.62	180	4.61	140	8.47	180	6.58
21	28.19	61	22.55	101	14.47	141	7.51	181	4.56	141	8.39	181	6.56
22	28.08	62	22.37	102	14.24	142	7.41	182	4.51	142	8.32	182	6.53
23	27.97	63	22.20	103	14.00	143	7.30	183	4.46	143	8.25	183	6.51
24	27.86	64	22.02	104	13.77	144	7.20	184	4.41	144	8.18	184	6.49
25	27.75	65	21.85	105	13.53	145	7.10	185	4.36	145	8.12	185	6.46
26	27.63	66	21.67	106	13.29	146	7.01	186	4.32	146	8.05	186	6.44
27	27.52	67	21.49	107	13.04	147	6.91	187	4.27	147	7.99	187	6.42
28	27.40	68	21.31	108	12.80	148	6.82	188	4.23	148	7.93	188	6.40
29	27.28	69	21.12	109	12.57	149	6.73	189	4.18	149	7.87	189	6.38
30	27.15	70	20.94	110	12.34	150	6.64	190	4.14	150	7.81	190	6.36
31	27.03	71	20.75	111	12.12	151	6.55	191	4.09	151	7.75	191	6.35
32	26.90	72	20.56	112	11.90	152	6.46	192	4.05	152	7.69	192	6.33
33	26.77	73	20.38	113	11.69	153	6.38	193	4.01	153	7.64	193	6.31
34	26.64	74	20.19	114	11.49	154	6.30	194	3.97	154	7.59	194	6.30
35	26.51	75	19.99	115	11.29	155	6.22	195	3.93	155	7.53	195	6.28
36	26.38	76	19.80	116	11.10	156	6.14	196	3.89	156	7.48	196	6.27
37	26.25	77	19.61	117	10.91	157	6.06	197	3.85	157	7.43	197	6.26
38	26.11	78	19.41	118	10.72	158	5.98	198	3.81	158	7.39	198	6.24
39	25.97	79	19.21	119	10.55	159	5.91	199	3.77	159	7.34	199	6.23
40	25.83	80	19.01	120	10.37	160	5.83	200	3.73	160	7.29	200	6.22

[a] K taken as 1.0 for secondary members.

[b] Values also applicable for steel of any yield stress ≥ 39 ksi.

Note: $C_c = 107.0$

$$d/t = \frac{640}{\sqrt{F_y}} \left(1 - 3.74 \frac{f_a}{F_y} \right) \qquad \text{when } f_a/F_y \leq 0.16 \qquad (1.5\text{-}4\text{a})$$

$$d/t = 257/\sqrt{F_y} \qquad \text{when } f_a/F_y > 0.16 \qquad (1.5\text{-}4\text{b})$$

5. The laterally unsupported length of the compression flange of members other than circular or box members shall not exceed the value

$$\frac{76b_f}{\sqrt{F_y}} \qquad \text{nor} \qquad \frac{20,000}{(d/A_f)F_y}$$

6. The laterally unsupported length of the compression flange of a box-shaped member of rectangular cross section whose depth is not more than 6 times the width and whose flange thickness is not more than 2 times the web thickness shall not exceed the value

$$\left(1950 + 1200 \frac{M_1}{M_2} \right) \frac{b}{F_y}$$

except that it need not be less than $1200(b/F_y)$.

7. The diameter-thickness ratio of hollow circular sections shall not exceed $3300/F_y$.

Except for hybrid girders and members of A514 steel, beams and girders (including members designed on the basis of composite action) which meet the requirements of subparagraphs 1 through 7, above, and are continuous over supports or are rigidly framed to columns by means of rivets, high-strength bolts, or welds, may be proportioned for $9/10$ of the negative moments produced by gravity loading which are maximum at points of support, provided that, for such members, the maximum positive moment shall be increased by $1/10$ of the average negative moments. This reduction shall not apply to moments produced by loading on cantilevers. If the negative moment is resisted by a column rigidly framed to the beam or girder, the $1/10$ reduction may be used in proportioning the column for the combined axial and bending loading, provided that the stress, f_a, due to any concurrent axial load on the member, does not exceed $0.15F_a$.

1.5.1.4.2 Members (except hybrid girders and members of A514 steel) which meet the requirements of Sect. 1.5.1.4.1, except that $b_f/2t_f$ exceeds $65/\sqrt{F_y}$ but is less than $95/\sqrt{F_y}$, may be designed on the basis of an allowable bending stress

$$F_b = F_y \left[0.79 - 0.002 \left(\frac{b_f}{2t_f} \right) \sqrt{F_y} \right] \qquad (1.5\text{-}5\text{a})$$

1.5.1.4.3 Tension and compression on extreme fibers of doubly-symmetrical I- and H-shape members meeting the requirements of Sect. 1.5.1.4.1, subparagraphs 1 and 2, and bent about their minor axis (except members of A514 steel);

solid round and square bars;   solid rectangular sections bent about their weaker axis:

$$F_b = 0.75F_y$$

Doubly-symmetrical I- and H-shape members bent about their minor axis (except hybrid girders and members of A514 steel) meeting the requirements of Sect. 1.5.1.4.1, subparagraph 1, except where $b_f/2t_f$ exceeds $65/\sqrt{F_y}$ but is less than $95/\sqrt{F_y}$, may be designed on the basis of an allowable bending stress

$$F_b = F_y \left[1.075 - 0.005 \left(\frac{b_f}{2t_f} \right) \sqrt{F_y} \right] \qquad (1.5\text{-}5b)$$

Rectangular tubular sections meeting the requirements of Sect. 1.5.1.4.1, subparagraphs 1, 3, and 4, and bent about their minor axis, may be designed on the basis of an allowable bending stress

$$F_b = 0.66F_y$$

1.5.1.4.4   Tension and compression on extreme fibers of box-type flexural members whose compression flange or web width-thickness ratio does not meet the requirements of Sect. 1.5.1.4.1, but does conform to the requirements of Sect. 1.9:

$$F_b = 0.60F_y$$

Lateral torsional buckling need not be investigated for a box section whose depth is less than 6 times its width.   Lateral support requirements for box sections of larger depth-to-width ratios must be determined by special analysis.

1.5.1.4.5   On extreme fibers of flexural members not covered in Sect. 1.5.1.4.1, 1.5.1.4.2, 1.5.1.4.3, or 1.5.1.4.4:

1. Tension:

$$F_b = 0.60F_y$$

2. Compression:

    a. For members meeting the requirements of Sect. 1.9.1.2, having an axis of symmetry in, and loaded in, the plane of their web, and compression on extreme fibers of channels bent about their major axis:

    The larger value computed by Formulas (1.5-6a) or (1.5-6b) and

(1.5-7), as applicable* (unless a higher value can be justified on the basis of a more precise analysis**), but not more than $0.60F_y$.[†]

When $\sqrt{\dfrac{102 \times 10^3 C_b}{F_y}} \le \dfrac{l}{r_T} \le \sqrt{\dfrac{510 \times 10^3 C_b}{F_y}}$:

$$F_b = \left[\frac{2}{3} - \frac{F_y (l/r_T)^2}{1530 \times 10^3 C_b} \right] F_y \qquad (1.5\text{-}6a)$$

When $l/r_T \ge \sqrt{\dfrac{510 \times 10^3 C_b}{F_y}}$:

$$F_b = \frac{170 \times 10^3 C_b}{(l/r_T)^2} \qquad (1.5\text{-}6b)$$

Or, when the compression flange is solid and approximately rectangular in cross section and its area is not less than that of the tension flange:

$$F_b = \frac{12 \times 10^3 C_b}{ld/A_f} \qquad (1.5\text{-}7)$$

In the foregoing,

l = distance between cross sections braced against twist or lateral displacement of the compression flange, inches. For cantilevers braced against twist only at the support, l may conservatively be taken as the actual length.

r_T = radius of gyration of a section comprising the compression flange plus $\frac{1}{3}$ of the compression web area, taken about an axis in the plane of the web, inches

A_f = area of the compression flange, square inches

C_b = $1.75 + 1.05\,(M_1/M_2) + 0.3\,(M_1/M_2)^2$, but not more than 2.3, where M_1 is the smaller and M_2 the larger bending moment at the ends of the unbraced length, taken about the strong axis of the member, and where M_1/M_2, the ratio of end moments, is positive when M_1 and M_2 have the same sign (reverse curvature bending) and negative when they are of opposite signs (single curvature bending). When the bending moment at any point within an unbraced length is larger than that at both ends of this length, the value of C_b shall be taken as unity. When computing F_{bx} and F_{by} to be used in Formula (1.6-1a), C_b may be

---

* Only Formula (1.5-7) applicable to channels.
** See Commentary Sect. 1.5.1.4.5 for alternate procedures.
† See Sect. 1.10 for further limitations in plate girder flange stress.

computed by the formula given above for frames subject to joint translation, and it shall be taken as unity for frames braced against joint translation. C_b may conservatively be taken as unity for cantilever beams.

For hybrid plate girders, F_y for Formulas (1.5-6a) and (1.5-6b) is the yield stress of the compression flange. Formula (1.5-7) shall not apply to hybrid girders.

b. For members meeting the requirements of Sect. 1.9.1.2, but not included in subparagraph 2a of this Section:

$$F_b = 0.60F_y$$

provided that sections bent about their major axis are braced laterally in the region of compression stress at intervals not exceeding $76b_f/\sqrt{F_y}$.

• *Commentary on the AISC Specification (11/1/78)*

1.5.1.4.5 The allowable bending stress for all other flexural members is given as $0.60F_y$, provided the member is braced laterally at relatively close intervals $(l/b_f \leq 76/\sqrt{F_y})$.

Members bent about their major axis and having an axis of symmetry in the plane of loading may be adequately braced laterally at greater intervals if the maximum bending stress is reduced sufficiently to prevent premature buckling of the compression flange. Mathematical expressions affording an exact estimate of the buckling strength of such members, which take into account their torsional rigidity about their longitudinal axis (St. Venant torsion) as well as the bending stiffness of their compression flange between points of lateral support (warping torsion), are too complex for general design office use. Furthermore, their accuracy is dependent upon the validity of assumptions regarding restraint at points of lateral support and conditions of loading which, at best, can be no more than engineering judgments.

The combination of Formulas (1.5-6a) or (1.5-6b) and (1.5-7) provides a reasonable design criterion in convenient form. Formulas (1.5-6a) and (1.5-6b) are based on the assumption that only the bending stiffness of the compression flange will prevent the lateral displacement of that element between bracing points.

Formula (1.5-7) is a convenient approximation which assumes the presence of both lateral bending resistance and St. Venant torsional resistance. Its agreement with more exact expressions for the buckling strength of intermittently braced flexural members is closest for homogeneous sections having substantial resistance to St. Venant torsion, identifiable in the case of doubly-symmetrical sections by a relatively low d/A_f ratio. Due to the difference between flange and web yield strength of a hybrid girder, it is desirable to base the lateral buckling resistance solely on warping torsion of the flange.   Hence, use of Formula (1.5-7) is not permitted for such members.

For some sections having a compression flange area distinctly smaller than the tension flange area, Formula (1.5-7) may be unconservative; for this reason, its use is limited to sections whose compression flange area is at least as great as the tension flange.   In plate girders, which usually have a much higher d/A_f ratio than rolled W shapes, Formula (1.5-7) may err grossly on the conservative side. For such members, the larger stress permitted by Formula (1.5-6a), and at times by Formula (1.5-6b), affords the better estimate of buckling strength.   While these latter formulas underestimate the buckling strength somewhat because they ignore the St. Venant torsional rigidity of the profile, this rigidity for such sections is relatively small and the margin of overconservatism, therefore, is likewise small.

It should be noted that Formula (1.5-7) is written for the case of elastic buckling.   A transition is not provided for this formula in the inelastic stress range because, when actual conditions of load application and variation in bending moment are considered, any unconservative error without the transition must be small.

Singly-symmetrical, built-up, I-shape members, such as some crane girders, often have an increased compression flange area in order to resist bending due to lateral loading acting in conjunction with the vertical loads.   Such members usually can be proportioned for the full permissible bending stress when the stress is produced by the combined vertical and horizontal loading.   Where the failure mode of a singly-symmetrical I-shape member having a larger compression than tension flange would be by lateral buckling, the permissible bending stress can be obtained by using Formula (1.5-6a) or (1.5-7).

Through the introduction of the modifier C_b, some liberalization in stress is permissible when there is moment gradient over the unbraced length, except that C_b must be taken as unity when computing F_{bx} for use in Formula (1.6-1a) for frames braced against joint translation.

Formulas (1.5-6a) and (1.5-6b) may be refined to include both St. Venant and warping torsion by substituting a derived value for r_T.   The equivalent radius of gyration, r_{Tequiv} , can be obtained by equating the appropriate expression giving the critical elastic bending stress for the compression flange of a beam with that of an axially loaded column.

For the case of a doubly-symmetrical I-shape beam,

$$(r_{Tequiv})^2 \;=\; \frac{I_y}{2S_x} \sqrt{d^2 + \frac{0.156 l^2 J}{I_y}}$$

where I_y is the minor axis moment of inertia of the member, S_x is its major axis section modulus, and

$$J \;=\; \frac{2b_f t_f^3}{3} + \frac{dt^3}{3}$$

1.5.6   Wind and Seismic Stresses

Allowable stresses may be increased $\frac{1}{3}$ above the values otherwise provided when produced by wind or seismic loading, acting alone or in combination with the design dead and live loads, provided the required section computed on this basis is not less than that required for the design dead and live load and impact (if any), computed without the $\frac{1}{3}$ stress increase, and further provided that stresses are not otherwise required to be calculated on the basis of reduction factors applied to design loads in combinations.   The above stress increase does not apply to allowable stress ranges provided in Appendix B of the AISC specifications.

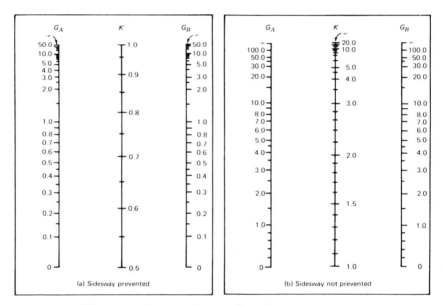

Figure B-1   Effective length factors for centrally loaded columns.

SECTION 1.6   COMBINED STRESSES

1.6.1   Axial Compression and Bending

Members subjected to both axial compression and bending stresses shall be proportioned to satisfy the following requirements:

$$\frac{f_a}{F_a} + \frac{C_{mx}f_{bx}}{\left(1 - \dfrac{f_a}{F'_{ex}}\right) F_{bx}} + \frac{C_{my}f_{by}}{\left(1 - \dfrac{f_a}{F'_{ey}}\right) F_{by}} \leq 1.0 \qquad (1.6\text{-}1a)$$

$$\frac{f_a}{0.60F_y} + \frac{f_{bx}}{F_{bx}} + \frac{f_{by}}{F_{by}} \leq 1.0 \qquad (1.6\text{-}1b)$$

When $f_a/F_a \leq 0.15$, Formula (1.6-2) may be used in lieu of Formulas (1.6-1a) and (1.6-1b):

$$\frac{f_a}{F_a} + \frac{f_{bx}}{F_{bx}} + \frac{f_{by}}{F_{by}} \leq 1.0 \qquad (1.6\text{-}2)$$

In Formulas (1.6-1a), (1.6-1b), and (1.6-2), the subscripts x and y, combined with subscripts b, m, and e, indicate the axis of bending about which a particular stress or design property applies, and

F_a = axial compressive stress that would be permitted if axial force alone existed, kips per square inch

F_b = compressive bending stress that would be permitted if bending moment alone existed, kips per square inch

$$F'_e = \frac{12\,\pi^2 E}{23(Kl_b/r_b)^2}$$

= Euler stress divided by a factor of safety, kips per square inch. (In the expression for F'_e, l_b is the actual unbraced length *in the plane of bending* and r_b is the corresponding radius of gyration. K is the effective length factor *in the plane of bending*. As in the case of F_a, F_b, and $0.60F_y$, F'_e may be increased $\frac{1}{3}$ in accordance with Sect. 1.5.6)

f_a = computed axial stress, kips per square inch

f_b = computed compressive bending stress at the point under consideration, kips per square inch

C_m = a coefficient whose value shall be taken as follows:

1. For compression members in frames subject to joint translation (sidesway), $C_m = 0.85$.

2. For restrained compression members in frames braced against joint translation and not subject to transverse loading between their supports in the plane of bending,

$$C_m = 0.6 - 0.4\frac{M_1}{M_2}, \quad \text{but not less than } 0.4$$

where M_1/M_2 is the ratio of the smaller to larger moments at the ends of that portion of the member unbraced in the plane of bending under consideration. M_1/M_2 is positive when the member is bent in reverse curvature, negative when bent in single curvature.

3. For compression members in frames braced against joint translation in the plane of loading and subjected to transverse loading between their supports, the value of C_m may be determined by rational analysis. However, in lieu of such analysis, the following values may be used:

   a. For members whose ends are restrained . . . $C_m = 0.85$
   b. For members whose ends are unrestrained . . $C_m = 1.0$

TABLE 9

VALUES OF F'_e

For Use in Formula (1.6-1a), Sect. 1.6.1, for Steel of Any Yield Stress

$\frac{Kl_b}{r_b}$	F'_e (ksi)	$\frac{Kl_b}{r_b}$	F'_e (ksi)	$\frac{Kl_b}{r_b}$	F'_e (ksi)	$\frac{Kl_b}{r_b}$	F'_e (ksi)	$\frac{Kl_b}{r_b}$	F'_e (ksi)	$\frac{Kl_b}{r_b}$	F'_e (ksi)
21	338.62	51	57.41	81	22.76	111	12.12	141	7.51	171	5.11
22	308.54	52	55.23	82	22.21	112	11.90	142	7.41	172	5.05
23	282.29	53	53.16	83	21.68	113	11.69	143	7.30	173	4.99
24	259.26	54	51.21	84	21.16	114	11.49	144	7.20	174	4.93
25	238.93	55	49.37	85	20.67	115	11.29	145	7.10	175	4.88
26	220.90	56	47.62	86	20.19	116	11.10	146	7.01	176	4.82
27	204.84	57	45.96	87	19.73	117	10.91	147	6.91	177	4.77
28	190.47	58	44.39	88	19.28	118	10.72	148	6.82	178	4.71
29	177.56	59	42.90	89	18.85	119	10.55	149	6.73	179	4.66
30	165.92	60	41.48	90	18.44	120	10.37	150	6.64	180	4.61
31	155.39	61	40.13	91	18.03	121	10.20	151	6.55	181	4.56
32	145.83	62	38.85	92	17.64	122	10.03	152	6.46	182	4.51
33	137.13	63	37.62	93	17.27	123	9.87	153	6.38	183	4.46
34	129.18	64	36.46	94	16.90	124	9.71	154	6.30	184	4.41
35	121.90	65	35.34	95	16.55	125	9.56	155	6.22	185	4.36
36	115.22	66	34.28	96	16.20	126	9.41	156	6.14	186	4.32
37	109.08	67	33.27	97	15.87	127	9.26	157	6.06	187	4.27
38	103.42	68	32.29	98	15.55	128	9.11	158	5.98	188	4.23
39	98.18	69	31.37	99	15.24	129	8.97	159	5.91	189	4.18
40	93.33	70	30.48	100	14.93	130	8.84	160	5.83	190	4.14
41	88.83	71	29.62	101	14.64	131	8.70	161	5.76	191	4.09
42	84.65	72	28.81	102	14.35	132	8.57	162	5.69	192	4.05
43	80.76	73	28.02	103	14.08	133	8.44	163	5.62	193	4.01
44	77.13	74	27.27	104	13.81	134	8.32	164	5.55	194	3.97
45	73.74	75	26.55	105	13.54	135	8.19	165	5.49	195	3.93
46	70.57	76	25.85	106	13.29	136	8.07	166	5.42	196	3.89
47	67.60	77	25.19	107	13.04	137	7.96	167	5.35	197	3.85
48	64.81	78	24.54	108	12.80	138	7.84	168	5.29	198	3.81
49	62.20	79	23.93	109	12.57	139	7.73	169	5.23	199	3.77
50	59.73	80	23.33	110	12.34	140	7.62	170	5.17	200	3.73

Note: $F'_e = \dfrac{12\pi^2 E}{23(Kl_b/r_b)^2}$ (1.6-1a)

All grades of steel

SECTION 1.9 WIDTH-THICKNESS RATIOS

1.9.1 Unstiffened Elements Under Compression

1.9.1.1 Unstiffened (projecting) compression elements are those having one free edge parallel to the direction of compression stress. The width of unstiffened plates shall be taken from the free edge to the first row of fasteners or welds; the width of legs of angles, channel and zee flanges, and stems of tees shall be taken as the full nominal dimension; the width of flanges of I- and H-shape members and tees shall be taken as $\frac{1}{2}$ the full nominal width. The thickness of a sloping flange shall be measured at a section half-way between a free edge and the corresponding face of the web.

1.9.1.2 Unstiffened elements subject to axial compression or compression due to bending shall be considered as fully effective when the ratio of width to thickness is not greater than the following:

Single-angle struts; double-angle struts with separators . . . $76/\sqrt{F_y}$

Struts comprising double angles in contact; angles or plates
   projecting from girders, columns, or other compression
   members; compression flanges of beams; stiffeners on
   plate girders . . . . $95/\sqrt{F_y}$

Stems of tees . . . . $127/\sqrt{F_y}$

When the actual width-to-thickness ratio exceeds these values, the design stress shall be governed by the provisions of Appendix C.

1.9.2   Stiffened Elements Under Compression

1.9.2.1   Stiffened compression elements are those having lateral support along both edges that are parallel to the direction of the compression stress. The width of such elements shall be taken as the distance between nearest lines of fasteners or welds, or between the roots of the flanges in the case of rolled sections.

1.9.2.2   Stiffened elements subject to axial compression, or to uniform compression due to bending as in the case of the flange of a flexural member, shall be considered as fully effective when the ratio of width to thickness is not greater than the following:

Flanges of square and rectangular box sections of
   uniform thickness . . . . $238/\sqrt{F_y}$

Unsupported width of cover plates perforated with
   a succession of access holes . . . . $317/\sqrt{F_y}$

All other uniformly compressed stiffened elements . . . . . . $253/\sqrt{F_y}$

Except in the case of perforated cover plates, when the actual width-to-thickness ratio exceeds these values the design shall be governed by the provisions of Appendix C.

1.9.2.3   Circular tubular elements subject to axial compression shall be considered as fully effective when the ratio of the outside diameter to the wall thickness is not greater than $3300/F_y$. For diameter-to-thickness ratios greater than $3300/F_y$ but less than $13,000/F_y$, see Appendix C.

1.10.5   Stiffeners

1.10.5.1   Bearing stiffeners shall be placed in pairs at unframed ends on the webs of plate girders and, where required, at points of concentrated loads. Such stiffeners shall have a close bearing against the flange, or flanges, through which they receive their loads or reactions, and shall extend approximately to the edge of the flange plates or flange angles. They shall be designed as columns subject to the provisions of Sect. 1.5.1, assuming the column section to comprise the pair of stiffeners and a centrally located strip of the web whose width is equal to not more than 25 times its thickness at interior stiffeners or not more than 12 times its thickness when the stiffeners are located at the end of the web. The effective length shall be taken as not less than ¾ of the length of the stiffeners in computing the ratio l/r. Only that portion of the stiffener outside of the flange angle fillet or the flange-to-web welds shall be considered effective in bearing.

1.10.5.2 Except as hereinafter provided, the largest average web shear, f_v, in kips per square inch, computed for any condition of complete or partial loading, shall not exceed the value given by Formula (1.10-1).

$$F_v = \frac{F_y}{2.89}(C_v) \le 0.40F_y \qquad (1.10\text{-}1)$$

where

$$C_v = \frac{45,000k}{F_y(h/t)^2} \quad \text{when } C_v \text{ is less than } 0.8$$

$$= \frac{190}{h/t}\sqrt{\frac{k}{F_y}} \quad \text{when } C_v \text{ is more than } 0.8$$

$$k = 4.00 + \frac{5.34}{(a/h)^2} \quad \text{when } a/h \text{ is less than } 1.0$$

$$= 5.34 + \frac{4.00}{(a/h)^2} \quad \text{when } a/h \text{ is more than } 1.0$$

t = thickness of web, inches
a = clear distance between transverse stiffeners, inches
h = clear distance between flanges at the section under investigation, inches

Alternatively, for girders other than hybrid girders, if intermediate stiffeners are provided and spaced to satisfy the provisions of Sect. 1.10.5.3 and if $C_v \le 1$, the allowable shear given by Formula (1.10-2) may be used in lieu of the value given by Formula (1.10-1).

$$F_v = \frac{F_y}{2.89}\left[C_v + \frac{1 - C_v}{1.15\sqrt{1 + (a/h)^2}}\right] \le 0.40F_y \qquad (1.10\text{-}2)$$

1.10.5.3 Subject to the limitations of Sect. 1.10.2, intermediate stiffeners are not required when the ratio h/t is less than 260 and the maximum web shear stress, f_v, is less than that permitted by Formula (1.10-1).

The spacing of intermediate stiffeners, where stiffeners are required, shall be such that the web shear stress will not exceed the value for F_v given by Formula

TABLE 10-50

ALLOWABLE SHEAR STRESS (KSI) IN WEBS OF PLATE GIRDERS BY FORMULA (1.10-1)

For 50 ksi Yield Stress Steel, Tension Field Action Not Included

h/t	Aspect Ratios a/h: Stiffener Spacing to Web Depth													
	0.5	0.6	0.7	0.8	0.9	1.0	1.2	1.4	1.6	1.8	2.0	2.5	3.0	over 3.0
60							20.0	20.0	20.0	19.9	19.5	18.9	18.6	17.9
70					20.0	20.0	18.9	18.0	17.4	17.0	16.7	16.2	16.0	15.3
80			20.0	20.0	18.9	17.8	16.6	15.8	15.3	14.9	14.6	14.2	14.0	13.0
90			19.9	18.1	16.8	15.8	14.7	14.0	13.3	12.6	12.2	11.5	11.1	10.3
100		20.0	17.9	16.3	15.1	14.2	12.6	11.5	10.7	10.2	9.9	9.3	9.0	8.3
110	20.0	18.3	16.3	14.8	13.6	12.0	10.4	9.5	8.9	8.5	8.2	7.7	7.4	6.9
120	19.5	16.8	15.0	13.3	11.5	10.1	8.8	8.0	7.5	7.1	6.9	6.5	6.3	5.8
130	18.0	15.5	13.7	11.4	9.8	8.6	7.5	6.8	6.4	6.1	5.8	5.5	5.3	4.9
140	16.7	14.4	11.8	9.8	8.4	7.4	6.4	5.9	5.5	5.2	5.0	4.8	4.6	4.2
150	15.6	13.0	10.3	8.5	7.3	6.5	5.6	5.1	4.8	4.5	4.4	4.1	4.0	3.7
160	14.6	11.5	9.1	7.5	6.4	5.7	4.9	4.5	4.2	4.0	3.9	3.6	3.5	3.2
170	13.7	10.1	8.0	6.7	5.7	5.0	4.4	4.0	3.7	3.5	3.4	3.2	3.1	2.9
180	12.2	9.1	7.2	5.9	5.1	4.5	3.9	3.5	3.3	3.2	3.0	2.9	2.8	2.6
200	9.9	7.3	5.8	4.8	4.1	3.6	3.2	2.9	2.7	2.6	2.5	2.3	2.3	2.1
220	8.2	6.1	4.8	4.0	3.4	3.0	2.6	2.4	2.2	2.1	2.0	1.9	1.9	1.7
240	6.9	5.1	4.0	3.3	2.9	2.5	2.2	2.0	1.9	1.8	1.7	1.6	1.6	1.4
260	5.8	4.3	3.4	2.8	2.4	2.2								
280	5.0	3.7	3.0	2.5										

(Left axis label: Web Depth to Web Thickness — Slenderness Ratios h/t:)

(1.10-1) or (1.10-2), as applicable, and the ratio a/h shall not exceed $[260/(h/t)]^2$ nor 3.0.

In girders designed on the basis of tension field action, the spacing between stiffeners at end panels, at panels containing large holes, and at panels adjacent to panels containing large holes shall be such that f_v does not exceed the value given by Formula (1.10-1).

1.10.6   Reduction in Flange Stress

When the web depth-to-thickness ratio exceeds $760/\sqrt{F_b}$, the maximum bending stress in the compression flange shall not exceed

$$F'_b \le F_b \left[1.0 - 0.0005 \frac{A_w}{A_f} \left(\frac{h}{t} - \frac{760}{\sqrt{F_b}} \right) \right] \qquad (1.10\text{-}5)$$

where

F_b = applicable bending stress given in Sect. 1.5.1.4, kips per square inch
A_w = area of web at the section under investigation, square inches
A_f = area of compression flange, square inches

The maximum stress in either flange of a hybrid girder shall not exceed the value given by Formula (1.10-5) nor

$$F'_b \leq F_b \left[\frac{12 + \left(\frac{A_w}{A_f}\right)(3\alpha - \alpha^3)}{12 + 2\left(\frac{A_w}{A_f}\right)} \right] \qquad (1.10\text{-}6)$$

where α = ratio of web yield stress to flange yield stress.

Appendix C

Determination of End Restraints for Tapered and Prismatic Members in a Rigid Frame

Appendix C: Determination of End Restraints

This Appendix is concerned with rigid frames of the type shown in Fig. C-1. The roof girders are composed of two tapered I-sections, each having a distinct and separate taper ratio:

$$\gamma_1 = \frac{d_1}{d_0} - 1 \quad \text{and} \quad \gamma_2 = \frac{d_2}{d_0} - 1 \tag{C-1}$$

where d_1 and d_2 are the cross-section depths at the left end and the right end, respectively, of the member under consideration. The common point has a depth d_0. (Of course, the element can be reduced to a single-taper segment by letting $\beta = 0$.)

In order to obtain an estimate of the end restraint for either the column

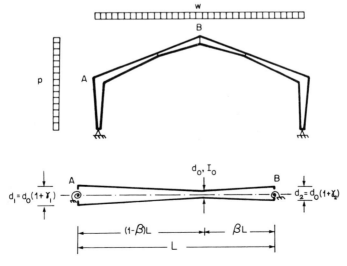

Figure C-1 Typical rigid frame with doubly-tapered rafter.

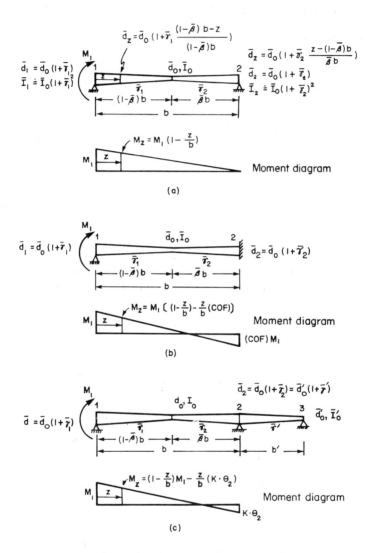

Figure C-2   Tapered members and the corresponding moment diagrams for the determination of the end restraining parameters.

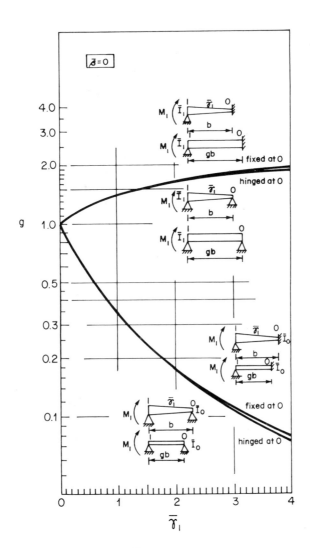

Figure C-3   Equivalent length factor ($\bar{\beta} = 0$).

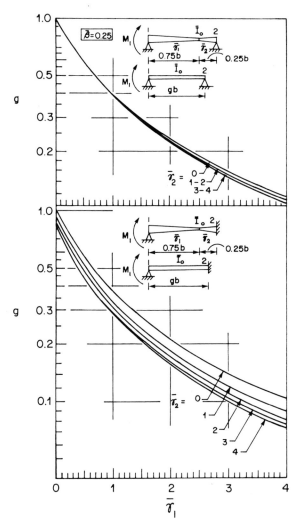

Figure C-4 Equivalent length factor ($\bar{\beta} = 0.25$).

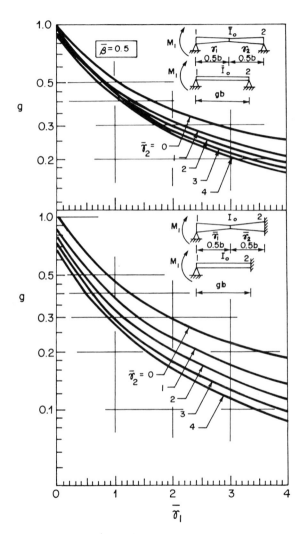

Figure C-5   Equivalent length factor ($\bar{\beta} = 0.5$).

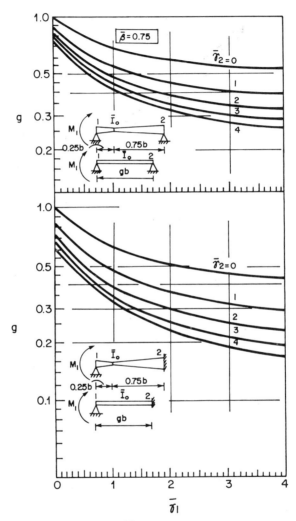

Figure C-6 Equivalent length factor ($\bar{\beta} = 0.75$).

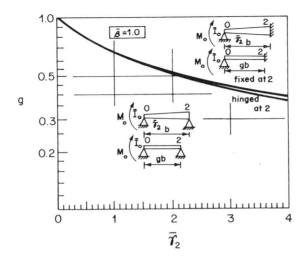

Figure C-7   Equivalent length factor ($\bar{\beta} = 1.0$).

or the roof girder, three separate cases of end-rotational stiffness must be investigated (Ref. [21]).

Case (i)—Fig. C-2(a): The adjacent member is presumed to be simply supported at the far end.

Case (ii)—Fig. C-2(b): The adjacent member is presumed to be fixed at the far end.

Case (iii)—Fig. C-2(c): The adjacent roof girder is connected to a tapered column whose far end is simply supported.

In Ref. [21], it is shown that the difference in equivalent length for either a simply supported or a fixed far end condition is negligibly small. For design purposes, then, the simply supported far end condition for the adjacent member can be presumed.

Figures C-3 through C-7 are equivalent length factors for all adjacent member cases—whether those members are prismatic or tapered. If they are tapered, they can be converted into prismatic members with cross-sectional properties equal to those of the smallest section of the tapered roof girder or tapered column, by using the appropriate length modification factor.

With the help of Figs. C-3 through C-7, the adjacent tapered members, either single or multiply segmented, can be converted into a prismatic member of length "gb". The stiffness of this hypothetical member is $\bar{I}_0/gb$, and may be used to evaluate the end restraining effects on the member in question. If the member is prismatic but connected to tapered adjacent members, $\overline{I_0}/gb$ can be used in the AISC provisions for the design of prismatic members. If the member in question is linearly tapered along its length, but connected to tapered members, $\overline{I_0}/gb$ can be used in conjunction with Appendix D to determine the effective length factor for the tapered member in question. Finally, $\overline{I_0}/gb$ may be used in conjunction with Appendix E for determining the effective length factor for gable roof girders of the type defined in Fig. C-1.

Appendix D

AISC Specifications for Web-Tapered Members

- *AISC Specification (Effective 11/1/78)*

SECTION D1   GENERAL

The design of tapered members meeting the requirements herein shall be governed by the provisions of Part 1, except as modified by this Appendix.

In order to qualify under this Specification, a tapered member must meet the following requirements:

1. It shall possess at least one axis of symmetry which shall be perpendicular to the plane of bending if moments are present.

2. The flanges shall be of equal and constant area.

3. The depth shall vary linearly as

$$d_o \left(1 + \gamma \frac{z}{l} \right)$$

where

d_o = depth at smaller end of member, inches
d_L = depth at larger end of member, inches
γ = $(d_L - d_o)/d_o \leq$ the smaller of $0.268l/d_o$ or 6.0
z = distance from the smaller end of member, inches
l = length of member, inches

SECTION D2   ALLOWABLE STRESSES—COMPRESSION

On the gross section of axially loaded tapered compression members, the axial compressive stress, in kips per square inch, shall not exceed the following:

When the effective slenderness ratio, S is less than C_c:

$$F_{a\gamma} = \frac{\left(1.0 - \frac{S^2}{2C_c{}^2} \right) F_y}{\frac{5}{3} + \frac{3S}{8C_c} - \frac{S^3}{8C_c{}^3}} \qquad (D2\text{-}1)$$

When the effective slenderness ratio, S, exceeds C_c:

$$F_{a\gamma} = \frac{12\pi^2 E}{23S^2} \tag{D2-2}$$

where

S = Kl/r_{oy} for weak axis bending and = $K_\gamma l/r_{ox}$ for strong axis bending
K = effective length factor for a prismatic member
K_γ = effective length factor for a tapered member as determined by a rational analysis*
l = actual unbraced length of member, inches
r_{ox} = strong axis radius of gyration at the smaller end of a tapered member, inches
r_{oy} = weak axis radius of gyration at the smaller end of a tapered member, inches

SECTION D3   ALLOWABLE STRESSES—BENDING**

Tension and compression stresses on extreme fibers of tapered flexural members, in kips per square inch, shall not exceed the following values:

Appendix D—Web-Tapered Members •

$$F_{b\gamma} = \frac{2}{3}\left[1.0 - \frac{F_y}{6B\sqrt{F_{s\gamma}^2 + F_{w\gamma}^2}}\right] F_y \le 0.60F_y \tag{D3-1}$$

unless $F_{b\gamma} \le F_y/3$, in which case

$$F_{b\gamma} = B\sqrt{F_{s\gamma}^2 + F_{w\gamma}^2} \tag{D3-2}$$

In the above Formulas,

$$F_{s\gamma} = \frac{12 \times 10^3}{h_s l d_o / A_f} \quad \text{and} \quad F_{w\gamma} = \frac{170 \times 10^3}{(h_w l / r_{To})^2}$$

where

h_s = factor equal to $1.0 + 0.0230\gamma\sqrt{ld_o/A_f}$
h_w = factor equal to $1.0 + 0.00385\gamma\sqrt{l/r_{To}}$
l = distance between cross sections braced against twist or lateral displacement of the compression flange, inches
r_{To} = radius of gyration of a section at the smaller end, considering only the compression flange plus $\frac{1}{3}$ of the compression web area, taken about an axis in the plane of the web, inches
A_f = area of the compression flange, square inches
γ = tapering ratio, equal to $(d_l - d_o)/d_o$
d_o = depth at smaller end of unbraced segment, inches
d_l = depth at larger end of unbraced segment, inches

---

* See Commentary Sect. D2.
** See Commentary Sect. D3.

and where B is determined as follows:

1. When the maximum moment, M_2, in three adjacent segments of approximately equal unbraced length is located within the central segment and M_1 is the larger moment at one end of the three-segment portion of a member:*

$$B = 1.0 + 0.37 \left[1.0 + \frac{M_1}{M_2} \right] + 0.50\gamma \left[1.0 + \frac{M_1}{M_2} \right] \geq 1.0$$

2. When the largest computed bending stress, f_{b2}, occurs at the larger end of two adjacent segments of approximately equal unbraced lengths and f_{b1} is the computed bending stress at the smaller end of the two-segment portion of a member:**

$$B = 1.0 + 0.58 \left[1.0 + \frac{f_{b1}}{f_{b2}} \right] - 0.70\gamma \left[1.0 + \frac{f_{b1}}{f_{b2}} \right] \geq 1.0$$

3. When the largest computed bending stress, f_{b2}, occurs at the small end of two adjacent segments of approximately equal unbraced length and f_{b1} is the computed bending stress at the larger end of the two-segment portion of a member:**

$$B = 1.0 + 0.55 \left[1.0 + \frac{f_{b1}}{f_{b2}} \right] + 2.2\gamma \left[1.0 + \frac{f_{b1}}{f_{b2}} \right] \geq 1.0$$

In the foregoing, $\gamma = (d_l - d_o)/d_o$, calculated for the unbraced length that contains the maximum computed bending stress.

- *AISC Specification (Effective 11/1/78)*

4. When the computed bending stress at the smaller end of a tapered member or segment thereof is equal to zero:

$$B = \frac{1.75}{1.0 + 0.25\sqrt{\gamma}}$$

where $\gamma = (d_l - d_o)/d_o$, calculated for the unbraced length adjacent to the point of zero bending stress.

SECTION D4   COMBINED STRESSES

Tapered members and unbraced segments thereof subjected to both axial compression and bending stresses shall be proportioned to satisfy the following requirements:

---

* M_1/M_2 is considered as negative when producing single curvature. In the rare case where M_1/M_2 is positive, it is recommended that it be taken as zero.

** f_{b1}/f_{b2} is considered as negative when producing single curvature. If a point of contraflexure occurs in one of two adjacent unbraced segments, f_{b1}/f_{b2} is considered as positive. The ratio $f_{b1}/f_{b2} \neq 0$.

$$\left(\frac{f_{ao}}{F_{a\gamma}}\right) + \frac{C'_m}{\left(1 - \frac{f_{ao}}{F'_{e\gamma}}\right)} \left(\frac{f_{bl}}{F_{b\gamma}}\right) \leq 1.0 \qquad \text{(D4-1a)}$$

and

$$\frac{f_a}{0.6F_y} + \frac{f_b}{F_{b\gamma}} \leq 1.0 \qquad \text{(D4-1b)}$$

When $f_{ao}/F_{a\gamma} \leq 0.15$, Formula (D4-2) may be used in lieu of Formulas (D4-1a) and (D4-1b).

$$\left(\frac{f_{ao}}{F_{a\gamma}}\right) + \left(\frac{f_{bl}}{F_{b\gamma}}\right) \leq 1.0 \qquad \text{(D4-2)}$$

where

$F_{a\gamma}$ = axial compressive stress permitted in the absence of bending moment, kips per square inch

$F_{b\gamma}$ = bending stress permitted in the absence of axial force, kips per square inch

$F'_{e\gamma}$ = Euler stress divided by factor of safety, kips per square inch; equal to

$$\frac{12\pi^2 E}{23(K_\gamma l_b/r_{bo})^2}$$

where l is the actual unbraced length in the plane of bending and r_{bo} is the corresponding radius of gyration at its smaller end

f_{ao} = computed axial stress at the smaller end of the member or unbraced segment thereof, as applicable, kips per square inch

f_{bl} = computed bending stress at the larger end of the member or unbraced segment thereof, as applicable, kips per square inch

C'_m = coefficient applied to bending term in interaction formula

$$= 1.0 + 0.1 \left(\frac{f_{ao}}{F'_{e\gamma}}\right) + 0.3 \left(\frac{f_{ao}}{F'_{e\gamma}}\right)^2$$

when the member is subjected to end moments which cause single curvature bending and approximately equal computed bending stresses at the ends

$$= 1.0 - 0.9 \left(\frac{f_{ao}}{F'_{e\gamma}}\right) + 0.6 \left(\frac{f_{ao}}{F'_{e\gamma}}\right)^2$$

when the computed bending stress at the smaller end of the unbraced length is equal to zero

When $Kl/r \geq C_c$ and combined stresses are checked incrementally along the length, f_{ao} may be replaced by f_a, and f_{bl} may be replaced by f_b, in Formulas (D4-1a) and (D4-2).

• *Commentary on the AISC Specification* (11/1/78)

APPENDIX B—FATIGUE*

---

* See AISC Commentary Sect. 1.7 for discussion of Fatigue Provisions of Appendix B.

APPENDIX C—SLENDER COMPRESSION ELEMENTS*

APPENDIX D—TAPERED MEMBERS

The provisions contained in Appendix D cover only those aspects of the design of tapered members that are unique to tapered members. For other criteria of design not specifically covered in Appendix D, see the appropriate portions of Part 1 of the Specification and Commentary.

SECTION D2 ALLOWABLE STRESSES—COMPRESSION

The approach in formulating $F_{a\gamma}$ of tapered columns is based on the concept that the critical stress for an axially loaded tapered column is equal to that of a prismatic column of different length, but of the same cross section as the smaller end of the tapered column. This has resulted in an equivalent effective length factor K_γ for a tapered member subjected to axial compression.[66] This factor, which is used to determine the value of S in Formulas (D2-1) and (D2-2), can be determined accurately for a symmetrical rectangular rigid frame composed of prismatic beams and tapered columns.

With modifying assumptions, such a frame can be used as a mathematical model to determine, with sufficient accuracy, the influence of the stiffness, $\Sigma(I/b)_R$, of beams and rafters which afford restraint at the ends of a tapered column in other cases, such as those shown in Fig. CD1.5.1. From Formulas (D2-1) and (D2-2), the critical load P_{cr} can be expressed as $\pi^2 EI_o/(K_\gamma l)^2$. The value of K_γ can be obtained by interpolation, using the appropriate chart (Figs. CD1.5.2 to CD1.5.17) and restraint modifiers G_T and G_B. In each of these modifiers the tapered column, treated as a prismatic member having a moment of inertia I_o, computed at the smaller end, and its actual length l, is assigned the stiffness I_o/l, which is then divided by the stiffness of the restraining members at the end of the tapered column under consideration. Such an approach is well documented.

SECTION D3 ALLOWABLE STRESSES—BENDING

The development of the allowable bending stress for tapered beams follows closely with that for prismatic beams. The basic concept is to replace a tapered beam by an equivalent prismatic beam with a different length, but with a cross section identical with that of the smaller end of the tapered beam.[66] This has led to the modified length factors h_s and h_w in Formulas (D3-1) and (D3-2).

Formulas (D3-1) and (D3-2) are based on total resistance to lateral buckling, using both St. Venant and warping resistance. The factor B modifies the basic $F_{b\gamma}$ to account for moment gradient and lateral restraint offered by adjacent segments. For members which are continuous past lateral supports, categories 1, 2, and 3 of Section D3 usually apply; however, it is to be noted that they apply

---

* See AISC Commentary Sect. 1.9 for discussion of Appendix C provisions for Slender Compression Elements.

only when the axial force is small and adjacent unbraced segments are approximately equal in length. For a single member, or segments which do not fall into category 1, 2, 3, or 4, the recommended value for B is unity. The value of B should also be taken as unity when computing the value of $F_{b\gamma}$ to be used in Formula (D4-1a), since the effect of moment gradient is provided for by the factor C_m. The background material is given in WRC Bulletin No. 192.[67]

Thus, it is to be noted that in these charts the values of K_γ represent the combined effects of end restraints and tapering. For the case $\gamma = 0$, K_γ becomes K, which can also be determined from the alignment chart for effective length of columns in continuous frames (Fig. C1.8.2). For cases when the restraining beams are also tapered, the procedure used in WRC Bulletin No. 173[66] can be followed, or appropriate estimation of K_γ can be made based on these charts.

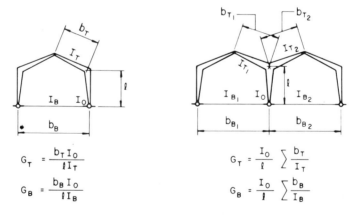

$$G_T = \frac{b_T I_0}{\ell I_T}$$

$$G_B = \frac{b_B I_0}{\ell I_B}$$

$$G_T = \frac{I_0}{\ell} \sum \frac{b_T}{I_T}$$

$$G_B = \frac{I_0}{\ell} \sum \frac{b_B}{I_B}$$

Fig. CD1.5.1

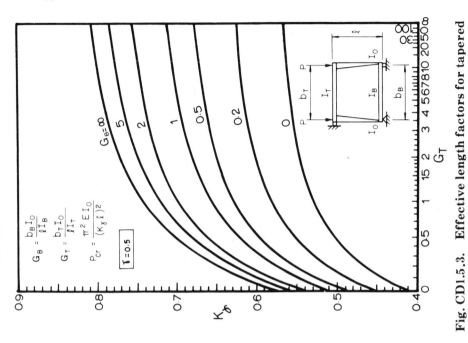

Fig. CD1.5.3. **Effective length factors for tapered columns: sidesway prevented ($\gamma = 0.5$)**

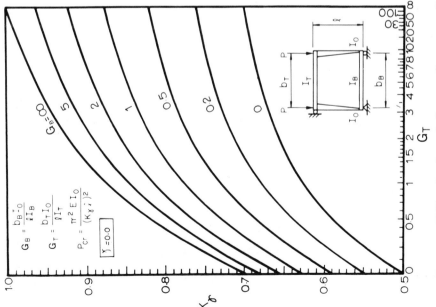

Fig. CD1.5.2. **Effective length factors for tapered columns: sidesway prevented ($\gamma = 0$)**

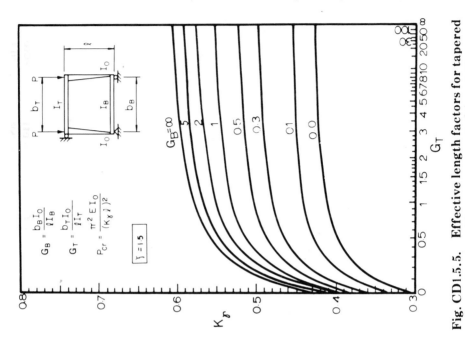

Fig. CD1.5.5. Effective length factors for tapered columns: sidesway prevented ($\gamma = 1.5$)

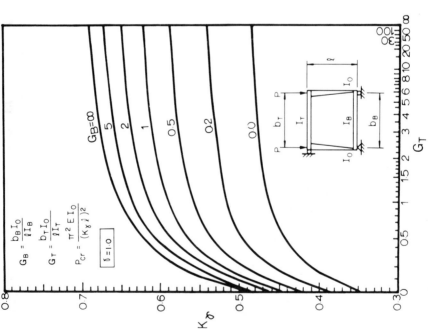

Fig. CD1.5.4. Effective length factors for tapered columns: sidesway prevented ($\gamma = 1.0$)

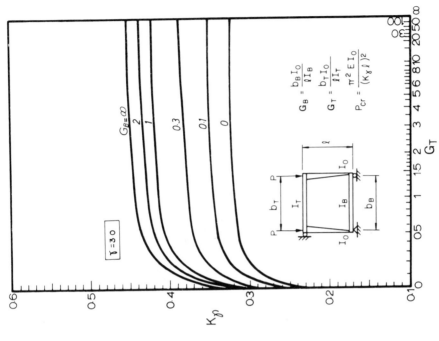

Fig. CD1.5.7. Effective length factors for tapered columns: sidesway prevented ($\gamma = 3.0$)

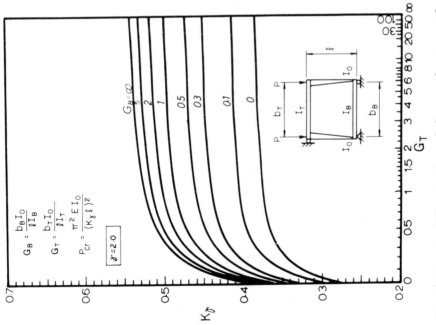

Fig. CD1.5.6. Effective length factors for tapered columns: sidesway prevented ($\gamma = 2.0$)

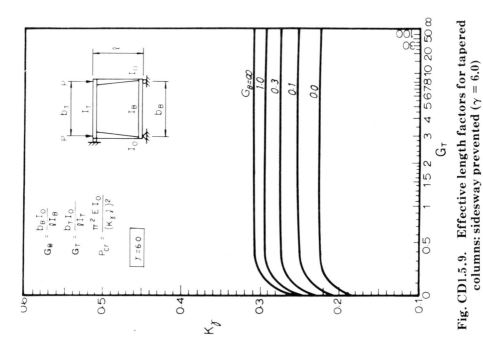

Fig. CD1.5.8. Effective length factors for tapered columns: sidesway prevented ($\gamma = 4.0$)

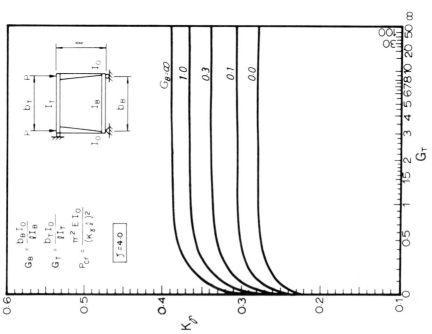

Fig. CD1.5.9. Effective length factors for tapered columns: sidesway prevented ($\gamma = 6.0$)

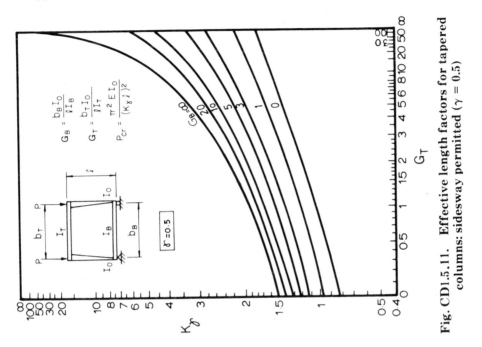

Fig. CD1.5.11. Effective length factors for tapered columns: sidesway permitted ($\gamma = 0.5$)

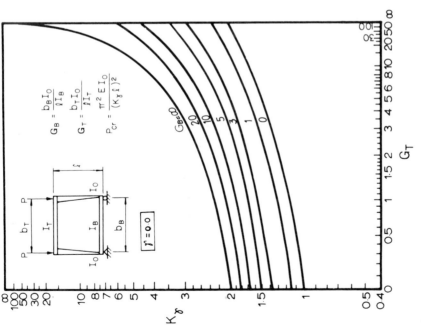

Fig. CD1.5.10. Effective length factors for tapered columns: sidesway permitted ($\gamma = 0$)

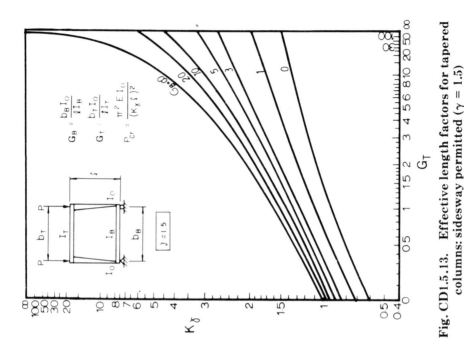

Fig. CD1.5.13. Effective length factors for tapered columns: sidesway permitted ($\gamma = 1.5$)

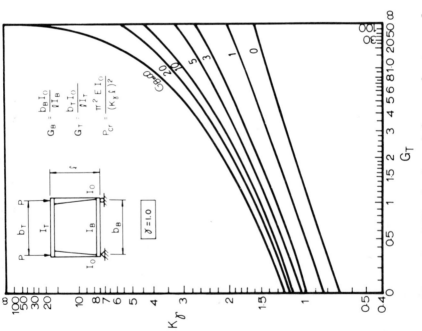

Fig. CD1.5.12. Effective length factors for tapered columns: sidesway permitted ($\gamma = 1.0$)

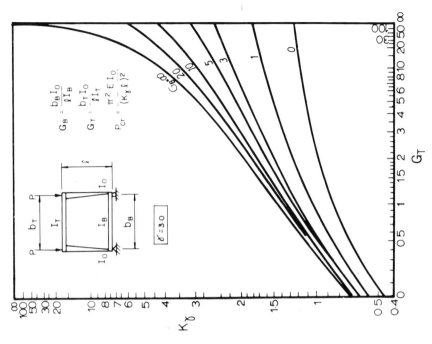

Fig. CD1.5.14. Effective length factors for tapered columns: sidesway permitted ($\gamma = 2.0$)

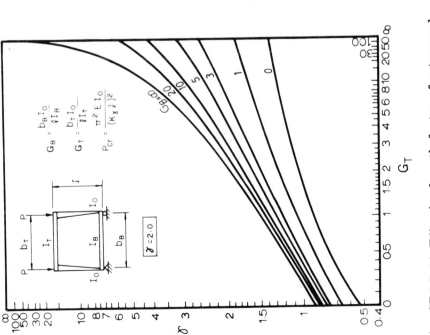

Fig. CD1.5.15. Effective length factors for tapered columns: sidesway permitted ($\gamma = 3.0$)

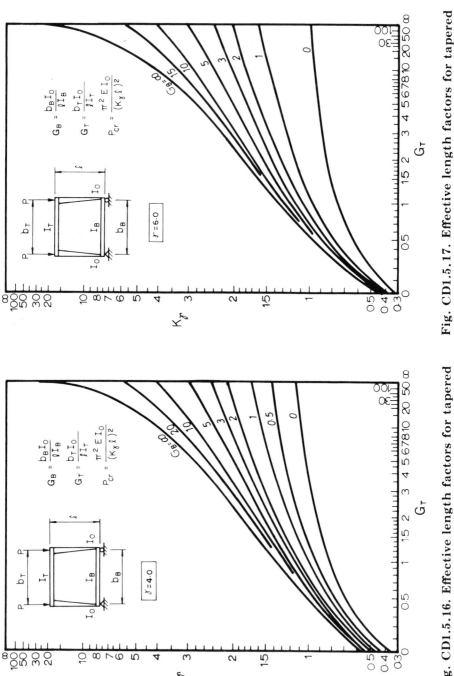

Fig. CD1.5.16. Effective length factors for tapered columns: sidesway permitted ($\gamma = 4.0$)

Fig. CD1.5.17. Effective length factors for tapered columns: sidesway permitted ($\gamma = 6.0$)

Appendix E

Effective Length Factors for Multi-Segment Tapered Members

Appendix E: Effective Length Factors for Multi-Segment Tapered Members

This Appendix contains curves for determining the effective length factor for tapered members of the type and kind defined in Fig. E-1. The curves are functions of the restraints that exist at the ends of the member.*

For the structures shown in Fig. E-2, the rotational stiffness at the top and bottom ends of the columns are as follows:

For sidesway prevented:

$$k_T = 2E \frac{I_T}{b} \tag{E-1}$$

and

$$k_B = 2E \frac{I_B}{b} \tag{E-2}$$

For sidesway permitted:

$$k_T = 6E \frac{I_T}{b} \tag{E-3}$$

and

$$k_B = 6E \frac{I_B}{b} \tag{E-4}$$

The end restraint factors are therefore

$$R_T = \frac{bI_0}{LI_T} = (G_T) \tag{E-5}$$

---

* In this Appendix—to emphasize that these curves are for tapered members—the symbols R_T and R_B are used for end restraints rather than the more normal prismatic member terms G_T and G_B.

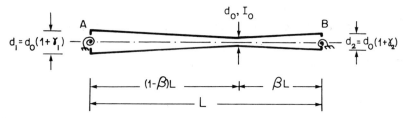

Figure E-1   Doubly-tapered member with end restraints.

$$R_B = \frac{bI_0}{LI_B} = (G_B) \tag{E-6}$$

(Had the top and bottom beams been tapered, the rotational spring constants would be modified using the equivalent length conversion factor given in Appendix C.)

The curves in Appendix E also can be used for tapered member gable frames. In using the equivalent length factors of Appendix C, the following adjustments should be made:

For sidesway prevented:

Equation E-1 becomes $k_1 = 2E \dfrac{\bar{I}_0}{g_e b}$

If the far end of the adjacent member is assumed to be hinged,

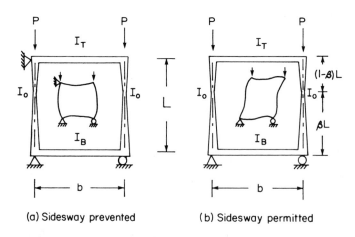

(a) Sidesway prevented   (b) Sidesway permitted

Figure E-2   Models of frame and conditions of restraint considered.

$$k_1 = 3E\frac{\bar{I}_0}{gb}$$

Equating these two yields

$$g_e = 0.67g \qquad (E\text{-}7)$$

If the far end of the adjacent member is presumed to be fixed,

$$k_1 = 4E\frac{\bar{I}_0}{gb}$$

which yields the modified equivalent length factor

$$g_e = 0.50g \qquad (E\text{-}8)$$

For sidesway permitted:

Equation E-3 becomes $k_1 = 6E\dfrac{\bar{I}_0}{g_e b}$

For the far end of the adjacent member hinged,

$$g_e = 2.0g \qquad (E\text{-}9)$$

For the far end fixed,

$$g_e = 1.5g \qquad (E\text{-}10)$$

Equations E-5 and E-6, therefore, may be written in the more general form:

$$R_T = \frac{(g_e b)_T \bar{I}_0}{L I_T} = (G_T) \qquad (E\text{-}11)$$

and

$$R_B = \frac{(g_e b)_B \bar{I}_0}{L I_B} = (G_B) \qquad (E\text{-}12)$$

(It is to be noted that for prismatic adjacent members in rectangular frames $g = g_e = 1.0$.)

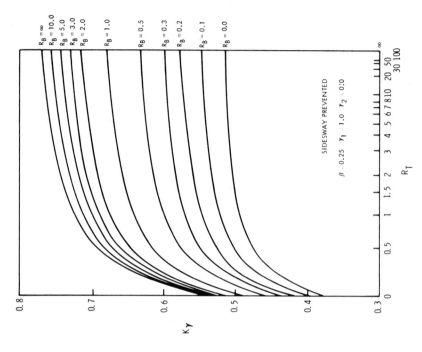

Figure E-3.2

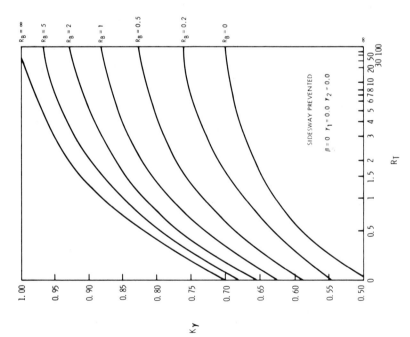

Figure E-3.1

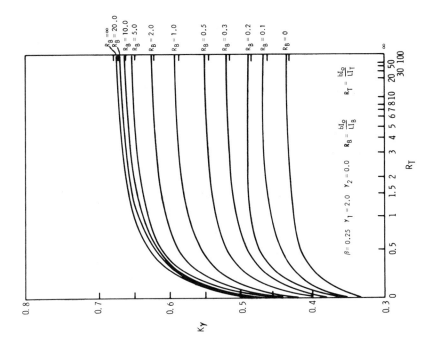

Figure E-3.4

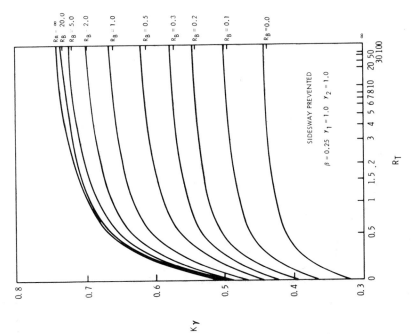

Figure E-3.3

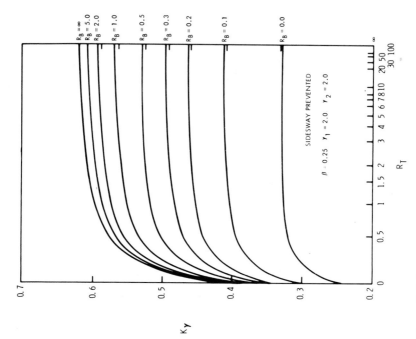

Figure E-3.6

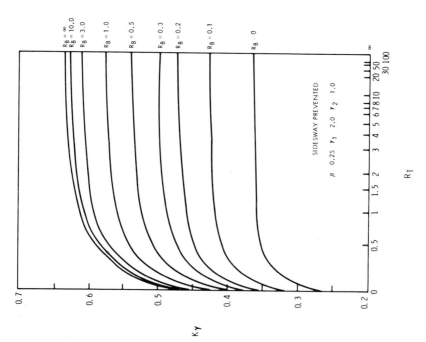

Figure E-3.5

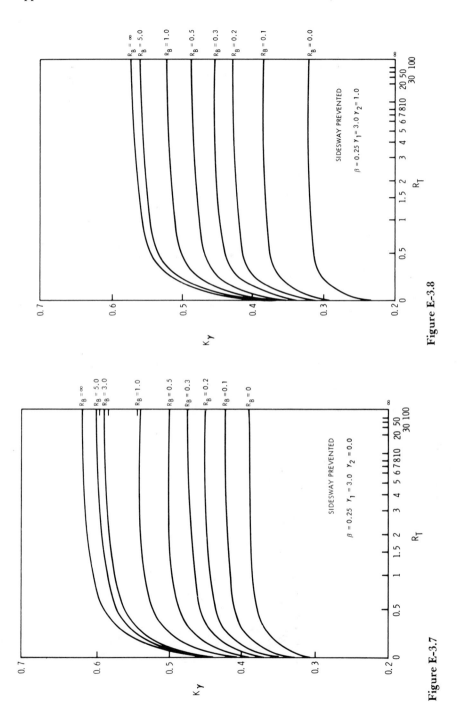

Figure E-3.8

Figure E-3.7

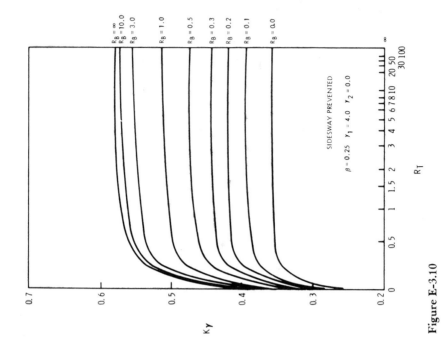

Figure E-3.10

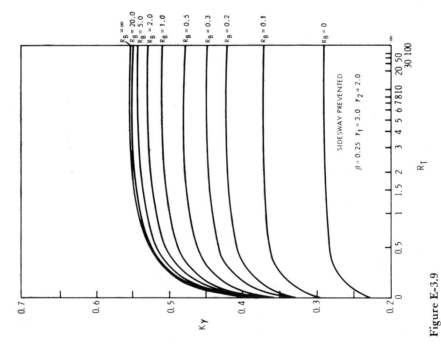

Figure E-3.9

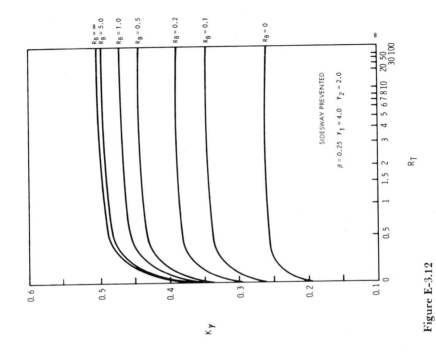

Figure E-3.12

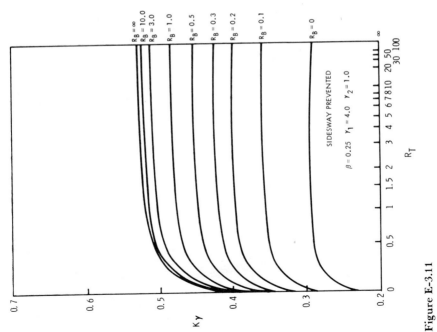

Figure E-3.11

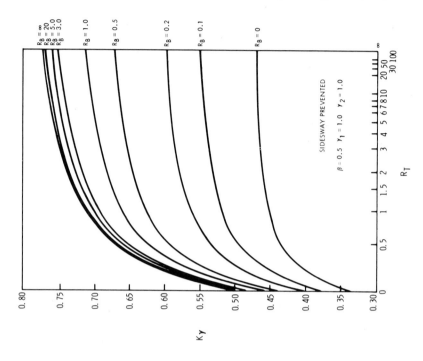

Figure E-3.14

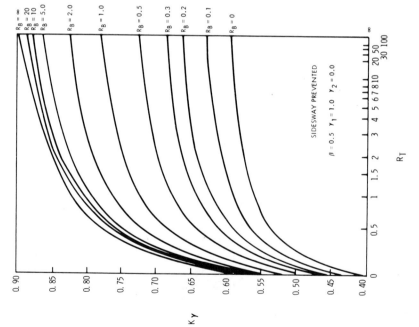

Figure E-3.13

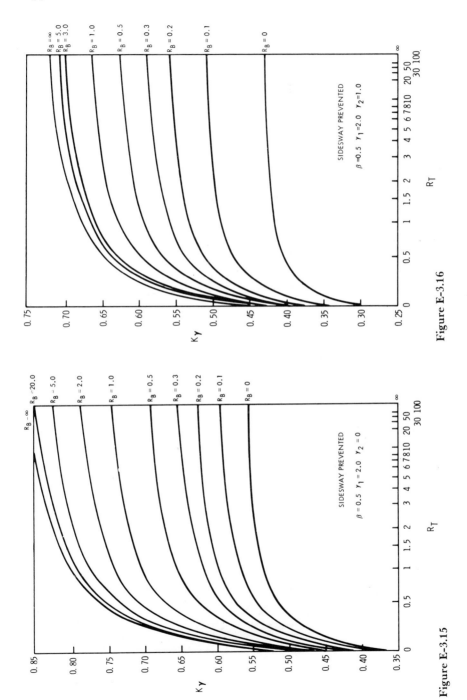

Figure E-3.16

Figure E-3.15

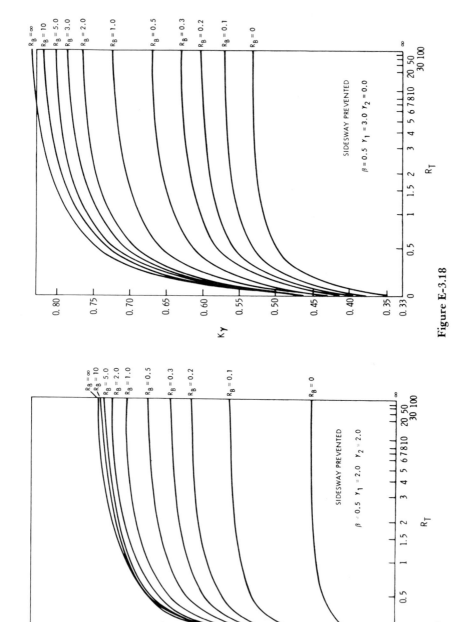

Figure E-3.18

Figure E-3.17

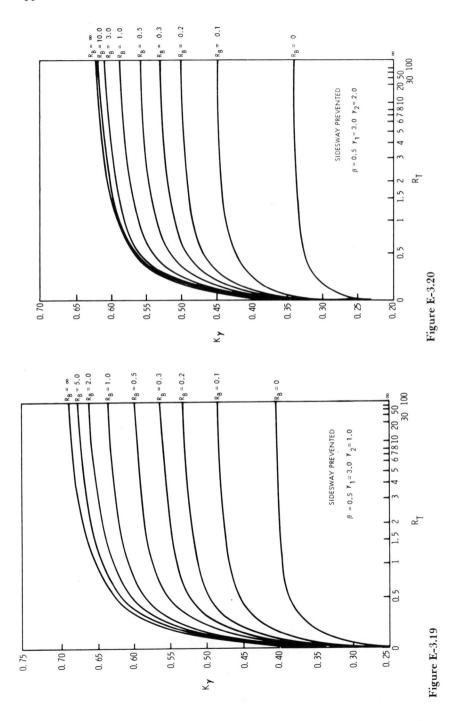

Figure E-3.20

Figure E-3.19

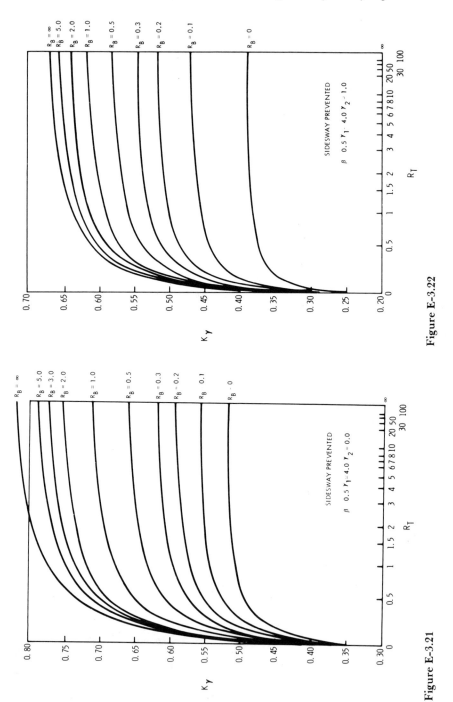

Figure E-3.22

Figure E-3.21

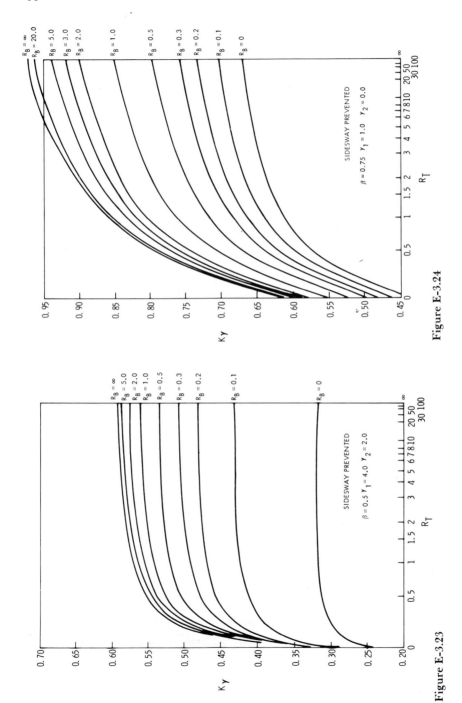

Figure E-3.24

Figure E-3.23

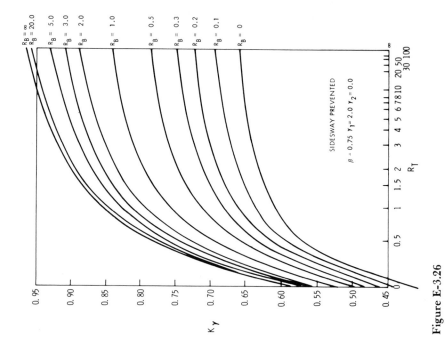

Figure E-3.26

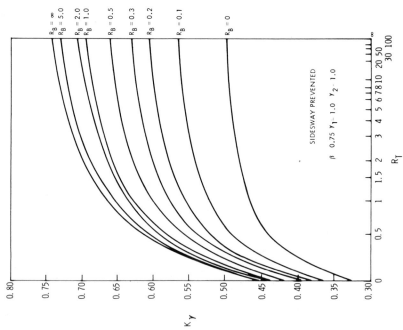

Figure E-3.25

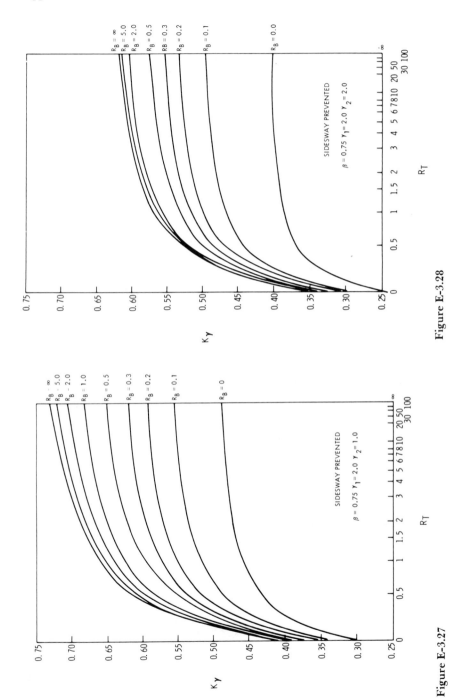

Figure E-3.28

Figure E-3.27

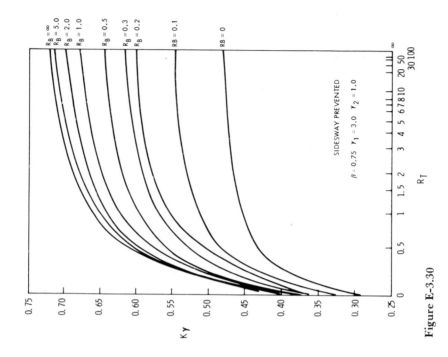

Figure E-3.30

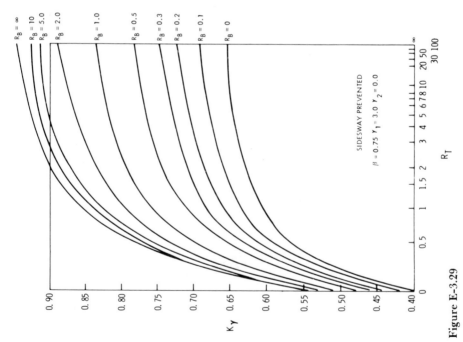

Figure E-3.29

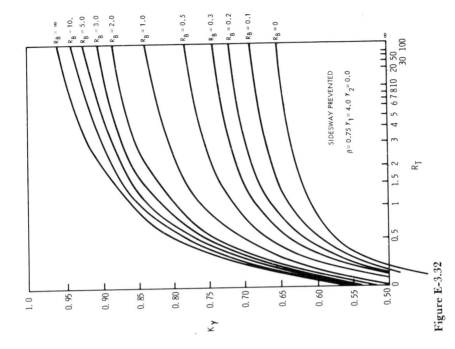

Figure E-3.32

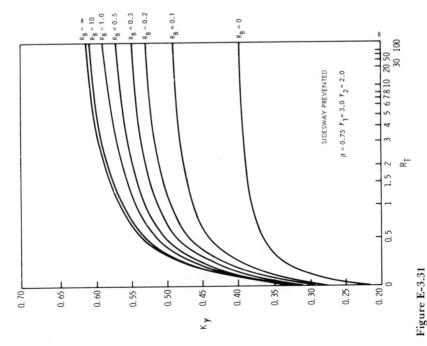

Figure E-3.31

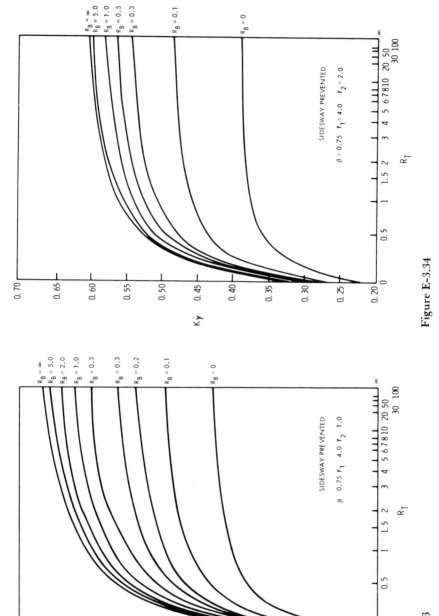

Figure E-3.34

Figure E-3.33

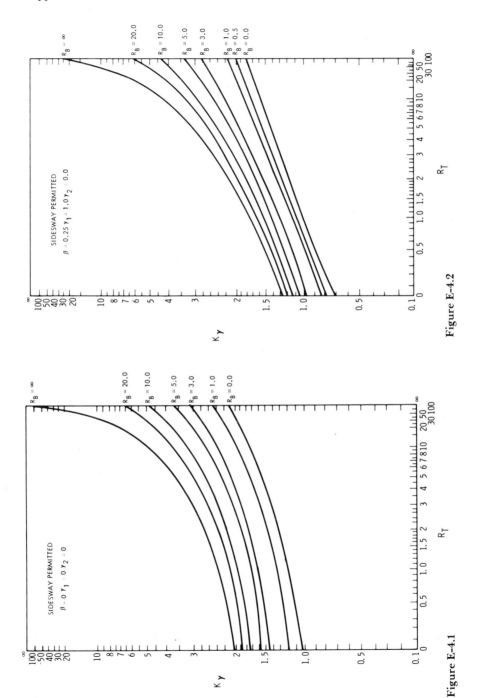

Figure E-4.2

Figure E-4.1

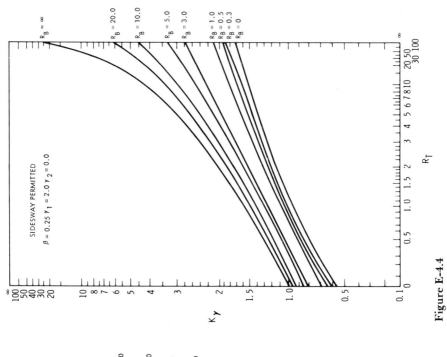

Figure E–4.4

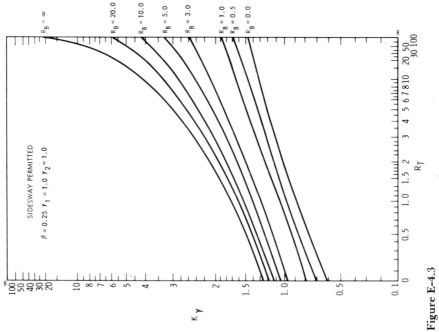

Figure E–4.3

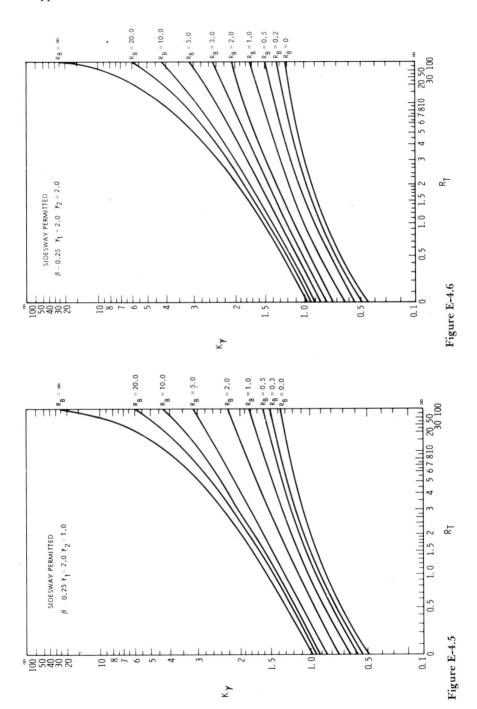

Figure E-4.6

Figure E-4.5

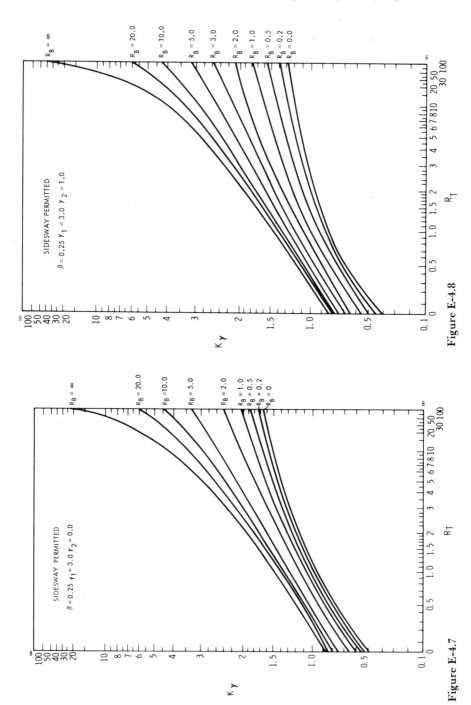

Figure E-4.8

Figure E-4.7

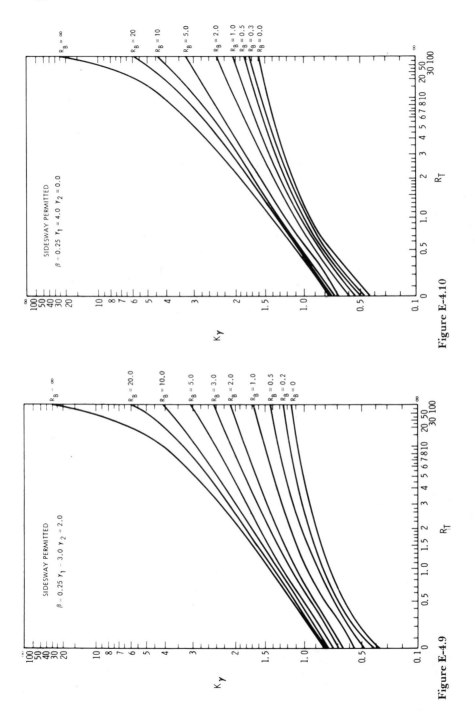

Figure E-4.10

Figure E-4.9

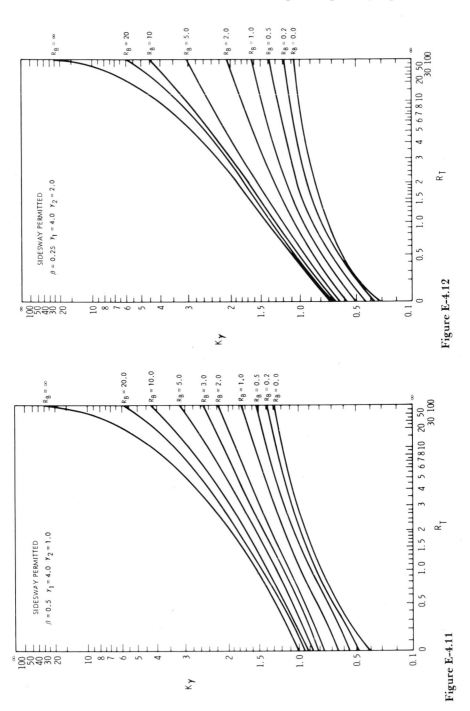

Figure E-4.12

Figure E-4.11

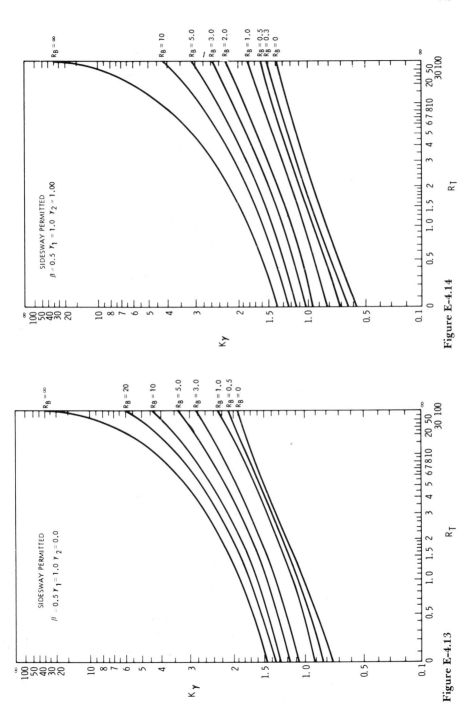

Figure E-4.14

Figure E-4.13

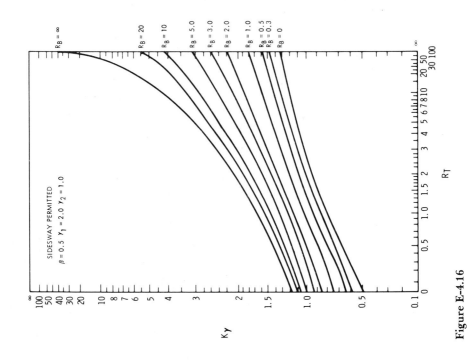

Figure E-4.16

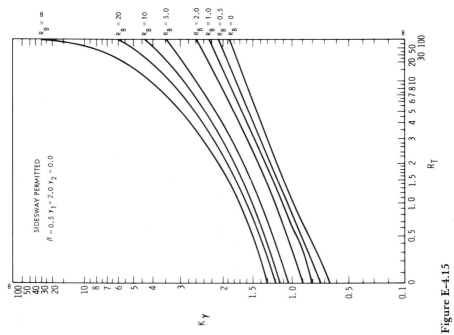

Figure E-4.15

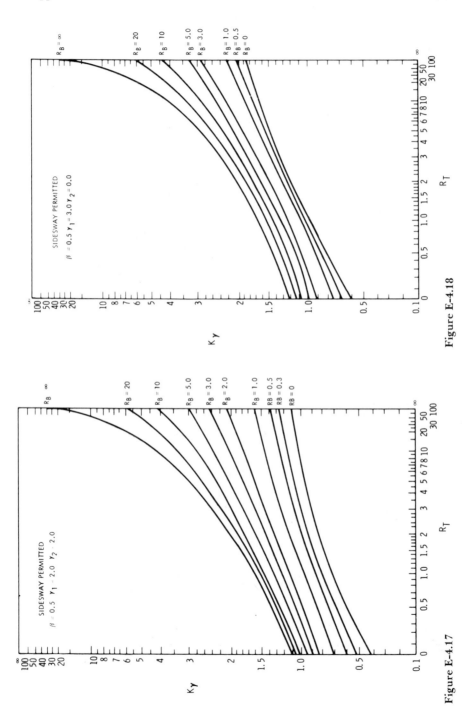

Figure E-4.18

Figure E-4.17

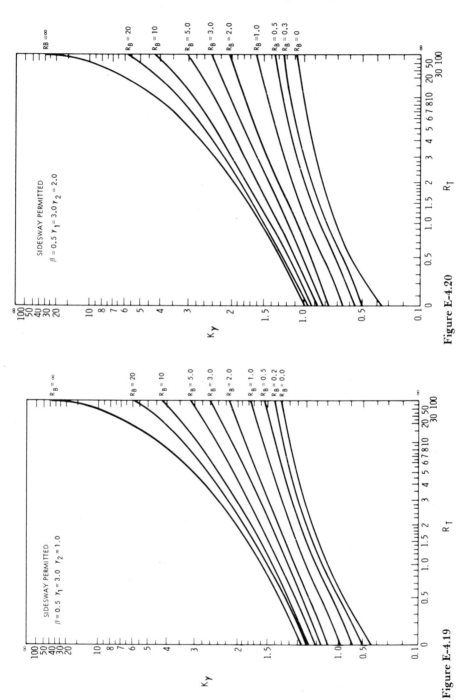

Figure E-4.20

Figure E-4.19

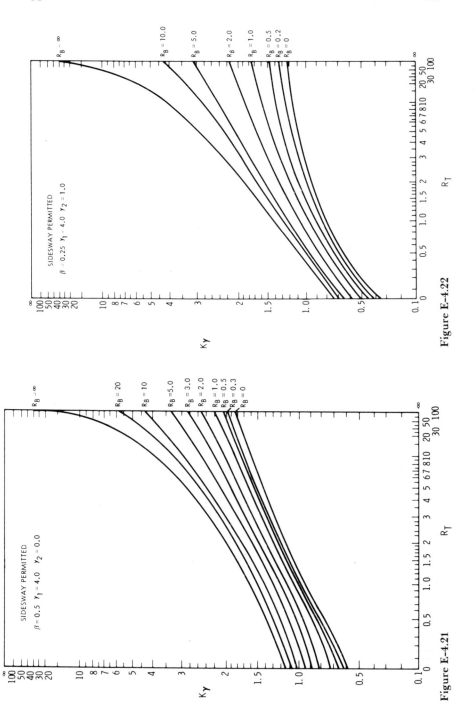

Figure E-4.22

Figure E-4.21

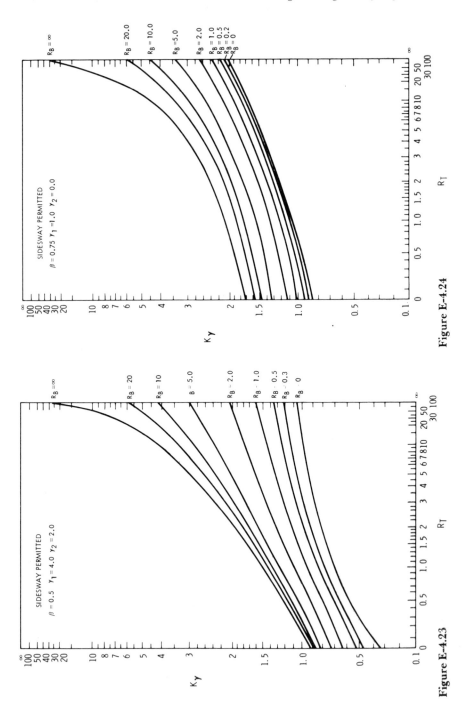

Figure E-4.24

Figure E-4.23

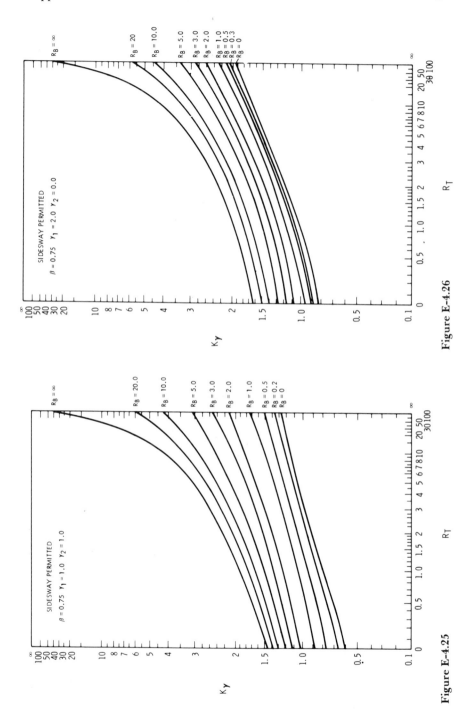

Figure E-4.26

Figure E-4.25

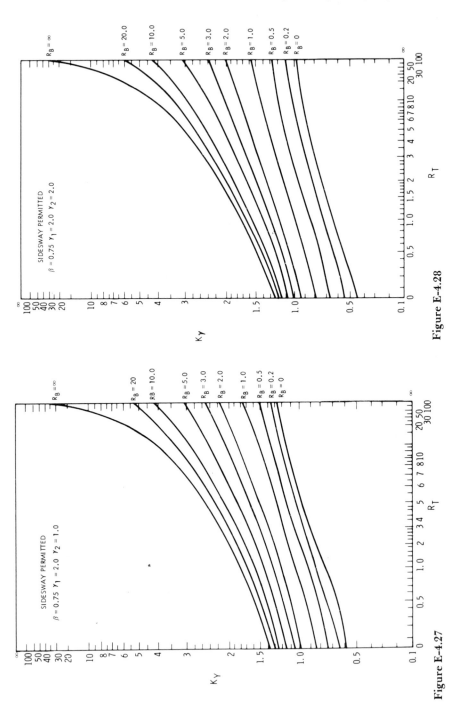

Figure E-4.28

Figure E-4.27

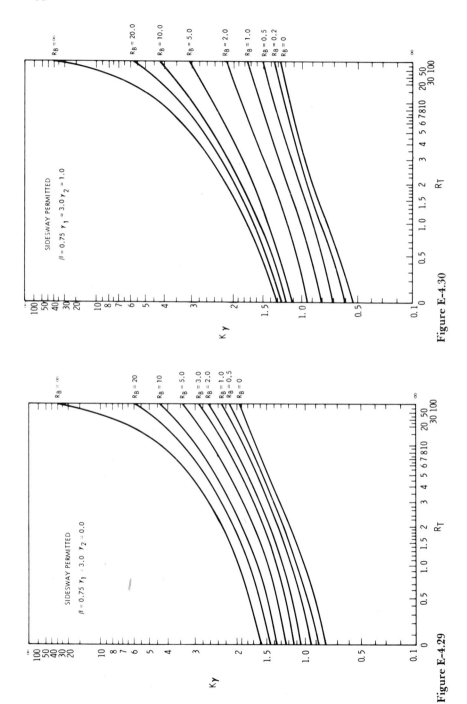

Figure E-4.30

Figure E-4.29

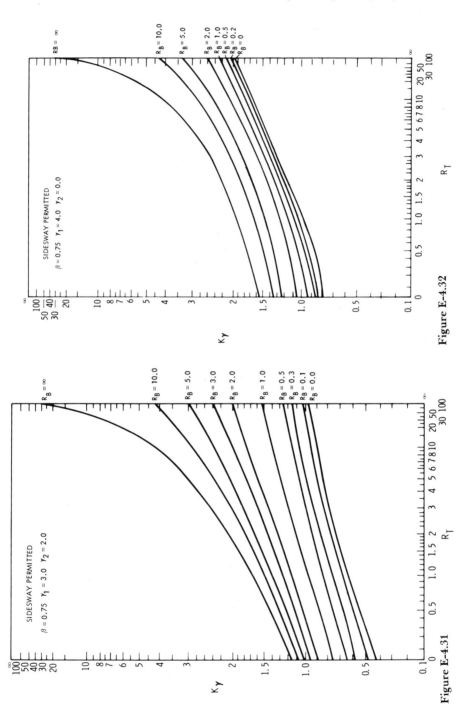

Figure E-4.32

Figure E-4.31

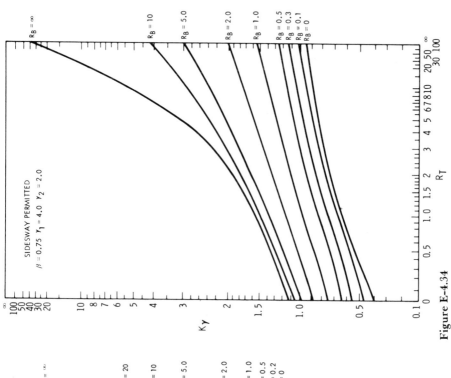

Figure E-4.34

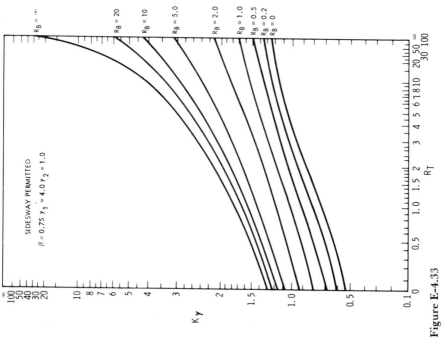

Figure E-4.33

Appendix F

Effective Length Factors for Laterally Continuous Beams

Appendix F: Effective Length Factors for Laterally Continuous Beams

For prismatic members, the effective length factors K_s and K_w are to be applied to the equivalent length $h_s L$ and $h_w L$ as indicated in Eqs. (3.33a) and (3.33b). For tapered members, the equations would be those given as Eqs. (3.37) and (3.38).

$$F_{b1} = \frac{170{,}000\ C_b}{\left(\dfrac{K_w L}{r_T}\right)^2} \tag{3.33a}$$

$$F_{b2} = \frac{12{,}000\ C_b}{\left(\dfrac{K_s L d}{A_f}\right)} \tag{3.33b}$$

$$F_{b1} = \frac{170{,}000}{\left(\dfrac{K_w\, h_w\, L}{r_T}\right)^2} \tag{3.37}$$

$$F_{b2} = \frac{12{,}000}{\left(\dfrac{K_s\, h_s\, L d}{A_f}\right)} \tag{3.38}$$

Values for K_s and K_w are given in Figs. F-1 and F-2, respectively.

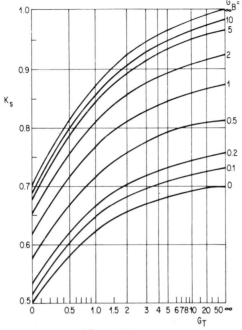

Figure F-1

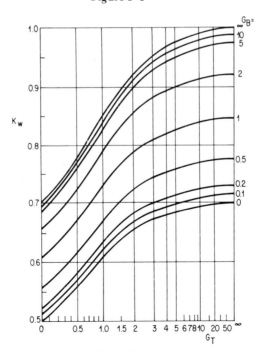

Figure F-2

Appendix G

Design Aids for Tapered Beam-Columns with Unequal Flanges

The control equation for design is

$$\frac{f_{a0}}{F_a} + \xi \frac{f_{bL}}{F_b} = 0 \qquad \text{(G-1)}$$

where

$$F_a = \sigma_a (F.S.)$$
$$F_b = \sigma_b (F.S.)$$

σ_a values are given in Figs. G-1.1 through G-1.6.
σ_b values are given in Figs. G-2.1 through G-2.3.
ξ values are given in Figs. G-3.1 through G-3.6.

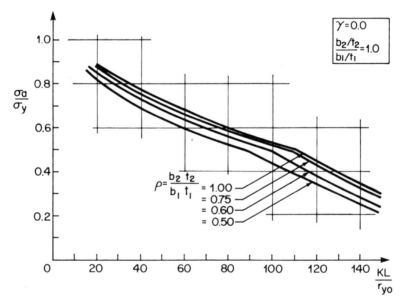

Figure G-1.1

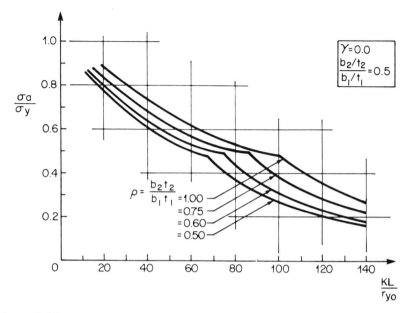

Figure G-1.2

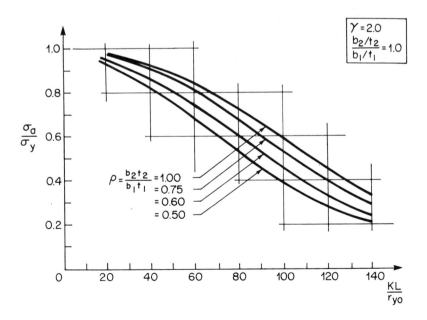

Figure G-1.3

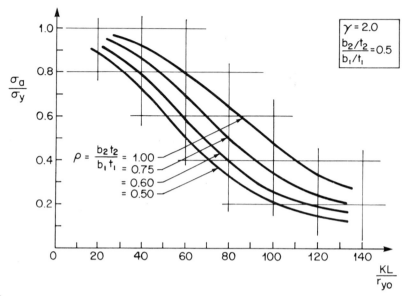

Figure G-1.4

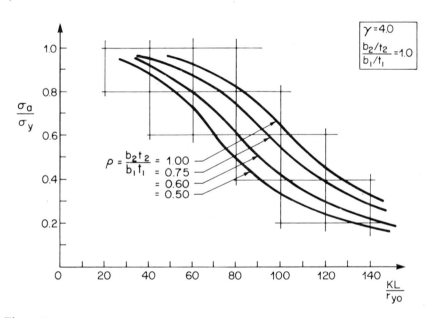

Figure G-1.5

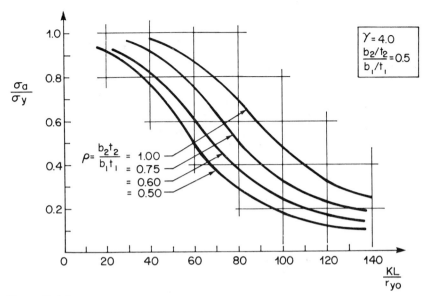

Figure G-1.6

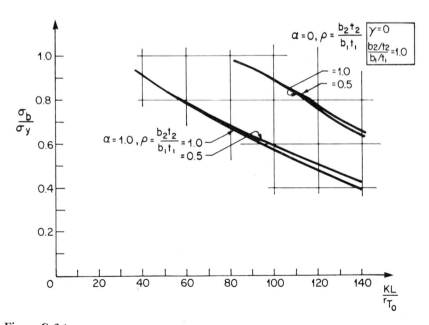

Figure G-2.1

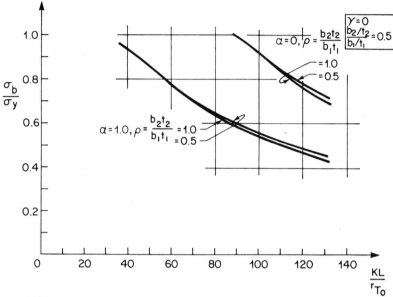

Figure G-2.2

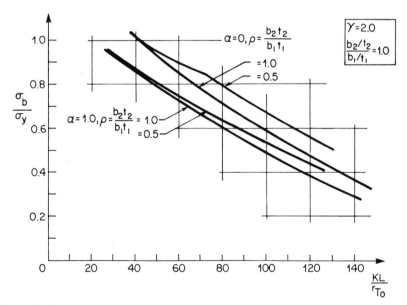

Figure G-2.3

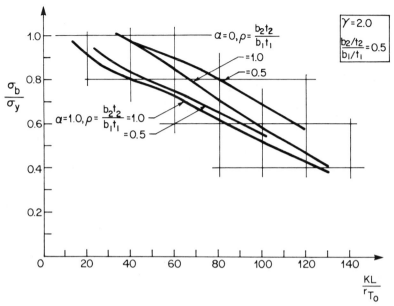

Figure G-2.4

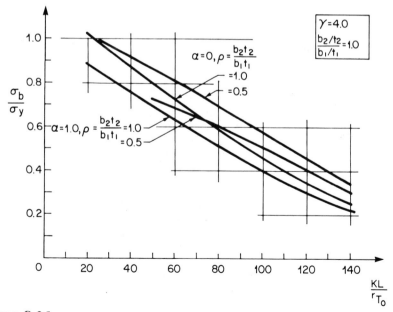

Figure G-2.5

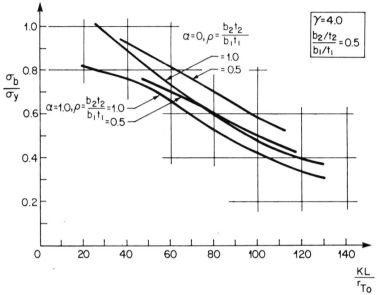

Figure G-2.6

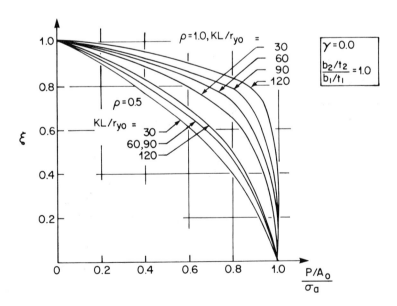

Figure G-3.1

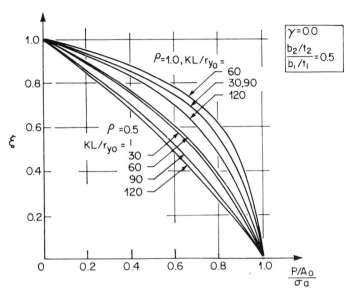

Figure G-3.2

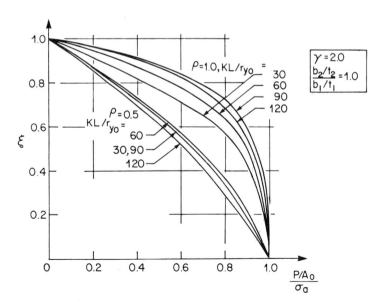

Figure G-3.3

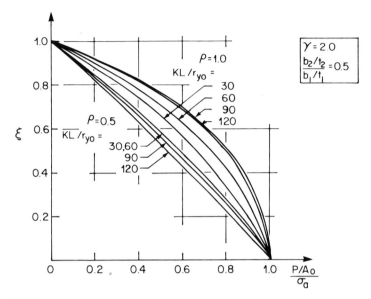

Figure G-3.4

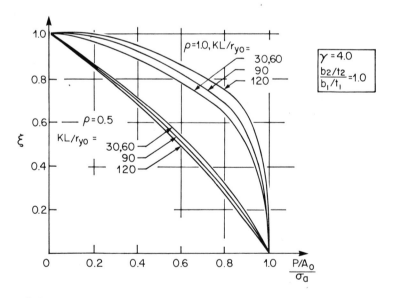

Figure G-3.5

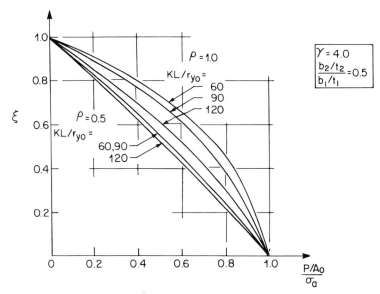

Figure G-3.6

The curves contained in this appendix are based on the work contained in Ref. [25]. The inelastic solutions are obtained assuming a maximum compression residual stress of $-0.5\ \sigma_y$ at the tips of flanges, and $+\sigma_y$ at the junction of the flange and the web. A linear variation in the flange between these two extreme values is assumed. Although these curves should not be regarded as exact solutions, they do provide appropriate approximations for design purposes.

NOTES

FOUNDATION DESIGN FOR RIGID FRAME STRUCTURES

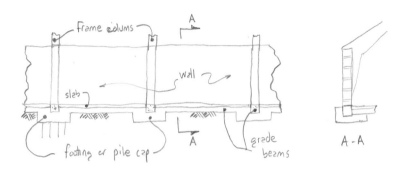

A-A

If slab/footing arrangement: Do not make recommendation to tie all members (slab, beams, cols, ftgs) together. Analyze settlements of footings based on loads from perimeter beams, and any column loads, plus a percentage of the slab loading. Analyze the remaining percentage of the slab loading as if it were a mat foundation with the entire area of the slab. At the footings, add the settlements obtained from the footing settlement analysis and that obtained from the slab settlement analysis. center, edge of long side, and corner of bldg are critical pts.

If pile cap arrangement: Recommend to tie all components together so that total load is carried by piles. No drag loads then from slab settlement. Besides, use of piles generally happens when can't tolerate deformation of slab/footing or independent arrangement.

In either case: Recommend elimination of lateral loads to foundation (tension slab, for instance), if at all possible.

NOTES

NOTES

NOTES

NOTES

NOTES